DIFFERENTIAL EQUATIONS

DIFFERENTIAL EQUATIONS

BY

MAX MORRIS, Ph.D.

AND

ORLEY E. BROWN, Ph.D.

ASSOCIATE PROFESSORS OF MATHEMATICS
CASE SCHOOL OF APPLIED SCIENCE

REVISED EDITION

New York
PRENTICE-HALL, INC.

Copyright, 1933, 1942, by

PRENTICE-HALL, INC.

70 Fifth Avenue, New York

First printing ....July, 1933
Second printing...... February, 1935
Third printing ....June, 1937
Fourth printing .....December, 1938
Fifth printing ....April, 1941

REVISED EDITION

Sixth printing ....June, 1942
Seventh printing......October, 1942
Eighth printing........October, 1945
Ninth printing...........July, 1946
Tenth printing..........June, 1947
Eleventh printing....December, 1948
Twelfth printing.....December, 1949

Preface to Revised Edition

IN REVISING this book, the authors have dealt lightly with the text, except where the interests of clarity or elegance have dictated a modification. Such is the case with the chapter on Linear Differential Equations, which has been considerably recast. Elsewhere, the text has been altered only occasionally and sparingly.

The main feature of the revised edition is an improved and augmented list of problems. Particularly, a void has been filled in the matter of problems exploiting the use of init'al conditions.

A section has been added to treat the Laplace Equation, with exercises to follow it. Also the chapter on Numerical Approximation has been enlarged by the inclusion of the Runge-Kutta method and Milne's method.

In the interest of completeness, brief tables of integrals and natural logarithms have been appended to the book.

M. M.

O. E. B.

Preface to First Edition

THE course in Differential Equations for which this text has been prepared is given, as a rule, in our colleges and engineering schools, to a class of student who brings to it the background of only a first year course in the Calculus. The teacher must make his terms with the limitations imposed by that background, implying as it does that the student has mastered only the merely manipulative aspects of the Calculus. Under such conditions, a searching and serious study of the more theoretical aspects of the subject of Differential Equations must of necessity be left in abeyance. On the other hand, the opportunity, as the subject is developed, for implanting in the student something like a feeling for mathematical rigor, presents itself frequently enough—and should be improved when met with. A course in which a generous amount of drill in integrating the various standard types of differential equations is accompanied by an exposure of the student, on as wide a front as possible, to the more exacting and searching aspects of mathematics, is a desideratum with every teacher of the subject.

This text has been prepared with the aim of assisting the teacher to come measurably near that end.

In the first place, the exercise material has been chosen with the greatest care. The exercises are numerous—generously so. The teacher will be pleased to find exercises in sufficient abundance to enable him to assign separate problems to individual students or groups of students, and also to enable him to select material for examinations, if desired, or for use in succeeding semesters.

The exercises have far more to commend them, however, than mere profusion. The authors have built them up carefully, all the way from those that serve no more than to illustrate a definite formula or a specific method, to such as lead the student on to something like independent study and criticism. Throughout, the text has been restricted to only as much as must be included, consistent with clearness and completeness, in the way of definition, proof, or discussion. Further treatment and elaboration of the

vii

subject matter has been relegated to the exercises, which have been supplemented with adequate hints where necessary.

A student cannot be led very far into the subject of Differential Equations, or indeed into any serious doctrine in mathematics, without being confronted with certain central ideas, such as linear dependence, functional dependence, the notion of the rank of a matrix, and so forth. Where germane to the subject of the text, such notions are introduced by an adequate treatment, though this treatment is not developed to such length as to become a digression. By this means, statements which would otherwise be loose, or even incorrect, are replaced with statements that are both precise and correct and the opportunities alluded to above are used to advantage.

The so-called applications—*i. e.*, the portrayal, by differential equations, of definite states of affairs that arise in Geometry, Mechanics, Engineering, and so forth—are numerous throughout the book. Care has been taken, in presenting such problems, to avoid a blunt statement of the equation, accompanied merely by an explanation of the terms involved; instead, an attempt has consistently been made to state briefly but adequately the background of the problem. Thus presented, each problem becomes indeed what it purports to be—an "application," and not just another manipulative exercise.

So far as possible, references have been restricted to two books which are very generally available, *viz.*, Wilson's "Advanced Calculus" and Dickson's "First Course in the Theory of Equations."

The authors are under obligation, for helpful criticism and suggestions, to various members of the mathematical staff at Case School. A particular debt of gratitude is due to Professor Wood of Northwestern University, who carefully read a considerable portion of the manuscript, and whose criticism was highly beneficial. Needless to say, the responsibility for such faults as the book may be found to possess is solely the authors'.

We also wish to acknowledge the unfailing courtesy and coöperation accorded us by our publishers.

M. M.

O. E. B.

Table of Contents

PAGE

PREFACE TO REVISED EDITION v

PREFACE TO FIRST EDITION............................ vii

CHAPTER

I. INTRODUCTION.................................... 1

    1. Definitions............................ 1
    2. Solutions of a differential equation.................. 3
    3. Primitives.......................... 4
    4. The general solution 7
    5. Equations of higher order.......................... 11
    6. Miscellaneous exercises on Chapter I................. 12

II. DIFFERENTIAL EQUATIONS OF THE FIRST ORDER AND FIRST DEGREE................................ 18

    7. Variables separable.............................. 18
    8. Exact differential equations......................... 19
    9. Integrating factors................................ 23
    10. Homogeneous equations........................... 28
    11. Equations reducible to homogeneous equations........ 31
    12. Linear equations of the first order.................. 33
    13. Equations reducible to linear equations.............. 37
    14. Riccati equation.................................. 38
    15. Applications of differential equations................. 42
    16. Miscellaneous exercises on Chapter II................ 50

III. EQUATIONS OF THE FIRST ORDER, BUT NOT OF THE FIRST DEGREE 55

    17. Introduction....................................... 55
    18. Equations solvable for p.......................... 55
    19. Equations solvable for y.......................... 56
    20. Equations solvable for x.......................... 57
    21. Clairaut's equation................................ 59
    22. Singular solutions................................. 61
    23. The c-discriminant............................... 62
    24. The p-discriminant............................... 63

IV. LINEAR DIFFERENTIAL EQUATIONS.................... 69

    25. General properties................................. 69
    26. General solution.................................. 69
    27. Homogeneous, with constant coefficients.............. 75
    28. The complementary function........................ 78
    29. Reduction of order................................ 80

CHAPTER   PAGE

IV. Linear Differential Equations—(*Cont.*)

30. Characteristic equation; equal or complex roots........ 84
31. Right-hand member not zero......................... 89
32. Inverse operators.................................... 94
33. The use of partial fractions......................... 98
34. Method of variation of parameters................... 102
35. Inverse operators corresponding to complex roots...... 106
36. The linear equation with variable coefficients......... 107
37. Cauchy's linear equation............................ 108
38. Exact linear equations.............................. 110
39. Simultaneous linear equations....................... 114
40. Miscellaneous exercises on Chapter IV............... 122

V. Numerical Approximation to Solutions............ 134

41. Picard's method................................... 134
42. Runge's method................................... 139
43. Milne's method................................... 144

VI. Integration in Series............................ 147

44. Equations of the first order......................... 147
45. Linear equations of the second order................. 151
46. Roots of indicial equation equal..................... 158
47. A coefficient in the series becoming infinite........... 161
48. The particular integral............................. 165
49. The Legendre equation............................. 170
50. The Bessel equation................................ 177
51. The Gauss equation................................ 184
52. Miscellaneous exercises on Chapter VI............... 188

VII. Ordinary Differential Equations in More Than Two Variables.............................. 191

53. Total differential equations; introductory remarks..... 191
54. Conditions for exactness............................ 192
55. Conditions for integrability......................... 193
56. Total differential equations which are integrable....... 194
57. Geometric significance.............................. 198
58. Pairs of total differential equations.................. 198
59. Solutions of a pair of total differential equations in three variables.. 199
60. Non-integrable equations........................... 206
61. Dependence and functional determinants............. 207
62. Determinate systems involving several variables....... 209
63. Jacobi's multipliers................................ 212
64. Indeterminate systems.............................. 217
65. Exercises... 218

VIII. Partial Differential Equations of the First Order 221

66. Illustrations and definitions........................ 221
67. Lagrange's equations............................... 223

CHAPTER · PAGE

VIII. PARTIAL DIFFERENTIAL EQUATIONS OF THE FIRST ORDER
(*Cont.*)

68. Functions of several variables........................ 227
69. Lagrange's equations; case of $n + 1$ variables......... 229
70. Equations not of the first degree; Charpit's method.... 230
71. Equations involving several variables; Jacobi's method 236

IX. LINEAR PARTIAL DIFFERENTIAL EQUATIONS WITH CONSTANT COEFFICIENTS........................... 242

72. Homogeneous linear equations with constant coefficients 242
73. Case of complex roots............................. 244
74. Case of multiple roots............................. 245
75. Right-hand member not zero........................ 248
76. Special cases.................................... 248
77. Inverse operators; factoring....................... 250
78. Partial fractions................................. 252
79. Case of α_i not all different from zero................. 254
80. Non-homogeneous equations........................ 256
81. Right-hand member zero........................... 256
82. Particular integrals.............................. 257
83. Other forms of $f(D_1, D_2)$........................... 260
84. Equations reducible to linear equations with constant coefficients....................................... 261
85. Laplace's equation................................ 262

X. PARTIAL DIFFERENTIAL EQUATIONS OF ORDER TWO... 268

86. Introduction.................................... 268
87. Intermediate integrals of a second order differential equation...................................... 269
88. Monge's method for $Rr + Ss + Tt = V$.............. 270
89. Integrability of $dz = p\, dx + q\, dy$................... 273
90. Monge's method for $Rr + Ss + Tt + U(rt - s^2) = V$.. 275
91. Laplace's transformation........................... 284

TABLE OF INTEGRALS.................................... 289

TABLE OF LOGARITHMS 297

ANSWERS TO EXERCISES................................. 303

INDEX,... 353

CHAPTER I

Introduction

1. Definitions. Let a curve be defined by the property that the slope of the tangent at any of its points equals the sum of the coördinates at that point. The student will readily express this property by the equation

$$\frac{dy}{dx} = x + y, \tag{1}$$

where x and y have the usual meaning of abscissa and ordinate, respectively.

Again, let the motion of a particle on a straight line be defined by the condition that the acceleration of the particle at any instant exceeds its velocity at that instant by a quantity equal to the displacement. If we denote the displacement and time by s and t, respectively, the condition is embodied in the equation

$$\frac{d^2s}{dt^2} - \frac{ds}{dt} = s. \tag{2}$$

Relations (1) and (2) are examples of equations which involve derivatives (or differentials), and which are, on that account, called *differential equations*. It is readily seen that such equations will arise in a great variety of problems in geometry, mechanics, and elsewhere.

We now lay down the following:

DEFINITION. *A differential equation of order* n *is one that involves a derivative of order* n *and none of higher order.*

Thus, (1) is of the first order, and (2) is of the second. We distinguish differential equations, as to their *degree*, in the light of the following:

DEFINITION. *The degree of a differential equation is the degree to which the highest ordered derivative enters into the equation, after it has been made rational and integral in all the derivatives.*

1

Thus, (1) and (2) are both of the first degree, while

$$\left(\frac{d^2y}{dx^2}\right)^2 + 3\left(\frac{dy}{dx}\right)^3 - x = 0$$

is of the second, as is also

$$\frac{d^2y}{dx^2} = \sqrt{1 + \frac{dy}{dx}},$$

which, when rationalized, becomes

$$\left(\frac{d^2y}{dx^2}\right)^2 = 1 + \frac{dy}{dx}.$$

Lastly, we shall classify differential equations as *ordinary* or *partial* by means of the following:

DEFINITION. *If an equation involves more than one independent variable, and partial derivatives with respect to the independent variables, it is said to be partial; otherwise, ordinary.*

Hence, all the equations displayed above are ordinary, while

$$\frac{\partial^2 z}{\partial x^2} + \frac{\partial^2 z}{\partial y^2} = xy$$

is partial (of order two and degree one).

Exercises

Classify the following into ordinary and partial differential equations; also name the order and degree of each:

1. $x^2\dfrac{dy}{dx} + \left(\dfrac{dy}{dx}\right)^2 = 0.$

2. $\dfrac{\partial z}{\partial y} + x\dfrac{\partial z}{\partial x} = y.$

3. $\dfrac{d^2y}{dx^2} = 3x\left[1 + \left(\dfrac{dy}{dx}\right)^2\right]^{3/2}.$

4. $\dfrac{d^3y}{dx^3} + \dfrac{2y}{\dfrac{d^3y}{dx^3}} = 2x.$

5. $\dfrac{\partial^4 z}{\partial x^4} - \left(\dfrac{\partial^2 z}{\partial x \partial y}\right)^2 = 0.$

6. $y\dfrac{d^2y}{dx^2} - x\dfrac{dy}{dx} = \sqrt{x}.$

7.* $e^{\frac{d^2y}{dx^2}} = x\dfrac{dy}{dx}.$

8. $\log\left(\dfrac{dy}{dx}\right) + \log x^2 = 2y.$

9. $x^2\dfrac{d^2y}{dx^2} - x\dfrac{dy}{dx} + y = 3x^3.$

---

* Note that the idea of degree is not applicable to this equation, inasmuch as a derivative enters exponentially.

2. Solutions of a differential equation. By a *solution* of a differential equation is meant a relation between the variables involved, free of derivatives and satisfying the equation identically. In other words,

$$f(x, y, y', y'', \cdots) = 0*$$

is said to have

$$y = g(x)$$

as a solution if

$$f[x, g(x), g'(x), g''(x), \cdots] \equiv 0\dagger$$

For example,

$$y'(x + 3x^2) - y(1 + 6x) = 0$$

has as a solution

$$y = 2x + 6x^2,$$

for, when y and y' are substituted from the latter, the former becomes

$$(2 + 12x)(x + 3x^2) - (2x + 6x^2)(1 + 6x) \equiv 0.$$

In like manner, the partial differential equation

$$F[x, y, z, z_x, z_y, z_{xx}, \cdots] = 0$$

is said to have

$$z = h(x, y)$$

as a solution if

$$F[x, y, h(x, y), h_x(x, y), h_y(x, y), h_{xx}(x, y), \cdots] \equiv 0.$$

Thus,

$$z = 4x^2 + 3y$$

is a solution of

$$z - \tfrac{1}{2}x^2 z_{xx} - y z_y = 0,$$

for, when z, z_{xx}, and z_y are substituted from the former, the latter becomes

$$4x^2 + 3y - 4x^2 - 3y \equiv 0.$$

We shall use freely the notation y', y'', $\cdots$ for $\dfrac{dy}{dx}, \dfrac{d^2y}{dx^2}, \cdots$, as well as $z_x, z_y, z_{xx}, z_{xy}, \cdots$ for $\dfrac{\partial z}{\partial x}, \dfrac{\partial z}{\partial y}, \dfrac{\partial^2 z}{\partial x^2}, \dfrac{\partial^2 z}{\partial y \partial x}, \cdots$.

† The notation $f(x) \equiv g(x)$ signifies that $f(x) = g(x)$ for every value of x for which f and g are defined, and it is read: "$f(x)$ equals $g(x)$, identically." The above, then, is read:

"$f[x, g(x), g'(x), g''(x), \cdots]$ equals zero, identically."

Exercises

Verify that the following are solutions of the corresponding differential equations.

1. $y = x + 3x^2$; $y'(x + 3x^2) - y(1 + 6x) = 0$.

2. $y = 0$; $y'(x + 3x^2) - y(1 + 6x) = 0$.

3. * $y = cx + 3cx^2$; $y'(x + 3x^2) - y(1 + 6x) = 0$.

4. $x^2 + y^2 = 5$; $yy' = -x$.

5. * $x^2 + y^2 = c$; $yy' = -x$.

6. $z = 3x^2 - y$; $z - \frac{1}{2}x^2 z_{xx} - yz_y = 0$.

7. † $z = ax^2 + by$; $z - \frac{1}{2}x^2 z_{xx} - yz_y = 0$.

8. † $y + ae^x + bx^2 = 0$; $y''(x^2 - 2x) + y'(2 - x^2)$
$$+ 2y(x - 1) = 0.$$

9. † $y = a \sin 2x + b \cos 2x$; $y'' + 4y = 0$.

10. $z = 2x^3 - xy$; $2xyz_{xy} + xz_x = 3z$.

11. $z = ax^3 + bxy$; $2xyz_{xy} + xz_x = 3z$.

12. $y = 1 + \dfrac{2}{x^2}$; $x^3 \dfrac{d^3y}{dx^3} + 2x^2 \dfrac{d^2y}{dx^2} - 6x \dfrac{dy}{dx} = 0$.

3. Primitives. Let us now consider the following problem: to find the differential equation satisfied by all relations of the form

$$y = cx^2 + x, \qquad (3)$$

where c is an arbitrary constant. By that we shall mean the differential equation of the lowest order satisfied by every one of the relations (3), regardless of the value assigned to c. If we differentiate (3), we obtain

$$y' = 2cx + 1, \qquad (4)$$

a differential equation obviously satisfied by (3). But (4) is not yet the equation we set out to find, for it is satisfied by (3) only if the same value of c is employed in (3) and (4) [thus, $y = 4x^2 + x$ is not a solution of (4) unless we set $c = 4$ in (4)]. To obtain an equation free of c and satisfied by (3) identically for every c, we eliminate c between (3) and (4), say as follows:

$$c = \frac{y' - 1}{2x} \text{ by (4),}$$

---

* Where c is any constant.   † Where a and b are any constants.

hence, by (3),

$$y = \frac{x^2(y' - 1)}{2x} + x,$$

or

$$y'x - 2y + x = 0. \tag{5}$$

From the mode of its derivation, (5) is satisfied by (3) for every c and is the equation we proposed to find.

More generally, if we set out with a relation of the form

$$f(x, y, c) = 0, \tag{6}$$

where c is an arbitrary constant, and propose the problem of forming the differential equation of the lowest order having (6) for its solutions, regardless of the value assigned to c, we differentiate (6), obtaining an equation which involves y' and which is certainly satisfied by (6). If that relation is free of c,* it is the differential equation desired; if it is not free of c, we eliminate c between it and (6), obtaining an equation of the form

$$F(x, y, y') = 0, \tag{7}$$

which is the equation we proposed to find.

We speak of (6) as the *primitive* of (7), and it is seen that a primitive involving one arbitrary constant gives rise to a differential equation of the first order.

If, next, our problem should be to build the differential equation having

$$f(x, y, c_1, c_2) = 0 \tag{8}$$

for its primitive—*i. e.*, the differential equation of lowest order satisfied by every one of the relations (8), regardless of the values of the arbitrary constants c_1 and c_2—our procedure clearly would be to differentiate (8) twice in succession, and then to eliminate c_1 and c_2 between (8) and the two derived equations. This procedure would yield a differential equation of type

$$F(x, y, y', y'') = 0. \tag{9}$$

On account of the mode of its formation, (9) is clearly satisfied by (8), independently of the particular values assigned to c_1 and c_2 (since (9) is free of c_1 and c_2).

---

* Thus, (A) $y = 2x^2 + c$ leads to the equation (B) $y' = 4x$, and (B) is the differential equation of lowest order satisfied by every relation (A), with c any constant whatsoever.

The elimination of c_1 and c_2 demanded three equations, and thus two successive differentiations of (8) were necessary. Hence, a primitive involving two arbitrary constants gives rise to a differential equation of the second order.

Illustration

Given

$$c_1 y + c_2 x - xy = 0 \tag{10}$$

as a primitive of a proposed differential equation, we adjoin to (10)

$$c_1 y' + c_2 - xy' - y = 0 \tag{11}$$

and

$$c_1 y'' - xy'' - 2y' = 0, \tag{12}$$

where (11) is the result of differentiating (10), and (12) the result of differentiating (11). The elimination of c_1 and c_2 may now be done, say, as follows. By (12),

$$c_1 = \frac{xy'' + 2y'}{y''};$$

hence, by (11),

$$c_2 = xy' + y - c_1 y' = xy' + y - \frac{xy'y'' + 2y'^2}{y''} = \frac{yy'' - 2y'^2}{y''}.$$

Now (10) becomes

$$\frac{xyy'' + 2yy'}{y''} + \frac{xyy'' - 2xy'^2}{y''} - xy = 0,$$

or

$$xyy'' - 2xy'^2 + 2yy' = 0, \tag{13}$$

which last is the differential equation having (10) for its primitive.*

It will be easy for the student to extend the argument to the case of a primitive involving n arbitrary constants, and to conclude that the differential equation of lowest order satisfied by the given

---

* A student familiar with the theory of eliminants, might have written directly as the eliminant of (10), (11), and (12):

$$\begin{vmatrix} y & x & -xy \\ y' & 1 & -xy' - y \\ y'' & 0 & -xy'' - 2y' \end{vmatrix} = 0,$$

which expands into (13). See Dickson's, *First Course in the Theory of Equations*, pp. 110–112.

primitive for all values whatsoever of the arbitrary constants (and hence free of those constants) will be of order n.

Exercises

1. In each of the following, form the differential equation having the given primitive:

(a) $y = x + cx^2$.

(b) $cx + 2cy = y$.

(c) $c^2 - cx = y$.

(d) $c_1 x + y = c_2$.

(e) $c_1 x^2 + c_2 y = x$.

(f) $c_1 y - x = c_2 xy$.

(g) $y = c_1 e^x + c_2 x e^x$.

(h) $y = c_1 \sin ax + c_2 \cos ax$, where a is a fixed constant.

(i) $y = e^x(c_2 \cos x + c_3 \sin x)$
$$+ c_1 + \frac{x}{4}$$

(j) $y = c_1 + c_2 e^x + c_3 x e^x + x^2$.

2. Form the differential equation representing all circles whose centers are at the origin. *Hint:* The differential equation is that having for its primitive $x^2 + y^2 = c^2$, where c is an arbitrary constant.

3. Form the differential equation representing all parabolas with vertices at the origin and foci on the x-axis.

4. Form the differential equation representing all straight lines in the xy-plane.

5. Form the differential equation representing all tangents to the parabola $y^2 = 4x$. Show that the equation of the parabola is a solution of the differential equation obtained. *Hint:* Derive the equation of an arbitrary tangent as $yy_0 = 2(x + x_0)$, where (x_0, y_0) is an arbitrary point of tangency on the parabola. Since (x_0, y_0) is on the parabola, this equation may be written, $yy_0 = 2\left(x + \frac{y_0^2}{4}\right)$, and may be taken as the primitive, with y_0 as an arbitrary constant.

4. The general solution. In the preceding section we found it a direct and generally soluble problem to form a differential equation whose solutions were prescribed in advance. On the other hand, it is by no means a soluble problem, in general, to start with a given differential equation and to obtain its solutions, though in the succeeding chapters, methods of attack will be developed for a great variety of special types of differential equations.

What is of importance, however, is to have some assurance, to begin with, that a differential equation, at least under specified conditions, actually has solutions. Furthermore, where a differential equation is derived from a given primitive, it is of significance to inquire whether that primitive includes all the solutions that the equation may have.

The argument involved, in considering the above, demands greater rigor than the scope of this book permits of, and hence we shall content ourselves with merely stating, without proof, the theorem pertaining to the questions raised; namely, the so-called

EXISTENCE THEOREM. *If, in a given differential equation,*

$$y' = F(x, y), \tag{14}$$

$F(x, y)$ *is continuous and single-valued for a certain range of values of* x *and* y, *and if, for all values of* x *and* y *within that range,* F_y *exists and is continuous,* * *then the equation admits of an infinity of solutions, where* c *is an arbitrary constant, such that one and only one of the curves* (15) *passes through an arbitrary point,* (x_0, y_0), *if* x = x_0 *and* y = y_0 *are within the range. Furthermore, all the solutions of* (14) *are included in* (15).

The result, (15), is called the *complete* or *general* solution of (14); any solution obtained by assigning to *c* a particular value is called a *particular solution.* The curves represented by (15) are called *integral curves* of (14).

The question raised above with regard to the primitive is now easily settled in the light of this theorem.

Let a primitive,

$$g(x, y, c) = 0, \tag{16}$$

give rise to the differential equation

$$y' = F(x, y), \tag{14}$$

satisfying the hyphotheses of the above theorem and having the complete solution,

$$f(x, y, c) = 0. \tag{15}$$

---

* A condition actually sufficient is the so-called condition of Lipschitz, *viz.:*

$$| F(x, y_1) - F(x, y_2) | < M | y_1 - y_2 |$$

where x, y_1, and y_2 are in the range, M is some constant, and the symbol $|\ |$ denotes absolute value. This condition, however, is always realized when F_y exists and is continuous.

Now all the equations (16), being solutions of (14), are to be found among the equations (15). On the other hand, should there be a curve (15) passing through a point (x_0, y_0) and not found among the curves (16), then through that point would be passing more than one integral curve, since there is a curve of (16) through (x_0, y_0) corresponding to the value of c determined by $g(x_0, y_0, c) = 0$. This would contradict the uniqueness statement of the Existence Theorem. The family of curves (16) is, then, identical with the family (15); in other words, the primitive is identical with the complete solution.

If a differential equation is of the first order and of the second degree, it defines y' in the form of two single-valued functions of x and y. For example,

$$y'^2 + y'(2x + 2y) + (y^2 + 2xy - 3x^2) = 0$$

yields

$$(y' + 3x + y)(y' - x + y) = 0,$$

whence,

$$y' = -3x - y$$

or

$$y' = x - y.$$

Each of these, within the range of values of x and y where it meets the requirements of the Existence Theorem, has a complete solution, so that through an arbitrary point (x_0, y_0), within both ranges, passes one integral curve of each. If both sets of solutions are embodied in a single equation involving one arbitrary constant c, it is evident that, in general, this equation must determine two values of c for an arbitrary point (x_0, y_0), corresponding to the two curves passing through it. Hence, such an equation will involve c to the second degree.

The student may now extend the argument to a differential equation of the first order and of any degree whatsoever, in order to conclude that the degree of the arbitrary constant in the complete solution will be the same as the degree of the differential equation.

A word should be added here about a type of solution called *singular*. In Exercise 5 of Section 3 the student built the differential equation representing all tangents to the parabola $y^2 = 4x$; in other words, the equation having for its primitive the one-parameter family of lines

$$yc = 2\left(x + \frac{c^2}{4}\right).$$

(The change in notation, from y_0 in the exercise to c, is immaterial.) The equation derived was

$$xy'^2 - yy' + 1 = 0,$$

and its complete solution would be expected to be the primitive with which we started. As a matter of fact, it is. However, as noticed in the exercise, the equation of the parabola, *viz.*, $y^2 = 4x$, is also a solution of the equation, and it is obviously not one included in the complete solution; *i. e.*, it is not a solution derivable from

$$yc = 2\left(x + \frac{c^2}{4}\right)$$

by assigning a fixed value to c.

We say that

$$y^2 = 4x$$

is a *singular solution* of

$$xy'^2 - yy' + 1 = 0,$$

and we define, in general, any solution of a differential equation which is not included in the general solution, as a *singular solution*.

The matter of singular solutions will be taken up in detail in Chapter III, but a brief remark at this point might be relevant. The above differential equation defines y' as a double-valued function of x and y; *viz.*,

$$y' = \frac{y \pm \sqrt{y^2 - 4x}}{2x},$$

so that through any point (x, y), not on the parabola $y^2 = 4x$, there are two integral curves with two distinct slopes. The points of the parabola are *singular*, *i. e.*, exceptional, in that for them the two values of y' are equal. The locus of these singular points is our singular solution.

Exercises

1. (a) Verify that the complete solution of $y' = y - 2x$ is $y = 2x + 2 + ce^x$. Find the particular solution satisfied by $x = 0$, $y = 1$ [*i. e.*, find the equation of the integral curve through $(0, 1)$].

(b) Verify that the complete solution of $y'^2x^2 - y'(2xy + 1) + y^2 = 0$ is $y = c^2x + c$. Find the two integral curves through $(2, 1)$.

(c) Verify that the complete solution of $y'^3 + xy' - y = 0$ is $y = cx + c^3$. Find the three integral curves through $(-1, 0)$.

2. (a) In the illustration on page 10, obtain the singular solution $y^2 = 4x$ as the locus of points whose coördinates (x, y) determine one value of c instead of two distinct values, in the complete solution $yc = 2\left(x + \dfrac{c^2}{4}\right)$. *Hint:* Solve this equation for c.

(b) Verify that $4xy = -1$ is a solution in Exercise 1 (b). It is a singular solution. Why?

(c) Obtain the singular solution of Exercise 1 (b) by two methods: first as the locus of points (x, y) at which y' has only one value, instead of two distinct values; then as the locus of points whose coördinates (x, y) determine only one value of c in the complete solution, instead of two distinct values.

3. Verify that the complete solution of $y = xy' + 2(y')^2 - y'$ is $y = cx + 2c^2 - c$. Obtain the singular solution by two methods as in Exercise 2 (c).

4. Write down the complete solution of $y' = -\dfrac{x}{y}$ directly from the fact that the tangent at any point (x, y) of an integral curve is perpendicular to the line joining (x, y) to the origin.

5. Using an argument similar to that in Exercise 4, write down directly the complete solution of $y'(3 - y) = x + 2$.

5. Equations of higher order. We have seen in Section 3 that a primitive representing an n-parameter family of curves, *i. e.*, one involving n arbitrary constants, gives rise to a differential equation of order n. Accordingly, we must expect the general solution of a differential equation of order n to involve n arbitrary constants. Otherwise, *i. e.*, if the general solution were to involve $m \neq n$ arbitrary constants, then, starting with that solution as primitive, we would derive an equation of order $m \neq n$—a contradiction.

It must be understood throughout that when we speak of an n-parameter family, the n arbitrary constants are meant to be essential, *i. e.*, that precisely n conditions are required to determine them. Thus,

$$y = c_1 x + c_2$$

is actually a two-parameter family, since two conditions, and only two, will serve to determine the constants c_1 and c_2. For example, the two conditions that a curve of the family pass through $(1, 3)$ and $(-1, 2)$ determine c_1 and c_2 by

$$3 = c_1 + c_2$$
$$2 = -c_1 + c_2$$

as $c_1 = \frac{1}{2}$ and $c_2 = \frac{5}{2}$, and the curve as

$$y = \frac{1}{2}x + \frac{5}{2}.$$

On the other hand,

$$y = c_1 x + c_2 x$$

is a one-parameter family involving only one essential constant, $c_1 + c_2$, which could be fixed only by imposing one condition. In fact, the equation of the family is essentially $y = cx$.

Exercises

1. (a) Verify that $y = c_1 e^x + c_2$ is the complete solution of $y'' - y' = 0$. Find the integral curve passing through $(0, 1)$ and $(1, e)$.

(b) Verify that $y = e^{2x}(c_1 \cos x + c_2 \sin x)$ is the complete solution of $y'' - 4y' + 5y = 0$. Find the integral curve passing through $(\pi, e^{2\pi})$ and $\left(\frac{\pi}{2}, 1\right)$.

(c) Verify that $y = e^{2x}(c_1 + c_2 x)$ is the complete solution of $y'' - 4y' + 4y = 0$. Find the integral curve passing through $(0, 0)$, with its slope equal to 1 at that point.

2. (a) Is $y = c_1 e^{x+c_2}$ a two-parameter family? If so, determine the curve of the family passing through $(0, 2)$ and $(1, -2)$. If not, write it as an equation with one arbitrary constant.

(b) Is $y = c_1 + \log c_2 x$ a two-parameter family? If not, write it as an equation with one arbitrary constant.

(c) Is $y = c_1 \sqrt{c_2 + x}$ a two-parameter family? If so, determine the curve of the family passing through $(0, 1)$, with slope equal to 2 at that point.

6. Miscellaneous exercises on Chapter I.

1. (a) Verify that the following are solutions of $xz_x + yz_y = 2z$:
$z = x^2 e^{\frac{x}{y}}; z = x^2 \log \frac{y}{x}; z = x^2 f\left(\frac{y}{x}\right)$, where $f\left(\frac{y}{x}\right)$ is an arbitrary function of $\frac{y}{x}$.

(b) Verify that the following are solutions of $y^2 z_x + xy z_y = xz$:
$z = y \sqrt{x^2 - y^2}; z = y \sin(x^2 - y^2); z = y f(x^2 - y^2)$, where $f(x^2 - y^2)$ is an arbitrary function of $(x^2 - y^2)$.

2. (a) Obtain the partial differential equation of the first order having $z = ax + by^2$ as its primitive (a, b being arbitrary constants). *Hint:* Differentiate the primitive with respect to x, also with respect to y; then eliminate a and b from the three equations.

(b) Obtain the partial differential equation of the first order having $z = ax^2 + bxy + by^2$ as its primitive (a, b being arbitrary constants).

(c) Obtain the differential equation of the first order having $z^2 = c_1 x + c_2 y^2$ as its primitive.

(d) Obtain the differential equation of the first order having $z = x^2 f(x + y)$ as its primitive, $f(x + y)$ being an arbitrary function of the quantity $x + y$.

(e) Obtain the differential equation of the first order having $z = f(x + y^2 - y)$ as its primitive, f being an arbitrary function.

3. (a) Find the differential equation of the family of tangents to the parabola $x^2 = 2y$.   Show that the equation of the parabola is a (singular) solution.

(b) Find the differential equation of all circles with centers on the y-axis.   *Hint:* The primitive is $x^2 + (y - a)^2 = r^2$ (a, r arbitrary constants).

(c) Find the differential equation of the family of ellipses with foci at $(a, 0)$ and $(-a, 0)$.

(d) Derive the singular solution in Exercise 3 (a) by the two methods of Exercise 2 (c) of Section 4.

(e) Find the differential equation of all circles tangent to the line $y = 2$.

(f) Find the differential equation representing all lines whose y-intercepts are twice their x-intercepts.

4. (a) Find the equation of the line tangent at $(3, -1)$ to an integral curve of $y' = 2xy - y^2$.

(b) Find the equation of the line tangent at $(\pi/2, 0)$ to an integral curve of $y' - 3y + \sin x = 0$.

(c) Find the radius of curvature at $(0, 2)$ of the integral curve of $y' - 2y + e^{xy} = 0$ which passes through that point.   *Hint:* The radius of curvature of a curve at (x, y) is given by $R = \dfrac{(1 + y'^2)^{3/2}}{y''}$.

(d) For each of the two integral curves of $y'^2 + y'(x - 2y) - xy + y^2 = 0$ which pass through $(1, -2)$, find the equation of the tangent at that point; also the radius of curvature at that point.

5. Obtain, in the form of an infinite series, the particular solution of $y' = 2x - y$ which passes through (2, 1). *Hint:* The equation defines the values of y' and of all the subsequent derivatives at (2, 1) by

$$y' = .(2 \cdot 2) - 1 = 3$$
$$y'' = 2 - y' = -1$$
$$y''' = -y'' = 1$$
$$y^{iv} = -y''' = -1, \text{ etc.}$$

Hence, by Taylor's Theorem, *viz.*,

$$y = y_0 + (x - x_0)y_0' + \frac{(x - x_0)^2}{2!} y_0'' + \frac{(x - x_0)^3}{3!} y_0''' + \cdots$$

with $x_0 = 2$, $y_0 = 1$, $y_0' = 3$, $y_0'' = -1$, $y_0''' = +1$, $\cdots$ we have

$$y = 1 + (x - 2) \, 3 + \frac{(x - 2)^2}{2!} (-1) + \frac{(x - 2)^3}{3!} (1) + \cdots,$$

the series sought. That the series so obtained is actually a Taylor expansion, in the neighborhood of (2, 1), of a function

$$y = f(x),$$

which is a solution of the given equation, is a matter vouched for by the Existence Theorem if $F(x, y)$ is assumed, in that theorem, to be a function capable of being developed into a power series

$$a_0 + a_1x + a_2y + a_3x^2 + a_4xy + a_5y^2 + \cdots,$$

as is $2x - y$ in the problem at hand.

Now verify that the above series is a Taylor expansion, about the point (2, 1), of

$$y = 2x - 2 - e^{2-x}.$$

6. By the method of the previous exercise, obtain, in the form of an infinite series:

(a) The particular solution of $y' = 3x + 2y$ passing through (0, 1).

(b) The particular solution of $y' = e^{-x} - y$ passing through (0, -1).

(c) The particular solution of $y' = 2xe^{-x^2/2} - xy$ passing through (0, 3).

7. Verify that the series obtained in Exercise 6(a) is a Taylor expansion, about (0, 1), of $y = -\frac{3}{4}(2x + 1) + \frac{7}{4}e^{2x}$; that the series obtained in Exercise 6(b) is a Taylor expansion, about (0, -1), of

$y = (x - 1)e^{-x}$; and that the series obtained in Exercise 6(c) is a Taylor expansion, about $(0, 3)$, of $y = (x^2 + 3)e^{-\frac{x^2}{2}}$.

8. Find, in the form of an infinite series:

(a) The particular solution of $y'' = \dfrac{2x - y + xy'}{x^2}$ passing through $(1, 2)$ with its slope equal to zero.

(b) The particular solution of $y'' - y' + 2y = \log x$ passing through. $(1, 3)$ with its slope equal to 1.

9. Obtain the general solution of $\dfrac{dy}{dx} = \dfrac{y}{x}$ directly from the fact that the tangent at any point (x, y) of an integral curve has the same slope as the line joining (x, y) to $(0, 0)$.

10. Given the equation $y' = xy - 1$, show:

(a) That the points on the branch of the curve $xy = 1$ which lies in the first quadrant are points of minimum ordinate for the integral curves through them.

(b) That the points on the other branch of $xy = 1$ are points of maximum ordinate for the integral curves through them.

(c) That the points of inflection of the integral curves lie on the locus $x^2y - x + y = 0$.

11. (a) Given the equation $y' = 2x - 3xy$, find the locus of the points which are points of maximum or minimum ordinate for the integral curves through them; also the locus of the points which are points of inflection for the integral curves through them.

(b) Obtain the same loci as described in (a) for the equation

$$y' = y + e^x.$$

12. Verify that $y = cx$ is the general solution of $y' = \dfrac{y}{x}$. Show that the origin is a singular point for this equation. *Hint:* Consider the number of integral curves through the origin. In what way does the behavior of the function $\dfrac{y}{x}$ at the origin fail to meet the requirements of the Existence Theorem?

13. Show that the system

$$\frac{dx}{dt} = -\frac{y}{t},$$

$$\frac{dy}{dt} = -\frac{x}{t},$$

is satisfied by

$$x = c_1 t + \frac{c_2}{t},$$

$$y = -c_1 t + \frac{c_2}{t}$$

where c_1 and c_2 are arbitrary constants.

Note. The above represents, in fact, the general solution, by the Existence Theorem, for a system of n simultaneous differential equations of the first order, with one independent variable and n dependent variables. We quote the

THEOREM. Given a system of n differential equations in one independent variable t and n dependent variables x, y, z, $\cdots$ *viz.*,

$$\begin{cases} \dfrac{dx}{dt} = F_1(x, y, z, \cdots, t), \\[2mm] \dfrac{dy}{dt} = F_2(x, y, z, \cdots, t), \\[2mm] \dfrac{dz}{dt} = F_3(x, y, z, \cdots, t), \\[2mm] \cdots\cdots\cdots\cdots\cdots\cdots\cdots, \end{cases} \tag{17}$$

where each function F_i is continuous and single valued for a certain range of values of t, x, y, z, $\cdots$ and has, within that range, a continuous partial derivative with respect to each dependent variable, then the system admits of an infinity of solutions

$$\begin{cases} f_1(x, t, c_1, c_2, \cdots, c_n) = 0, \\ f_2(y, t, c_1, c_2, \cdots, c_n) = 0, \\ f_3(z, t, c_1, c_2, \cdots, c_n) = 0, \\ \cdots\cdots\cdots\cdots\cdots\cdots\cdots, \end{cases} \tag{18}$$

(where the c's are arbitrary constants) such that an assigned set of values $(t_0, x_0, y_0, z_0, \cdots)$ within the range is satisfied by one, and only one, set of (18). (That is, $c_1, c_2, \cdots c_n$ are determined by the assigned set of values $t_0, x_0, y_0, z_0, \cdots$.)

14. Verify that the system

$$\frac{dx}{dt} = 1 - \frac{2x}{t},$$

$$\frac{dy}{dt} = x + y + \frac{2x}{t} - 1,$$

has for its general solution

$$x = \frac{t}{3} + \frac{c_1}{t^2},$$

$$y = c_2 e^t - \frac{t}{3} - \frac{c_1}{t^2}.$$

15. Derive the statement made in Section 5, *viz.*, that the general solution of a differential equation of order n contains n arbitrary constants, as a corollary to the Existence Theorem stated in Exercise 13.   *Hint:* Consider the equation

$$f(x, y, y', \cdots, y^{(n)}) = 0$$

as solved for $y^{(n)}$, *viz.*,

$$y^{(n)} = F(x, y, y', y'', \cdots, y^{(n-1)}).$$

Put the last equation in the form of a system of n simultaneous equations in one independent variable x and n dependent variables y, y', y'', $\cdots$, $y^{(n-1)}$; *viz.*,

$$\frac{dy}{dx} = y',$$

$$\frac{dy'}{dx} = y'',$$

$$\cdots \cdots \cdots \cdots$$
$$\cdots \cdots \cdots \cdots$$

$$\frac{dy^{(n-2)}}{dx} = y^{(n-1)},$$

$$\frac{dy^{(n-1)}}{dx} = F(x, y, y', \cdots, y^{(n-1)}).$$

16. Exhibit the equation $x^2 y''' + (1 - x)y'' - 2y' + xy = \sin x$ in the form of a system of equations of first order, as suggested in Exercise 15.

CHAPTER II

Differential Equations of the First Order and First Degree

7. Variables separable. A differential equation of the first order and first degree can be put into the form

$$M \, dx + N \, dy = 0, \tag{1}$$

where M and N are functions of x and y. It may happen that the function M contains x alone and that the function N contains y alone, or that the equation is reducible to one in which M and N have those properties. In such a case we may write the equation in the form

$$X(x) \, dx + Y(y) \, dy = 0. \tag{2}$$

The process of reducing an equation to the form (2) is called *separating the variables*. The resulting equation may be solved at once by an integration, giving

$$\int X(x) \, dx + \int Y(y) \, dy = c.*$$

As an illustration, consider the equation

$$3x^3(1 + y^2) \, dx + x \, dy = 0.$$

Upon dividing through by $x(1 + y^2)$, we have

$$3x^2 \, dx + \frac{dy}{1 + y^2} = 0,$$

whence, by integration,

$$x^3 + \text{arc tan } y = c.$$

Exercises

1. Solve the following by separating the variables:

(a) $dx - 2dy = 0$.

(b) $y(1 - x) \, dx + x^2(1 - y) \, dy = 0$.

---

* A differential equation is considered solved if it is reduced to quadratures.

(c) $5(1 - y) dx - xy(1 + x^2) dy = 0.$

(d) $2xy(4 - y^2) dx + (y - 1)(x^2 + 2) dy = 0.$

(e) $(1 + y) dx + \dfrac{dy}{x^2 - 2x} = 0.$

(f) $y \sqrt{y^2 - 1} dx - \sqrt{1 - x^2} dy = 0.$

(g) $\dfrac{ds}{dt} + \cos 2t = 0.$

(h) $e^{x^2 - y^2} + \dfrac{y}{x^2} \cdot \dfrac{dy}{dx} = 0.$

2. Find the system of all curves having the property that the normal at every point passes through the origin.

3. The acceleration of a particle moving in a straight line is the negative of its velocity. It starts from the origin with a velocity equal to 1. Find its position at the end of two units of time.

8. Exact differential equations. If we take the differential of the relation $x^2y - x + 3y^2 = c$, where c is constant, we obtain the differential equation

$$(2xy - 1) dx + (x^2 + 6y) dy = 0.$$

We may identify this with the equation

$$M \, dx + N \, dy = 0 \qquad (1)$$

by putting $M \equiv 2xy - 1$ and $N \equiv x^2 + 6y$. If we form the partial derivative of M with respect to y and the partial derivative of N with respect to x, we notice that each is equal to $2x$ and hence that

$$M_y \equiv N_x. \qquad (3)$$

Similarly, any relation of the form $f(x, y) = c$ in which the partial derivatives f_x and f_y exist, gives a differential equation

$$f_x \, dx + f_y \, dy = 0.$$

This is of the form (1), with $M \equiv f_x$ and $N \equiv f_y$, and, from the mode of its derivation, it is said to be *exact*. An equation of the form (1) will evidently be exact if, and only if, there exists a function $f(x, y)$ such that $f_x \equiv M$ and $f_y \equiv N$. If this function $f(x, y)$ not only exists but has second partial derivatives, we may note that $M_y \equiv f_{xy}$ and $N_x \equiv f_{yx}$. If, further, these second partial derivatives are continuous, the order of differentiation is immaterial, and we have (3). In other words, if (1) is exact and is obtained from the primitive $f(x, y) = c$ such that $f(x, y)$ has continuous first and second partial derivatives, then (3) holds.

Let us now ask whether or not relation (3) is a sufficient condition for the exactness of (1), $i.$ $e.$, whether or not there can be shown to exist a function $f(x, y)$ such that $f_x \equiv M$ and $f_y \equiv N$, whenever (3) holds. We first follow through the example

$$(2xy^2 - y \sin x + 2x - 1)\, dx + \left(2x^2y + \cos x + \frac{1}{y}\right) dy = 0. \quad (4)$$

Here we have:
$$M \equiv 2xy^2 - y \sin x + 2x - 1,$$
$$N \equiv 2x^2y + \cos x + \frac{1}{y},$$
$$M_y \equiv 4xy - \sin x \equiv N_x,$$

and hence (3) holds. We shall show the existence of a function $f(x, y)$ such that $f_x \equiv M$ and $f_y \equiv N$ by actually setting up the function in the form

$$f(x, y) \equiv \int_a^x M(x, y)\, dx + \int N(a, y)\, dy$$

$$= \int_a^x (2xy^2 - y \sin x + 2x - 1)\, dx + \int \left(2a^2y + \cos a + \frac{1}{y}\right) dy,$$

where a is any constant and where the definite integral is evaluated with y held constant. Carrying out these operations, we have

$$f(x, y) \equiv [x^2y^2 + y \cos x + x^2 - x]_a^x + a^2y^2 + y \cos a + \log y$$
$$\equiv x^2y^2 + y \cos x + x^2 - x + \log y - a^2 + a.$$

Forming the first partial derivatives of this function, we find

$$f_x \equiv 2xy^2 - y \sin x + 2x - 1 \equiv M$$

and

$$f_y \equiv 2x^2y + \cos x + \frac{1}{y} \equiv N.$$

This function $f(x, y)$, therefore, has the desired properties, and (4) is an exact differential equation having the complete solution

$$x^2y^2 + y \cos x + x^2 - x + \log y = c.$$

Following the method of the above illustration, we now prove that (3) is a sufficient condition for the exactness of (1). We assume, then, a differential equation (1) in which M and N are continuous and have continuous partial derivatives M_y and N_x

such that (3) holds.   To exhibit a function $f(x, y)$ such that $f_x \equiv M$ and $f_y \equiv N$, we set up the function

$$f(x, y) \equiv \int_a^x M(x, y)\, dx + \int N(a, y)\, dy,$$

where, again, the definite integral is evaluated with y held constant, and this time, a is any constant for which $N(a, y)$ is integrable. The second term is a function of y alone, and we see at once that

$$f_x(x, y) \equiv M(x, y).$$

Differentiation with respect to y gives

$$f_y(x, y) \equiv \frac{\partial}{\partial y} \int_a^x M(x, y)\, dx + \frac{\partial}{\partial y} \int N(a, y)\, dy.$$

The second term may be evaluated at once as $N(a, y)$, while we may put the symbol $\dfrac{\partial}{\partial y}$ under the first integral sign by Leibnitz's rule,* and thus reduce f_y to

$$\int_a^x M_y(x, y)\, dx + N(a, y).$$

Now, since (3) holds, this may be written

$$f_y \equiv \int_a^x N_x(x, y)\, dx + N(a, y)$$
$$\equiv N(x, y) \Big|_a^x + N(a, y)$$
$$\equiv N(x, y) - N(a, y) + N(a, y)$$
$$\equiv N(x, y).$$

Thus, we see that the function $f(x, y)$ has the required properties, and, therefore, that (3) is sufficient for the exactness of (1).   The complete solution is evidently

$$f(x, y) = c.$$

The student has seen, by the above illustration, how to find the complete solution of an exact differential equation.   In practice, he may prefer to proceed as in the following example.   To solve the equation

$$(2xy + e^z)\, dx + (x^2 - 1)\, dy = 0,$$

---

* See Wilson's *Advanced Calculus*, Section 119.

note that $M_y \equiv N_x$, and write

$$f(x, y) \equiv \int M \, dx \equiv \int (2xy + e^x) \, dx \equiv x^2 y + e^x + \varphi(y).$$

Here, $\varphi(y)$ must be evaluated so that

$$f_y(x, y) \equiv x^2 + \varphi'(y) \equiv N \equiv x^2 - 1,$$

i. e., so that

$$\varphi'(y) \equiv -1.$$

We see that this will be true if $\varphi(y) \equiv -y$, for which our function $f(x, y)$ takes the form

$$f(x, y) \equiv x^2 y + e^x - y,$$

and the equation has the solution

$$x^2 y + e^x - y = c.$$

Note: A direct way of integrating the above would be to group the terms as follows:

$$(2xy \, dx + x^2 \, dy) + e^x \, dx - dy = 0,$$

hence as

$$d(x^2 y) + e^x \, dx - dy = 0,$$

and the integration gives immediately

$$x^2 y + e^x - y = C.$$

Similarly, in the first illustration above, the terms might have been grouped as

$$(2xy^2 \, dx + 2x^2 y \, dy) + (-y \sin x \, dx + \cos x \, dy) + (2x - 1) \, dx + \frac{1}{y} \, dy = 0,$$

i. e.,

$$d(x^2 y^2) + d(y \cos x) + (2x - 1) \, dx + \frac{1}{y} \, dy = 0,$$

whence

$$x^2 y^2 + y \cos x + x^2 - x + \log y = C.$$

Exercises

1. Test the following for exactness, and solve those which are exact:

   (a) $(x + 3y) \, dx + (x - 2y) \, dy = 0$.
   (b) $(y + 3x) \, dx + x \, dy = 0$.

(c) $(x^2 - 4xy + 4y^2)\, dx + (2y^2 + 8xy - 6x^2)\, dy = 0.$

(d) $(ax^2 + 2bxy + cy^2)\, dx + (bx^2 + 2cxy + gy^2)\, dy = 0.$

(e) $(x^3 + 5xy^2)\, dx + (5x^2y + 2y^3)\, dy = 0.$

(f) $(x^2 + xy + y^2)\, dx + (4x^2 - 2xy + 3y^2)\, dy = 0.$

(g) $(7x - 3y + 2)\, dx + (4y - 3x - 5)\, dy = 0.$

(h) $(5xy^4 + x)\, dx - (2 + 3y^2 - 10x^2y^3)\, dy = 0.$

(i) $x^{-2}y^{-1}(e^{-\frac{1}{xy}} - 1)\, dx + y^{-2}x^{-1}(e^{-\frac{1}{xy}} - 1)\, dy = 0.$

(j) $\sec^2 x \tan y\, dx + \sec^2 y \tan x\, dy = 0.$

(k) $(2xy - \cos x)\, dx + (x^2 - 1)\, dy = 0.$

(l) $(\tan y - 3x^2)\, dx + x \sec^2 y\, dy = 0.$

(m) $ye^x\, dx + e^x\, dy = 0.$

(n) $\cosh x \cosh y\, dx - \sinh x \sinh y\, dy = 0.$

(o) $\cosh x\, (\cosh y - 1)\, dx + \sinh y\, (\sinh x + 1)\, dy = 0.$

(p) $2x \tan y + \sin 2y + (x^2 \sec^2 y + 2x \cos 2y - e^y)y' = 0.$

2. Solve Exercise 1 (j) by separating the variables.

3. Prove that an equation is exact if its variables have been separated.

4. Determine b so that the equation $(3x - 5y + 7)\, dx + (bx + 6y + 10)\, dy = 0$ will be exact.

9. Integrating factors. As we saw in Chapter I, the general solution of a differential equation of the form

$$M\, dx + N\, dy = 0 \tag{1}$$

is a relation of the form

$$f(x, y, c) = 0,$$

where c is an arbitrary constant. If we solve this equation for c, we may write it in the form

$$\varphi(x, y) = c.$$

Differentiated, this gives

$$\varphi_x\, dx + \varphi_y\, dy = 0. \tag{5}$$

In order that Equations (1) and (5) may be simultaneously satisfied by quantities dx and dy, not both zero, it is necessary and sufficient* that the determinant

$$\begin{vmatrix} M & N \\ \varphi_x & \varphi_y \end{vmatrix}$$

---

* See Dickson's *Theory of Equations*, p. 119.

have the value zero. Then the elements in the second row are proportional to those in the first. The factor of proportionality being, in general, a function of x and y, we have

$$\varphi_x \equiv \mu(x, y) \cdot M,$$
$$\varphi_y \equiv \mu(x, y) \cdot N.$$

If (1) is multiplied through by $\mu(x, y)$, the result is the exact differential equation (5). The function $\mu(x, y)$, as employed here, is called an *integrating factor* of Equation (1). The integrating factor μ is by no means unique. As a matter of fact, it can be shown that if an equation of form (1) satisfies the hypotheses of the Existence Theorem, and hence has a general solution, it has an infinite number of integrating factors. The demonstration is left to the student in an exercise at the close of this chapter.

Illustrations

If the differential equation

$$x\, dy - y\, dx = 0$$

is multiplied through by $\dfrac{1}{x^2}$, it becomes

$$\frac{dy}{x} - \frac{y}{x^2}\, dx = 0,$$

in which $N \equiv \dfrac{1}{x}$, $M \equiv -\dfrac{y}{x^2}$, $M_y \equiv -\dfrac{1}{x^2} \equiv N_x$, and hence (3) holds and the equation is exact. The student may readily show that $\dfrac{1}{y^2}$, $\dfrac{1}{xy}$, and $\dfrac{1}{x^2 \pm y^2}$ are other integrating factors of this equation. If we solve the equation by using each of these five integrating factors in turn, we obtain

$$\frac{y}{x} = c, \; \frac{x}{y} = c, \; \log\frac{y}{x} = c, \; \tan^{-1}\frac{y}{x} = c, \; \tfrac{1}{2}\log\frac{y+x}{y-x} = c$$

in the respective cases. These solutions may be seen to be essentially the same by observing that, when considered geometrically, each represents a family of straight lines through the origin.

The student's success in finding integrating factors by inspection will depend largely upon his experience and ingenuity, but he might do well to keep in mind the following differentials of common functions:

$$d(xy) = y \, dx + x \, dy;$$
$$d(x^2 \pm y^2) = 2x \, dx \pm 2y \, dy;$$
$$d\left(\frac{y}{x}\right) = \frac{x \, dy - y \, dx}{x^2};$$
$$d\left(\tan^{-1}\frac{y}{x}\right) = \frac{x \, dy - y \, dx}{x^2 + y^2};$$
$$d\left(\log\frac{y-x}{y+x}\right) = \frac{2x \, dy - 2y \, dx}{y^2 - x^2};$$
$$d\left(\frac{x+y}{x-y}\right) = \frac{2x \, dy - 2y \, dx}{(x-y)^2};$$
$$d\left(\frac{x-y}{x+y}\right) = \frac{2y \, dx - 2x \, dy}{(x+y)^2}.$$

The form of the algebraic expressions in the differential equation may suggest an integrating factor, as in the examples below.

Illustration 1

To find an integrating factor of

$$y \, dx - x \, dy + \log x \, dx = 0,$$

note that $\log x$ suggests $\dfrac{1}{x}$, while $y \, dx - x \, dy$ suggests $\dfrac{1}{x^2}$. Trying the latter, we obtain

$$\frac{y + \log x}{x^2} \, dx - \frac{1}{x} \, dy = 0,$$

which is exact.

Illustration 2

Given the equation

$$(x^2 + y^2)(x \, dx + y \, dy) + (1 + x^2 + y^2)^{\frac{1}{2}}(y \, dx - x \, dy) = 0,$$

the algebraic factor $x^2 + y^2$ in one term and the differential factor $y \, dx - x \, dy$ in the other both suggest $\dfrac{1}{x^2 + y^2}$, while the algebraic factor $(1 + x^2 + y^2)^{\frac{1}{2}}$ in one term and $x \, dx + y \, dy$ in the other both suggest $\dfrac{1}{(1 + x^2 + y^2)^{\frac{1}{2}}}$. Trying the product, we obtain

$$\frac{x\,dx + y\,dy}{(1 + x^2 + y^2)^{\frac{1}{2}}} + \frac{y\,dx - x\,dy}{x^2 + y^2} = 0,$$

the left member of which is the differential of

$$(1 + x^2 + y^2)^{\frac{1}{2}} + \tan^{-1}\frac{x}{y},$$

and the equation is therefore exact.

Exercises

1. In each of the following, find an integrating factor by inspection:

(a) $\dfrac{x^3\,dy - yx^2\,dx}{x^2 + y^2} + x^2\,dy = 0.$

(b) $(2x + y)\,dx - (x - 2y)\,dy = 0.$

(c) $(x^2y + y^2)\,dx - x^3\,dy = 0.$

(d) $\dfrac{1}{x}(2x - y^3)\,dx - 3y^2\,dy = 0.$

(e) $(x^2 + y^2)\,dx = x(x\,dy - y\,dx).$

(f) $y\,dx + (x + x^2y^2)\,dy = 0.$

(g) $(2x^3y^3 - y)\,dx + (2x^3y^3 - x)\,dy = 0.$

(h) $2y\,dx + (1 - \log y - 2x)\,dy = 0.$

(i) $(x^2y + xy^2 - y^3)\,dx + (y^2x + yx^2 - x^3)\,dy = 0.$

(j) $a(3x\,dy + 2xy\,dx) + 3y\,dx = 0.$

(k) $(x^4\cos x + 2py^2x)\,dx - 2px^2y\,dy = 0.$

(l) $(y + \sinh y\,\operatorname{sech} x)\,dx + (x\,\operatorname{sech} x\,\cosh y + \tanh x)\,dy = 0.$

(m) $(xy - y)\,dx + (x^2 - 2x + y)\,dy = 0.$

(n) $\sqrt{x^2 + y^2} - x + (\sqrt{x^2 + y^2} - y)\dfrac{dy}{dx} = 0.$

2. Derive the partial differential equation which must be satisfied by an integrating factor $\mu(x, y)$ of the differential equation $M\,dx + N\,dy = 0.$

3. If $M \equiv yf(xy)$ and $N \equiv xg(xy)$ where f and g are functions of the product xy, show that $\dfrac{1}{Mx - Ny}$ is an integrating factor provided $Mx - Ny$ is not identically zero.

4. Solve $(y - xy^2)\,dx + (3x - x^2y)\,dy = 0.$

5. Solve $y(1 + 2xy - x^2y^2)\,dx + x(1 + 2xy)\,dy = 0.$

6. Solve $(y - xy^2 + x^{3/2}y^{5/4})\,dx + x(1 - xy - 2x^{3/2}y^{3/2})\,dy = 0.$

7. Solve $(y - xy^2 \sin xy)\, dx + (4x - x^2y \sin xy)\, dy = 0$.

8. If the functions M and N are of the form of Exercise 3 above, but $Mx - Ny$ is identically zero, find an integrating factor.

9. Solve $(xy^2 - y)\, dx + x(xy - 1)\, dy = 0$.

10. Show that the substitution $v = xy \left(\therefore y = \dfrac{v}{x}\right)$ will reduce the equation of Exercise 3 above to an equation in x and v in which the variables are separable.

11. Solve the equation of Exercise 5 by the substitution $v = xy$.

12. Solve $(2y - xy^2 - x^2y^3)\, dx + (2x - x^2y)\, dy = 0$ by the substitution $v = xy$.

13. Solve Exercise 7 by the substitution $v = xy$.

14. Show that an equation of the form $x^r y^s (my\, dx + nx\, dy) = 0$ has an infinite number of integrating factors of the form $x^a y^b$, and find expressions for a and b.

15. Solve $x^{-1}y^3(3y\, dx - 2x\, dy) = 0$.

16. Solve $5x^2y^6\, dx - x^3y^5\, dy = 0$.

17. Show that a differential equation of the form $x^r y^s (my\, dx + nx\, dy) + x^p y^\sigma (\mu y\, dx + vx\, dy) = 0$ has an integrating factor of the form $x^a y^b$, if the determinant $\begin{vmatrix} m & n \\ \mu & v \end{vmatrix}$ is not zero, and find the values of a and b.

18. Solve $x^4y(3y\, dx + 2x\, dy) - x(y\, dx - 2x\, dy) = 0$.

19. Solve $y^2(3y\, dx - 6x\, dy) - x(y\, dx + x\, dy) = 0$.

20. Solve $(2x^3y - 2y)\, dx + (x - 2x^4)\, dy = 0$.

21. Solve $a(x\, dy - 3y\, dx) = bxy\, dx$.

22. Find an integrating factor for an equation of the form of Exercise 17 in case $\begin{vmatrix} m & n \\ \mu & v \end{vmatrix}$ vanishes.

23. Solve $x^2(4y\, dx + 3x\, dy) - y^2(8y\, dx + 6x\, dy) = 0$.

24. Solve $(2x^3 + 4xy^2)\, dy - (3x^2y + 6y^3)\, dx = 0$.

25. If $\dfrac{M_y - N_x}{N} \equiv f(x)$, a function of x alone, show that $e^{\int f(x)\, dx}$ is an integrating factor of $M\, dx + N\, dy = 0$.

26. Find an integrating factor of $M\, dx + N\, dy = 0$ in case $\dfrac{N_x - M_y}{M} \equiv g(y)$, a function of y alone.

27. Solve $(y^4 - 5y)\,dx + (7xy^3 - 5x + y)\,dy = 0$.

28. Solve $(3x^2 + 6xy + 3y^2)\,dx + (2x^2 + 3xy)\,dy = 0$.

29. Solve $(3xy - 8y + x^2)\,dx + (x^2 - 5x + 6)\,dy = 0$.

30. Solve $(4x^2y^3 + 2x^2y)\,dx + 4x^3y^2\,dy = 0$.

31. Solve $(3xy - x^2)\,dx + x^2\,dy = 0$.

10. Homogeneous equations. A function $f(x, y, z, \cdots)$ of any number of variables is said to be *homogeneous* in those variables and of *degree n* if the effect of multiplying each variable by any number t is to multiply the function by t^n, *i. e.*, if

$$f(xt, yt, zt, \cdots) \equiv t^n f(x, y, z, \cdots). \tag{6}$$

Thus, $xe^{y/x} + \dfrac{y^2}{x}\log\dfrac{x^2}{y^2}$ is homogeneous and of degree 1, since

$$txe^{ty/tx} + \frac{t^2y^2}{tx}\log\frac{t^2x^2}{t^2y^2} \equiv t\left(xe^{y/x} + \frac{y^2}{x}\log\frac{x^2}{y^2}\right).$$

Let the student verify, as an exercise, that:

   (a) $\dfrac{(x^2 + y^2)^{\frac{1}{2}}}{x} + \cos\dfrac{y}{x}$ is homogeneous and of degree 0;

   (b) The polynomial $ax^n + bx^{n-1}y + cx^{n-2}y^2 + \cdots + kx^{n-i}y^i + \cdots + py^n$ is homogeneous and of degree n.

We now define the differential equation

$$M\,dx + N\,dy = 0 \tag{1}$$

as *homogeneous* if M and N are homogeneous functions of x and y and of the same degree. A method of solving such an equation is suggested by the significant fact that the quotient of two homogeneous functions of x and y of the same degree is a function of $\dfrac{y}{x}$,*

---

  * Apply (6) to $M(x, y)$ with $t = \dfrac{1}{x}$ and obtain $M\left(1, \dfrac{y}{x}\right) \equiv \dfrac{1}{x^n}\,M(x, y)$.

Hence, $M(x, y) \equiv x^n M\left(1, \dfrac{y}{x}\right) \equiv x^n f\left(\dfrac{y}{x}\right)$. Similarly, $N(x, y) \equiv x^n g\left(\dfrac{y}{x}\right)$.

Thus, $-\dfrac{M}{N} \equiv -\dfrac{x^n f\left(\dfrac{y}{x}\right)}{x^n g\left(\dfrac{y}{x}\right)} \equiv F\left(\dfrac{y}{x}\right)$.

so that (1) is equivalent to $\dfrac{dy}{dx} = -\dfrac{M(x, y)}{N(x, y)} \equiv F\left(\dfrac{y}{x}\right)$. It is therefore natural to introduce a new variable v, defined by $v = \dfrac{y}{x}$ $(y = vx)$. This reduces the given equation to $\dfrac{v\,dx + x\,dv}{dx} = F(v)$, with the variables obviously separable. After solving this equation, it remains to replace v by $\dfrac{y}{x}$ to obtain the solution of (1).

Illustration

To solve $(y^2 + xy)\,dx - x^2\,dy = 0$, where M and N are evidently homogeneous and of degree 2, put $y = vx$ and obtain

$$x^2(v^2 + v)\,dx - x^2(v\,dx + x\,dv) = 0,$$

or

$$v^2\,dx - x\,dv = 0.$$

The solution is $\log x = c - \dfrac{1}{v} = c - \dfrac{x}{y}$, or $x = e^{-x/y}e^c$, or, lastly, $x = ce^{-x/y}$.

Note: In dividing by x^2, in the course of our solution, we have apparently suppressed a root $x = 0$ which obviously satisfies the equation.* However, the solution is recovered from the general solution by assigning to c the value zero. Hence, the division is legitimate.

Exercises

1. Solve $(2x + y)\,dy = (x - 2y)\,dx$. $\quad (x(x^2 + y^2))$

2. Solve $y' = \dfrac{4y^2 + xy - 3x^2}{x^2}$.

3. Solve $\dfrac{y}{x}\,dx = dy + \sec^2\dfrac{y}{x}\,dx$.

4. Solve $(x^2 - y^2)\,dx - \dfrac{2y^3}{x}\,dy = 0$.

5. Solve $\dfrac{dy}{dx} = e^{y/x} + \dfrac{y}{x} + 1$.

6. Solve $x\,dy - y\,dx = \sqrt{x^2 + y^2}\,dx$.

7. Show that the substitution $x = vy$ will separate the variables in the homogeneous equation $M\,dx + N\,dy = 0$.

---

* Let the student satisfy himself that $x = 0$ is a solution.

8. Solve Exercises 1, 3, and 5 by use of the substitution of Exercise 7.

9. Show that a straight line through the origin intersects at a constant angle all integral curves of a homogeneous equation.

10. Prove that $\dfrac{1}{Mx + Ny}$ is an integrating factor for the homogeneous equation $M\,dx + N\,dy = 0$ if $Mx + Ny$ is not identically zero.*

11. Solve the following by employing an integrating factor:

(a) $(y^4 - 2x^3y)\,dx + (x^4 - 2xy^3)\,dy = 0.$

(b) $\left(2x \sinh \dfrac{y}{x} - y \cosh \dfrac{y}{x}\right) dx + x \cosh \dfrac{y}{x}\,dy = 0.$

(c) $\dfrac{y - x}{x}\,dx = dy + \cos \dfrac{y}{x}\,dx.$

12. The method of Exercise 10 obviously does not apply if $Mx + Ny$ is identically zero. Find an integrating factor in that case.

13. Prove that if $M\,dx + N\,dy = 0$ is exact and homogeneous of degree not equal to -1, its solution is $Mx + Ny = c$. (Hence, the solution is written down at sight, without a quadrature.) *Hint:* Employ the footnote to Exercise 10.

14. Apply the principle of Exercise 13 to the following:

(a) $(2x + y)\,dx + (x - 2y)\,dy = 0.$
(b) $(3x^2 - 2xy + y^2)\,dx - (x^2 - 2xy + y^2)\,dy = 0.$

15. Prove that if $M\,dx + N\,dy = 0$ is exact and homogeneous of degree -1, then $Mx + Ny$ is identically equal to some constant. Find that constant for the equation $\dfrac{1 + e^{x/y}}{x + ye^{x/y}}\,dx + \dfrac{(y - x)e^{x/y}}{xy + y^2e^{x/y}}\,dy = 0.$

Note: This shows why the principle of Exercise 13 is subject to the exception stated.

---

* In completing this exercise, the student may find it well to resort to an important theorem on homogeneous functions, due to Euler and bearing his name; *viz.*, if $f(x, y, z, \cdots)$ is homogeneous and of degree n, then $xf_x + yf_y + zf_z + \cdots \equiv nf$. This theorem will be frequently used, and hence if the student is not already familiar with it, he should refer to any good book on the calculus for its proof and discussion.

16. (a) Discuss the equation of the text, $\dfrac{x\,dv + v\,dx}{dx} = F(v)$, for the case when $F(v)$ is identically equal to v.

(b) If α is a root of $F(v) = v$, show that $y = \alpha x$ is a solution of $y' = F(y/x)$.

(c) Solve $y' = \dfrac{y^2}{x^2} + \dfrac{y}{x} - 1$.

17. Prove. If in a homogeneous equation a change is made to polar coordinates (*i. e.*, by $x = r \cos \theta$, $y = r \sin \theta$) the variables are separable in the resulting equation.

18. Prove that the non-homogeneous equation $\dfrac{dy}{dx} = \dfrac{y}{x} + x^m y^n f\left(\dfrac{y}{x}\right)$ can be solved by the substitution $y = vx$.

19. Use the method of Exercise 18 to solve the following non-homogeneous equations:

(a) $\dfrac{dy}{dx} = \dfrac{y}{x} + x^2 e^{\frac{-2y}{x}}$. (b) $\dfrac{dy}{dx} = \dfrac{y}{x} + \dfrac{\sec^2 \frac{y}{x}}{y^2}$.

(c) $x \dfrac{dy}{dx} = y + y^2 \sqrt{\dfrac{3y - x}{x}}$.

20. At any point, P, of a curve, the inclination of OP, where O is the origin, is equal to the angle from OP to the tangent drawn at P to the curve. Find the equation of the curve.

11. Equations reducible to homogeneous equations. Consider the non-homogeneous equation

$$(2x - y + 3)\,dx + (x + y - 1)\,dy = 0. \tag{7}$$

If we introduce new variables defined by

$$\begin{aligned} u &= 2x - y + 3 \\ v &= x + y - 1 \end{aligned} \tag{8}$$

whence $du = 2dx - dy$, $dv = dx + dy$, and hence, $dx = \dfrac{du + dv}{3}$ and $dy = \dfrac{-du + 2dv}{3}$, the equation becomes

$$(u - v)\,du + (u + 2v)\,dv = 0,$$

which is homogeneous and may therefore be solved by the method of the preceding section.   Its solution is

$$\log (u^2 + 2v^2)^{1/2} = c - \frac{1}{\sqrt{2}} \tan^{-1} \left(\frac{v}{u} \sqrt{2} \right),$$

or

$$e^{-\frac{\sqrt{2}}{2} \tan^{-1} \frac{v\sqrt{2}}{u}} = c(u^2 + 2v^2)^{1/2}.$$

(The student should solve the last differential equation and obtain this result.)   We now replace u and v by their equivalents in (8), and obtain, as the solution of (7),

$$e^{-\frac{\sqrt{2}}{2} \tan^{-1} \frac{(x+y-1)\sqrt{2}}{2x-y+3}} = c[(2x - y + 3)^2 + 2(x + y - 1)^2]^{1/2}.$$

Evidently, this method is applicable to any equation of the form

$$(ax + by + c)\, dx + (\alpha x + \beta y + \gamma)\, dy = 0, \tag{9}$$

where a, b, c, α, β, γ are constants such that $\begin{vmatrix} a & b \\ \alpha & \beta \end{vmatrix} \neq 0.$

Exercises

1. Solve $(2x - 5y + 3)\, dx - (5x - 12y + 8)\, dy = 0.$

2. Solve $(8x + 25y - 62)\, dx + (-11x - 4y + 11)\, dy = 0.$

3. Solve $(x - y + 1)\, dx + (2x + y - 2)\, dy = 0.$

4. Show that the method of this section is applicable to any equation of the form

$$\frac{dy}{dx} = f \left(\frac{ax + by + c}{\alpha x + \beta y + \gamma} \right)$$

in which the determinant $\begin{vmatrix} a & b \\ \alpha & \beta \end{vmatrix}$ is not zero.

5. Solve

$$\frac{dy}{dx} = \left(\frac{6x + 4y - 3}{3x + y - 1} \right)^2 - 2 \left(\frac{6x + 4y - 3}{3x + y - 1} \right).$$

Note: The method here presented obviously fails for an equation of the form (9) in which $a\beta - b\alpha = 0$, since the substitutions $u = ax + by + c$, $v = \alpha x + \beta y + \gamma$, lead to $dx = \dfrac{\beta\, du - b\, dv}{a\beta - b\alpha}$, $dy = \dfrac{-\alpha\, du + a\, dv}{a\beta - b\alpha}.$ But in that case, since $a\beta - b\alpha = 0$ implies

$\frac{a}{\alpha} = \frac{b}{\beta} = k$, we have $ax + by = k(\alpha x + \beta y)$, and the substitution $z = \alpha x + \beta y$ will separate the variables.   Indeed, (9) becomes

$$(kz + c)\, dx + (z + \gamma)\, \frac{dz - \alpha\, dx}{\beta} = 0,*$$

or

$$(\beta kz + \beta c - \alpha z - \alpha\gamma)\, dx + (z + \gamma)\, dz = 0,$$

or

$$dx + \frac{z + \gamma}{z(\beta k - \alpha) + (\beta c - \alpha\gamma)}\, dz = 0.$$

   6. Solve $(x - 2y + 1)\, dx + (2x - 4y + 3)\, dy = 0$.

   7. Solve $(3x - y + 2)\, dx - (6x - 2y)\, dy = 0$.

   8. Solve $\dfrac{dy}{dx} = \dfrac{x + 2y - 1}{x + 2y + 1}$.

   9. Show that the substitution $ax + by = z$ will separate the variables in any equation of the form $\dfrac{dy}{dx} = f\left(\dfrac{ax + by + c}{\alpha x + \beta y + \gamma}\right)$ if $a\beta = b\alpha$.

   10. Solve $y' = \dfrac{(2x - y)^2}{(4x - 2y - 1)^2}$.

   11. Solve $(x + 2y^3)\, dx + 6xy^2\, dy = 0$.   *Hint:* Put $u = y^3$.

   12. Solve $y' = \dfrac{3x + 2}{-2x + y - 1} + \dfrac{-2x + y - 1}{3x + 2} + 1$.

   13. Solve $y' = \dfrac{3y - 2x - 3}{4x - 6y}$.

   12. Linear equations of the first order.   An equation of the form

$$y' + yP(x) = Q(x), \tag{10}$$

in which the dependent variable and its derivative enter to the first degree, is called *linear*.   The linear equation

$$y' + yP(x) = 0$$

is said to be *homogeneous*.†   Its solution is obtained at once as

$$y = ke^{-\int P\, dx}. \tag{11}$$

---

* The case $\beta = 0$ now presents an apparent difficulty, but since $\dfrac{b}{\beta} = k$, then $b = 0$, and (9) has its variables immediately separable.

   † Obviously, the term *homogeneous* is used here in a different sense from that of Section 10.

We now inquire in what way the constant k in (11) can be replaced by a function of x, such that the solution of (10) will be the same in form as (11). Under this hypothesis (k, a function of x, to be determined presently) we have

$$y' = e^{-\int P \, dx} \cdot k' - Pk e^{-\int P \, dx}. \tag{12}$$

Substituting (11) and (12) into (10), we obtain, as an equation from which to determine k,

$$e^{-\int P \, dx} \cdot k' \equiv Q(x),$$

whence

$$k' \equiv Q(x) \cdot e^{\int P \, dx}$$

and

$$k \equiv \int Q(x) \cdot e^{\int P \, dx} \, dx + c,$$

where c is an arbitrary constant. The solution of (10) is now obtained as

$$y = \left[\int Q(x) \cdot e^{\int P \, dx} \, dx + c \right] e^{-\int P \, dx}. \tag{13}$$

Illustration

Given the equation

$$y' - 2y = e^{3x},$$

we first solve the corresponding homogeneous equation

$$y' - 2y = 0$$

and obtain

$$y = ke^{2x}.$$

Now considering k as a function of x, we have

$$y' = 2ke^{2x} + e^{2x} \cdot k'$$

and, by substituting into the given equation, we obtain

$$2ke^{2x} + e^{2x} \cdot k' - 2ke^{2x} \equiv e^{3x},$$

whence, $k' \equiv e^x$, $k \equiv e^x + c$, and the solution of our equation is

$$y = (e^x + c)e^{2x}.$$

We might have obtained the solution directly from (13) by setting $P(x) \equiv -2$ and $Q(x) \equiv e^{3x}$, but the student is advised to familiarize himself with a method rather than to memorize a formula.

Note: The method by which the quantity k is here treated is one that the student will meet frequently in the solution of linear differential equations, and it is called *the method of variation of constants*, or, also, *the method of variation of parameters*.

An alternative method of treating (10) is to employ an integrating factor. That $e^{\int P\,dx}$ is such a factor, the student will perceive immediately. Indeed, when it is introduced, (10) becomes

$$e^{\int P\,dx} \cdot y' + Py\,e^{\int P\,dx} = Qe^{\int P\,dx},$$

or

$$\frac{d}{dx}\,(ye^{\int P\,dx}) = Qe^{\int P\,dx}.$$

Hence,

$$ye^{\int P\,dx} = \int Qe^{\int P\,dx}\,dx + c,$$

or

$$y = e^{-\int P\,dx}\left[\int Qe^{\int P\,dx}\,dx + c\right],$$

that is, (13) once again.

In the illustration worked above, the integrating factor is

$$e^{\int -2dx} \equiv e^{-2x}.$$

The equation becomes

$$e^{-2x} \cdot y' - 2ye^{-2x} = e^x;$$

that is,

$$\frac{d}{dx}\,(ye^{-2x}) = e^x,$$

whence,

$$ye^{-2x} = e^x + c,$$

or

$$y = e^{2x}(e^x + c).$$

Exercises

1. Solve the following:

(a) $y' + y \cos x = e^{-\sin x}$.

(b) $2x\,dy = (2x^3 - y)\,dx$.

(c) $3xy\,dx = \sin 2x\,dx - dy$.

(d) $2yy' - \dfrac{y^2}{x^2} = e^{\frac{x^2-1}{x}}$.   *Hint:* Put $u = y^2$.

(e) $y' \sec^2 y + \dfrac{x \tan y}{x^2 + 1} = x.$

(f) $y' + 2xy + x = e^{-x^2}.$

(g) $x^2 y'' + 2xy' = 2.$ *Hint:* Set $p = y'.$

2. (a) Adapt the methods of the text to the equation

$$\frac{dx}{dy} + xP(y) = Q(y),$$

and obtain a solution for it corresponding to (13).

(b) Solve $dx - dy\,(x + \log y) = 0.$

(c) Solve $\cos x\, dx - 4 \sin x\, dy = y^2\, dy.$

(d) Solve $\cos y + x \sin y \log x \cdot y' = x \cos^2 y.$

(e) Solve $dx + \dfrac{x}{\sqrt{1 - y^2}}\, dy = e^{\cos^{-1} y}\, dy.$

3. Solve the following:

(a) $\cos y \dfrac{dy}{dx} + \dfrac{\sin y}{x} = \sin 2x.$

(b) $y \sec^2 x\, dx + 3 \tan x\, dy = y \cos^2 2y\, dy.$

4. Show that if $y = f(x)$ is a solution of $y' + yP(x) = 0$, then $y = c \cdot f(x)$ is also a solution, where c is any constant.

5. Show that $y = e^{-\int P\, dx} \cdot \displaystyle\int Q(x) e^{\int P\, dx}\, dx$ satisfies Equation (10) of the text.

6. Show that if $y = f(x)$ is any solution of (10), then $y = f(x) + ce^{-\int P\, dx}$ is the general solution of (10); *i. e.*, that any solution of (10) added to the general solution of the corresponding homogeneous equation $y' + yP(x) = 0$ gives the general solution of (10). (Consider Formula (13) in the light of Exercise 5.)

7. If $y = f(x)$ and $y = g(x)$ are two distinct solutions of (10), show that the complete solution is given by

$$\frac{y - f(x)}{g(x) - f(x)} = c.$$

8. Assume $y = f(x)$ to be a known solution of $y' + y \cdot P(x) = 0$. To find the solution of $y' + y \cdot P(x) = Q(x)$, set $y = v \cdot f(x)$ and determine v. Compare the result with Formula (13). This provides another method of treating the linear equation.

9. Solve by the method of Exercise 8 the example worked out in the text.

13. Equations reducible to linear equations.   An equation easily reducible to the linear form is the so-called *Bernoulli* * *equation,*

$$y' + yP(x) = y^nQ(x) \quad (n \neq 0,\ n \neq 1). \quad (14)$$

If we divide through by y^n, to obtain

$$y^{-n}y' + y^{-n+1}P(x) = Q(x),$$

an obvious change of variable is to set $y^{-n+1} = z$.   From this we have $z' = (1 - n)y^{-n}y'$, leading to

$$\frac{1}{1 - n} z' + zP(x) = Q(x),$$

a linear equation.

To illustrate, consider the equation $y' - \dfrac{y}{3x} = y^4 \log x$.   Dividing through by y^4, we have

$$y^{-4}y' - y^{-3} \cdot \frac{1}{3x} = \log x.$$

Setting $y^{-3} = z$, and hence $z' = -3y^{-4}y'$, we have the new equation

$$-\frac{1}{3} z' - \frac{1}{3x} \cdot z = \log x, \quad (15)$$

which is linear.   Let us solve this by the method of Exercise 8 of the preceding section.   (The other methods would apply as well, of course.)   The solution of the corresponding homogeneous equation, *i. e.*, of

$$-\frac{1}{3} z' - \frac{1}{3x} \cdot z = 0,$$

is $z = \dfrac{c}{x}.$ $\Big($For simplicity, a particular solution may be taken, say $z = \dfrac{1}{x}.\Big)$ Now let $z = \dfrac{1}{x} \cdot v$, hence $z' = \dfrac{v'}{x} - \dfrac{v}{x^2}$; then substitute in

---

* So named after James Bernoulli (1654–1705), a member of a family that contributed several illustrious names to the mathematics of the 17th and 18th centuries.

(15), to obtain

$$-\frac{1}{3x} \cdot v' + \frac{v}{3x^2} - \frac{v}{3x^2} = \log x,$$

or

$$dv = -3x \log x \, dx,$$

whence,

$$v = \int -3x \log x \, dx + c \equiv -3x^2 \left(\frac{\log x}{2} - \frac{1}{4}\right) + c$$

From this we have

$$z = \frac{v}{x} = -\frac{3x}{4}(2 \log x - 1) + \frac{c}{x} = y^{-3},$$

and hence

$$y = \left[-\frac{3x}{4}(2 \log x - 1) + \frac{c}{x}\right]^{-\frac{1}{3}}.$$

Exercises

1. Solve the following:

    (a) $dy = (xy^2 + 3xy) \, dx$.
    (b) $t \, dx \, (2xt^2 \log x + 1) = 2x \, dt$.
    (c) $(2y + 1) \, dx = (2y^3x^2 + x^2y^2 - 2x) \, dy$.
    (d) $yy' + y^2 \cdot \cot x = \csc^2 x$.
    (e) $(4 - x^2)y' + 4y = (2 + x)y^2$.
    (f) $x \, dy + y \, dx = xy^2 \, dx$.

2. Solve $y' \cos y - \sin y = \cos x \cdot \sin^2 y$.   *Hint:* Put $u = \sin y$.

3. Solve $\sec^2 u \, du - \tan^3 u \, dx = -x \tan u \, dx$.

4. Discuss Equation (14) of the text for the cases $n = 0$ and $n = 1$.

14. Riccati equation. The student may have noted that up to this point the differential equations presented as illustrations and exercises have usually had solutions expressible in terms of elementary functions.* He should guard against any tendency to suppose that all functions may be so expressed, and should be prepared to accept as solutions of a differential equation functions which are not so expressible. Suppose, for example, we consider

---

* By an *elementary function* we mean a function defined in a finite formula involving algebraic, trigonometric, exponential, and logarithmic functions.

the problem of determining the length of arc of the ellipse

$$x = a \cos \theta$$
$$y = b \sin \theta$$

from the point $\theta = \dfrac{\pi}{2}$ to a variable point θ. From the relation $ds^2 = dx^2 + dy^2$ we have

$$ds = (a^2 \sin^2 \theta + b^2 \cos^2 \theta)^{1/2} \, d\theta.$$

It is not possible to solve this equation in terms of elementary functions, although the nature of the problem indicates that s is a perfectly definite function of θ and is, furthermore, a continuous function having a derivative. We may indicate the solution of the above equation in the form

$$s = \int_{\pi/2}^{\theta} (a^2 \sin^2 \theta + b^2 \cos^2 \theta)^{1/2} \, d\theta.$$

The integral is known as an elliptic integral, in terms of which elliptic functions may be defined. The subject of elliptic integrals and elliptic functions occurs in many branches of mathematics, and many volumes have been written on its exposition.

One differential equation of the first order and first degree which is not always solvable in terms of elementary functions is

$$y' + Py^2 + Qy + R = 0, \tag{16}$$

where P, Q, and R are functions of x alone. This is usually called a *Riccati equation*, after Count Riccati (1676–1754), an Italian mathematician who studied the special case $y' + by^2 = cx^m$. While (16) cannot always be solved in terms of elementary functions, we easily establish the following properties of the equation and its solutions:

PROPERTY 1. *If a particular solution,* y = y$_1$(x), *is known, we may reduce the equation to a linear equation of the first order.*

To establish this property, let $y = y_1 + u$. Then $y' = y_1' + u'$, and the equation becomes

$$u' + u(Q + 2Py_1) + u^2P = 0.$$

This is recognized as a Bernoulli equation and, after the manner of Section 13, we put $v = \dfrac{1}{u}$, to obtain

$$v' - v(Q + 2Py_1) - P = 0,$$

which is linear.

PROPERTY 2. *If three distinct particular solutions* $y = y_1(x)$, $y = y_2(x)$, *and* $y = y_3(x)$ *are known, we may write down the complete solution without a quadrature.*

To show this, let us first substitute $y = y_3(x) + \dfrac{1}{v}$, and thus derive the linear equation

$$v' - v(Q + 2Py_3) - P = 0, \tag{17}$$

as in Property 1. The other two solutions $y = y_1(x)$ and $y = y_2(x)$ of (16) furnish two solutions of (17); *viz.,*

$$v = v_1(x) \equiv \frac{1}{y_1(x) - y_3(x)}$$

and

$$v = v_2(x) \equiv \frac{1}{y_2(x) - y_3(x)},$$

whence, by Exercise 7, Section 12, the complete solution of (17) is given by

$$\frac{v - v_1}{v_2 - v_1} = c.$$

Replacing v by $\dfrac{1}{y - y_3}$, and v_1 and v_2 by their values, we have

$$\frac{\dfrac{1}{y - y_3} - \dfrac{1}{y_1 - y_3}}{\dfrac{1}{y_2 - y_3} - \dfrac{1}{y_1 - y_3}} = c,$$

which is easily reduced to

$$\frac{y - y_1}{y - y_3} \cdot \frac{y_2 - y_3}{y_2 - y_1} = c.$$

This is, then, the general solution of (16), and its form at once establishes

PROPERTY 3. *The cross ratio* of any four solutions of (16) is independent of* x.

---

* By the cross ratio of four numbers a, b, c and d is meant the fraction $\dfrac{\dfrac{a - b}{a - d}}{\dfrac{c - b}{c - d}}$. If a, b, c, and d are metric or projective coördinates of four points A, B, C, and D on a line, this same fraction is said to be the cross ratio of the four points. Its value is invariant under projective transformations, a fact which renders it of fundamental importance in projective geometry.

PROPERTY 4.   *If* P *is identically zero, equation* (16) *is linear and of first order.   If* P *is not identically zero,* (16) *may be reduced to an equation of the form*

$$v'' + x_1v' + x_2v = 0.^*$$

The first statement of the property is obvious.   If $P \not\equiv 0$, let us substitute $y = \dfrac{z}{P}$ and multiply by P to obtain

$$z' + z^2 + \left(Q - \frac{P'}{P}\right)z + PR = 0.$$

If, now, we put $z = \dfrac{v'}{v}$ and multiply by v, we have

$$v'' + \left(Q - \frac{P'}{P}\right)v' + PRv = 0.$$

Note: The general solution of this equation involves two arbitrary constants.   However, they enter into the corresponding solution of the original Riccati equation in such a manner that their ratio only is significant and furnishes the one constant essential for a first order equation.

Exercises

1. Form the differential equation whose solution expresses the length of arc s on the hyperbola $x = a \sec \theta$, $y = b \tan \theta$.   Do not try to solve the equation obtained.

2. Using $y = \tan x$, an obvious solution, find the complete solution of $y' - y^2 - y \sin 2x + 2 \sin^2 x - 1 = 0$.

3. Show that if two different particular solutions of (16), $y = y_1(x)$ and $y = y_2(x)$, are known, the complete solution can be obtained with only one quadrature.   *Hint:* Put $y = \dfrac{y_1 - uy_2}{1 - u}$.

4. Show that $y = 0$, $y = x$, and $y = x^2$ are all solutions of the Riccati equation $y' + \dfrac{y^2}{x^2 - x^3} + y\dfrac{x - 2}{x - x^2} = 0$, and write the general solution.

5. Find the Riccati equation which has as particular solutions $y = \dfrac{1}{x}$, $y = \log x$, $y = 2x$.

---

* Later we shall know this as a linear equation of the second order.

6. Show that $y = 1$, $y = 2x$, and $y = 2x + 1$ are all solutions of the Riccati equation $y' + \dfrac{y^2}{2x^2 - x} - \dfrac{y(1 + 4x)}{2x^2 - x} + \dfrac{4x}{2x^2 - x} = 0$, and write the general solution. Find the cross ratio of the original three solutions and the solution obtained by putting the arbitrary constant equal to one in the general solution $\dfrac{y - 1}{2x(y - 2x)} = c$; when $x = 1$, when $x = 5$, when $x = a$.

7. Take the three given solutions of the equation of Exercise 6 and the solution corresponding to $c = 3$, and find their cross ratio. Do the same when $c = b$.

8. Show that $y = \tan x$ is a particular solution of the Riccati equation $y' + \dfrac{y^2}{\cos x - 1} + \dfrac{y}{\sin x} = 0$, and thus reduce the equation to a linear equation of the first order, and solve.

15. Applications of differential equations. A class of problems to which differential equations lend themselves effectively may be found in geometry. If one desires to determine the equation of a curve whose slope at each of its points (x, y) is equal to some predetermined function $f(x, y)$ of the coördinates of the point, he has merely to set

$$y' = f(x, y).$$

Solutions of this equation will represent curves having the desired property. Instead of the slope, one may be interested in some other quantity connected with a curve, whose value, at any point, is expressible in terms of the slope at that point, such as the subtangent, $y\dfrac{dx}{dy}$, and the subnormal, yy'. Many other quantities whose measures, at any point, depend only upon the position of the point and the direction of the curve through the point, may be readily expressed in terms of x, y, and y'.

If two one-parameter families of curves occupy the same plane in such a way that each curve of either family crosses, at right angles, every curve of the other family, each of the two families is said to be the system of *orthogonal trajectories* with reference to the other. Systems of curves related in this way have numerous uses in applied science, particularly in connection with fluid flow and potential theory.

If the position of a particle moving in a straight line is given by a coördinate x, and the time after some fixed instant is denoted by t, then the instantaneous velocity v of the particle at the position x and time t is defined by $\frac{dx}{dt}$. The condition that the velocity v shall be given by some function f of x and t produces the differential equation

$$\frac{dx}{dt} = f(x,\ t).$$

In the same manner,

$$\frac{dv}{dt} = g(v,\ t)$$

expresses the acceleration in terms of the velocity v and the time t.

In electrical work, a condenser is a device capable of holding a quantity q of electricity, spoken of as a *charge*. The presence of such a charge on a condenser is accompanied by a difference in potential e across the terminals, which is proportional to the amount of electricity stored. This fact can be expressed by the equation

$$e = \frac{q}{C}.$$

If q is measured in coulombs and e in volts, then C is said to be the *capacity* of the condenser, in farads.

If a condenser is charged or discharged through a conductor, the instantaneous rate of change of the charge is given by $\frac{dq}{dt}$. This quantity is a measure of the current flowing in the conductor, and we may express the fact by the equation

$$i = \frac{dq}{dt},$$

where i will be the current flowing into the condenser, in amperes, if q is in coulombs and t in seconds. The amount of current which a conductor carries when subject to a constant e.m.f. is proportional to that e.m.f., and is given by the relation

$$e = Ri,$$

where R is called the *resistance* of the conductor. If i is in amperes and e in volts, then R is in ohms.

A (pure) *inductor* is a device which, when placed in an electrical circuit, opposes any change in the current by a difference in potential proportional to the rate of the change. In a circuit containing only a driving e.m.f. of e volts and an inductor, we have the relation

$$e = L \frac{di}{dt},$$

where L is said to be the *inductance* of the inductor and is measured in henries if i is in amperes and t in seconds. If a current i is driven through a resistance R and an inductance L, we have the relation

$$e = Ri + L \frac{di}{dt}.$$

Whether the driving electromotive force, e, is a constant or a function of t, it is seen that the above equation is linear and of the first order.

Exercises

1. Find the system of curves having the property that the tangent at any point passes through $(2, -4)$.

2. Find the system of curves having the property that the subtangent at any point exceeds twice the abscissa of the point by 1.

3. Find the polar equation of the curve passing through $\left(1, \frac{\pi}{3}\right)$ and such that the polar subtangent, $\rho^2 \frac{d\theta}{d\rho}$, at any point is equal to 2 divided by the radius vector, ρ, of the point.

4. The perpendicular from the origin to the tangent line of a curve is equal to the abscissa of the point of contact. Find the equation of the curve if it passes through $(1, -3)$.

5. Find the equation of the system of curves having the subnormal at every point equal to twice the ordinate of the point of contact, diminished by its abscissa.

6. The normal at any point of a curve and the line joining that point to the origin form an isosceles triangle, with the x-axis as base. Find the equation of the curve.

7. Find the differential equation of the family of orthogonal trajectories of the integral curves of $M\, dx + N\, dy = 0$.

8. Find the orthogonal trajectories of the integral curves of $y(1 - x)\, dx + x^2(1 - y)\, dy = 0$.

9. Find the orthogonal trajectories of the integral curves of the differential equation $(21x + 8y + 1)\, dx - (48x + y + 29)\, dy = 0$.

10. Find the orthogonal trajectories:

(a) of the system of parabolas $x^2 = ky$.
(b) of the system of parabolas $y^2 = kx + k$.

11. The area bounded by an arc of a curve, the x-axis, the ordinate $x = a$ and a variable ordinate is twice the length of that arc.   Find the equation of the curve.

12. Find the orthogonal trajectories of the system of equilateral hyperbolas $xy = c$, and show that they too are equilateral hyperbolas.

13. Find the orthogonal trajectories of the system of conics $x^2 + \dfrac{y^2}{1 - e^2} = a^2$, in which e is fixed and a is the parameter of the family.

14. Work Exercise 13, modified to have a fixed and e variable.

15. Find the orthogonal trajectories of the system of parabolas whose foci are at $(0, 0)$ and directrices $y = c$, where c is taken as the parameter of the system.

16. A body moves in a straight line with its velocity exceeding by 1 its distance from a fixed point on the line.   Find the equation of the motion, if the velocity is 2 when the time is zero.

17. A body moving in a straight line has its acceleration equal to 10 divided by 1 more than the time which has elapsed after a given instant.   Find the equation of the motion, if at the given instant the body is 3 units from the origin and has a velocity equal to 2.

18. A body moves in a straight line in such a way that $v = \dfrac{k}{t^{1/2}} + \sin t$.   Express the distance in terms of t.

19. A body falling in a liquid is subject to a steady pull of gravity and to a resistance which is proportional to the cube of the velocity. Find the equation of the motion.   (*Hint:* Take the mass as unity, and write $v' = g - kv^3$.   Rationalize the factors of $g - kv^3$ by the substitution $g = kb^{-3}$.)   Show that the velocity approaches a constant.

20. A body of mass m pounds is projected upward at an initial velocity of v_0 feet per second.   It encounters resistance equal to kv, and is affected by the steady pull of gravity. Find the equation, expressing v in terms of t. *Hint:* Take v as positive downward, and write $mv' = mg - kv$.

21. An electrical circuit contains a condenser of capacity C farads, and a resistance of R ohms connected in series. The condenser has a charge of q_0 coulombs at the time t_0. Express q in terms of t. *Hint:* $R \dfrac{dq}{dt} + \dfrac{q}{C} = 0$.

22. An electrical circuit contains an inductance of L henries and a resistance of R ohms connected in series. A current i_0 is flowing at the time t_0. Express i in terms of t. (Consider all e.m.f. removed.)

23. A series circuit, with no resistance, contains an inductance L measured in henries, and a constant electromotive force of e volts. Show that the current increases linearly with the time.

24. An electrical circuit contains a resistance of R ohms, a condenser whose capacity is C farads, and a constant electromotive force of E volts. If the charge on the condenser is q_0 when $t = t_0$, find the relation between q and t. Show that q approaches a constant which is independent of R.

25. Under the conditions of Exercise 24, express i in terms of t.

26. A resistance of R ohms is connected in series with an inductance of L henries and a constant voltage v. At the time t_0, a current i_0 is flowing. Express i in terms of t, and show that i approaches a constant as t increases.

27. Assume that the air pressure p at a point of altitude h above sea level is proportional to the mass of air above the point, and that a portion of air Δm will occupy a volume Δv such that $pk \cdot \Delta v = \Delta m$. Show that $p = c \cdot e^{-kh}$, where c and k are constants.

28. The rate at which a body cools is proportional to the difference in temperature between the body and the surrounding atmosphere. If a body in air at $10°$ will cool from $200°$ to $100°$ in 40 minutes, how long will it take the body to cool from $100°$ to $10°$ in air at $5°$?

29. The rate at which a substance decomposes is assumed to be proportional to the amount of the substance remaining. Write the differential equation expressing this fact, and find its solution. If the amount of the substance not decomposed changes from 6 pounds to 1 pound in 2 hours, find the constant of proportionality and the constant of integration.

30. Find the equation of the Catenary, or curve of equilibrium of a hanging chain. *Hint:* Take the y-axis as the axis of symmetry, and the origin at the minimum point. Let the tension at the point (x, y) be $T(x, y)$, the length of the curve from $(0, 0)$ to (x, y) be $s(x, y)$, the weight of the chain from $(0, 0)$ to (x, y) be ks, and recognize that the y component of the tension T is equal to ks, while the x component of T is constant, say ka. This gives the two equations

$$T \frac{dx}{ds} = ka,$$

$$T \frac{dy}{ds} = ks.$$

If we square and add, we obtain $T^2 = k^2(a^2 + s^2)$. The value of T, thus defined, may be placed in the two differential equations, one of which will be in x and s, and the other of which will be in y and s. Elimination of s between the solutions should give the desired equation.

31. Liquid is discharged from a vessel through an orifice at the rate given by $ca(2gh)^{1/2}$, where h is the head, or height, of the surface of the water above the center of the orifice, g is the acceleration of gravity (about 32 feet per second^2), a is the area of the cross section of the orifice, and c is a constant, $\leqq 1$, called the coefficient of discharge, which is dependent upon the physical characteristics of the liquid and the vessel and upon the shape and size of the orifice, but which is ordinarily about 0.6. If the head changes from 10 feet to 9 feet in the first 15 minutes, in what time will the head be 1 foot, assuming that the vessel is cylindrical?

32. A cylindrical tank with vertical axis has a base 12 sq. ft. in area. Near the bottom is an orifice whose area is 2 sq. in., and whose coefficient of discharge is 0.6. It was observed that the discharge through the orifice lowered the head 1 inch in 20 seconds. What was the head to start with? What will the head be after 10 more seconds?

33. A vertical cylindrical tank 4 feet in diameter contains a first liquid with a head of 9 feet above a circular orifice 1 inch in diameter whose coefficient of discharge is $\frac{3}{5}$. A second liquid is flowing into the tank through a pipe $\frac{4}{5}$ inch in inside diameter at a constant linear velocity of 15 feet per second. Assuming g to be 32 feet per second², express the time t in terms of h. Find the value of h at which it would remain constant.

34. In Exercise 33, find the value of t at which the contents of the tank will be half of each kind of liquid, if the head was 4 feet when the process began: (a) liquids mixed; (b) second liquid floating.

35. If the number of bacteria in a quart of milk doubles in 4 hours, in how much time will the number be multiplied by 25?

36. The rate at which one substance combines with another is supposed to be proportional to the amount of the first substance remaining. If there are 15 pounds of the first substance when $t = 0$, and 5 pounds when $t = 8$, find how much will be left when $t = 5$. Also find the value of t when there is 1 pound left.

37. Two substances are combining in such a way as to produce a third substance. If in x pounds of the product there are αx pounds of the first substance and βx pounds of the second, and if at the beginning of the process there are αa pounds of the first and βb pounds of the second, then the amounts of the two substances remaining after x pounds of the product have been produced are $\alpha(a - x)$ and $\beta(b - x)$, respectively. If the rate of combination is proportional to the product of the remaining amounts, we have $\frac{dx}{dt} = k\alpha\beta(a - x)(b - x)$. If $\alpha = \frac{3}{5}$ and there are 300 pounds of the first substance and 200 pounds of the second substance when $t = 0$, and 100 pounds of the product when $t = 1$ hour, find the value of t when there are 400 pounds of the product. Note that $\alpha + \beta = 1$.

38. With the conditions similar to those of Exercise 37, except that $\alpha = \frac{3}{4}$, let the amounts of the first and second substances present when $t = 0$ be 20 and 25 pounds, respectively. If, when $t = 30$ minutes, 20 pounds of the second substance remain, how much of the first substance will remain? How much of each parent substance will there be when $t = 60$ minutes?

39. If a quantity $a - x$ of a substance A is present and changes into a substance B at a rate $k_1(a - x)$, while the substance B is changing into the substance A at a rate $k_2 x$, express x in terms of t.

40. The compound amount A, in dollars, realized if a principal of P dollars is invested at the nominal rate of r per year compounded n times per year for t years is

$$A = P\left(1 + \frac{r}{n}\right)^{nt} \equiv P\left[\left(1 + \frac{r}{n}\right)^{\frac{n}{r}}\right]^{rt}.$$

As the number of times per year for compounding interest increases indefinitely, the amount A approaches the value

$$A = Pe^{rt},$$

which is the formula for the amount after t years if interest is compounded continuously on a principal of P dollars at the nominal rate r. The effective rate, or corresponding rate, for yearly conversion is $(e^r - 1)$, and r is called the *force of interest* corresponding to the effective rate $(e^r - 1)$. Show that the effective rate of 5 per cent is very nearly equivalent to the force 4.9 per cent.

41. A man works for a banking institution which pays him, in addition to his weekly salary, the equivalent of a dollar a day continuously deposited, and continuously converted at the force of 4 per cent. Find the amount in the account at the end of the first 10 years.

42. By natural increase the population of a city doubles every 50 years. Find the expression giving the number of people at a time t years after the period when the population was equal to n_0.

43. The normal growth of the population of a city is the same as in Exercise 42, and each year 1000 people move in from other cities. If the city has 10,000 inhabitants in 1940, what will be its population 50 years later?

44. A circular plate loaded symmetrically with respect to the center is freely supported around its edge. If the angle between the vertical and the normal at a point r units from the center is θ, the plate bends in such a way that the equation $r^2 \dfrac{d^2\theta}{dr^2} + r \dfrac{d\theta}{dr} - \theta = kr^3$ holds, with k a constant. To solve this equation, divide through by r^2, and note that in this form, $\theta'' + \dfrac{\theta'}{r} - \dfrac{\theta}{r^2} = kr$, the equation may be written $\theta'' + \left(\dfrac{\theta}{r}\right)' = kr$. One quadrature produces one arbitrary constant and a linear equation of the first order, $\theta' + \dfrac{\theta}{r} = \dfrac{kr^2}{2}$ $+ c.$ Find the complete solution.

45. Water is running at the rate of 2 gallons per minute into a tank containing brine.   The mixture is running out at the same rate, the concentration being kept uniform by stirring.   Find the amount of salt in the tank at the end of one-half hour, if there are always 150 gallons of liquid in the tank and at the beginning the brine contained 60 pounds of salt.

46. Under the same conditions as in Exercise 45, except that the tank contains 150 gallons only at the beginning and the mixture runs out at the rate of 3 gallons per minute, find the amount of salt in the tank at the end of one-half hour.

47. The air in a room 20 feet by 30 feet by 12 feet tested .09 per cent carbon dioxide.   Find the percentage of carbon dioxide in the room at the end of 18 minutes if 1000 cubic feet of air containing .04 per cent carbon dioxide is admitted into the room per minute.

16. Miscellaneous exercises on Chapter II. Solve the following:

1. $\left(\dfrac{y - x}{xy}\right) dx + \left(\dfrac{2y^3 + x + y}{y^2}\right) dy = 0.$

2. $\sin \theta \, dr + r \cos \theta \, d\theta = 0.$

3. $(x^2 + y^2) \, dx = x(x \, dy - y \, dx).$

4. $x(5y \, dx + 3x \, dy) - y^2(2y \, dx + x \, dy) = 0.$

5. $(x^2 + y^2) \, dx - 4xy \, dy = 0.$

6. $y \, dx - [x + (x^2 + y^2)^{1/2}] \, dy = 0.$

7. $xy' - 6y = 2x + 1.$

8. $u \dfrac{du}{dv} + vu^2 = v.$

9. $x \, dz + (z - 2z^2 \log x) \, dx = 0.$

10. $(v^3 - 3u) \, dv + (u^2 - 3v) \, du = 0.$

11. $(x + y^2) \, dx - 2xy \, dy = 0.$

12. $\tan x \cot y \, dx + dy = 0.$

13. $y'' = (x - y') \cot x + 1.$ *Hint:* Let $y' = p.$

14. $3y^3(x - 1)\, dx + xy^2(x - 7)\, dy = 0.$

15. $y'' - y' = 1.$

16. $\cos y\, dx + (x \sin y - 1)\, dy = 0.$

17. $\dfrac{dr}{d\theta} - r \tan \theta = r^4 \sec \theta.$

18. $xy'' - y' = 0.$

19. $(1 + e^{u/v})\, du + e^{u/v}\left(1 - \dfrac{u}{v}\right) dv = 0.$

20. $(2x - y + 4)\, dx + (2y + x + 7)\, dy = 0.$

21. $(6y + 3x - 5)\, dx + (2y + x + 2)\, dy = 0.$

22. $y(1 + 2xy)\, dx + x(1 - 2xy)\, dy = 0.$

23. $(\sqrt{st} - 1)s\, dt - (\sqrt{st} + 1)t\, ds = 0.$

24. $y(1 + 3xye^{xy} + 2xye^{-xy})\, dx + x^2y(3e^{xy} + 2e^{-xy})\, dy = 0.$

25. $(12x^2y^2 + y^3)\, dx + (4x^3y + 2xy^2)\, dy = 0.$

26. $(\pi + 2xy - 6y^2)\, dx + (x - 6y)^2\, dy = 0.$

27. $(4x^2 + y^2 + 4x)\, dx + y\, dy = 0.$

28. $3 \sin^2 \theta \sin \varphi \cos \varphi\, d\varphi + 5 \sin \theta \cos \theta \cos^4 \varphi\, d\theta = 0.$

29. $y^2(y\, dx + 2x\, dy) - x^2(y\, dx - 10x\, dy) = 0.$

30. $dr + (r \sec \theta + 1 + \sin \theta)\, d\theta = 0.$

31. $(2u + 1)\, dv + (2 - 4e^{-v})\, du = 0.$

32. $(2y^2 - 4)\, dx + y(1 + 2xy^2)\, dy = 0.$

33. $(x^2 + 4y^2)\, dy = xy\, dx.$

34. $xy' + (x \tan y/x - y) = 0.$

35. $y' = \left(\dfrac{2x - 3y + 4}{3x - 2y - 1}\right)^2.$

36. $(3y - xy^2 - 5x^2y^3)\, dx - x(2 + xy + 10x^2y^2)\, dy = 0.$

37. $(6xy + 6x^2y - 2y^3 + 3e^x)\, dx + (3x^2 - 3y^2)\, dy = 0.$

38. $(1 + x^2)\, y' + xy = \dfrac{2}{x}.$

39. $y\, dy + (xy^2 - 4x)\, dx = 0.$

40. $(ax^2 + 2bxy + cy^2)\, dx + (bx^2 + 2cxy + gy^2)\, dy = 0.$

41. In the differential equation $M\, dx + N\, dy = 0$, M and N are homogeneous polynomials in x and y, of degree 3. If the equation is exact, what are the most general forms for the quantities M and N? Solve the equation formed.

42. Solve the equation $(4x^3 + 9x^2y + 6xy^2 - y^3)\,dx + (3x^3 + 6x^2y - 3xy^2 + 20y^3)\,dy = 0$.

43. The triangle formed by the line tangent to a curve at any point, (x, y), the radius vector to the point, (x, y), and the y-axis, is isosceles, and has the y-axis as base. Find the equation of the curve.

44. A water tank has vertical sides, and by means of an orifice at the bottom its level is lowered from 10 feet to 9 feet in 10 minutes. Find the time required for the level to fall from 7 feet to 1 foot.

45. The x-intercept of a line tangent to a curve at the point (x, y) is proportional to $x^m y^n$. Find the equation of the curve.

46. An electrical current i is driven by a voltage $v = V \sin \omega t$ through an inductance L. (V and ω are constant.) Express i in terms of t.

47. An electrical current i is driven through a resistance R and a condenser of capacity c, by a variable electromotive force $v = V \sin \omega t$. (V and ω are constant.) The initial charge on the condenser is q_0, the initial time t_0, and the initial current i_0. Express q as a function of t.   *Hint:* The equation is $R\dfrac{dq}{dt} + \dfrac{q}{c} = V \sin \omega t$.

48. Under the conditions of Exercise 47, express i in terms of t.

49. A constant e.m.f. of V volts is applied to a resistance of R ohms and an inductance of L henries, connected in series. At the time t_0 a current i_0 is flowing. Express i in terms of t, and show that it approaches a constant as t increases.

50. Replace V in Exercise 49 by $V \sin \omega t$, and solve the problem.

51. A vessel containing liquid is rotated about a vertical axis at a uniform angular velocity ω. Find the shape assumed by the surface of the liquid.

52. Prove that the differential equation of the orthogonal trajectories of the integral curves of a homogeneous equation is also homogeneous.

53. Find the equation of the family of curves which make the angle $\tan^{-1} \frac{3}{4}$ with each of the integral curves of the differential equation $(7x - 3y + 2)\,dx + (4y - 3x - 5)\,dy = 0$.

54. In books on Calculus* it is shown that if two functions $F(x, y)$ and $G(x, y)$ are so related that $F \equiv \Phi(G)$, then, and only then,

$$\begin{vmatrix} F_x & F_y \\ G_x & G_y \end{vmatrix} \equiv 0.$$

---

* Wilson's *Advanced Calculus*, page 62.

This determinant is known as the *functional determinant*, or *Jacobian*, of the two functions F and G.   Thus, if $G \equiv \dfrac{1}{x^2y}$ and $F \equiv 2 \log x +$ $\log y$, the relation is obviously $F \equiv - \log G$.   Let the student show that the *Jacobian* of F and G vanishes identically for this case.

55. Find the Jacobian of the following pairs of functions; if it vanishes identically, find the functional relationship:

(a) $F \equiv x^2 + y^2$, $G \equiv 2xy$.

(b) $F \equiv \dfrac{(x + y)^2}{x^2 - y^2}$, $G \equiv \dfrac{3x - y}{x - y}$.

56. Show that if $F(x, y) = c$ and $G(x, y) = c$ are two general solutions of the differential equation $M\,dx + N\,dy = 0$, then F is a function of G.   *Hint:* Evidently

$$M \equiv \mu(x,\, y)F_x \equiv \nu(x,\, y)G_x$$

and

$$N \equiv \mu(x,\, y)F_y \equiv \nu(x,\, y)G_y,$$

where μ and ν are reciprocals of appropriate integrating factors of $M\,dx + N\,dy = 0$.

57. State and prove the converse of Exercise 56.

58. On page 24 are listed five general solutions of the equation $x\,dy - y\,dx = 0$.   Verify that Exercise 56 holds for the first and last by finding the Jacobian of $\dfrac{y}{x}$ and $\dfrac{1}{2} \log \dfrac{y + x}{y - x}$.   Find the relation between these functions.

59. Verify by substitution that, since $\dfrac{y}{x} = c$ is the solution of $x\,dy - y\,dx = 0$, the following are also solutions:

(a) $e^{x/y} = c$.   (c) $\tan^{-1} \dfrac{y}{x} = c$.

(b) $\sin \dfrac{x}{y} = c$.   (d) $x^2 - 3xy - y^2 = cy^2$.

60. If $\mu(x, y)$ and $\nu(x, y)$ are two integrating factors of $M\,dx +$ $N\,dy = 0$, show that either $\dfrac{\mu}{\nu}$ is identically equal to some constant, or that $\dfrac{\mu}{\nu} = c$ is a solution of the equation.

61. Find several solutions of the equation $x\,dy - y\,dx = 0$ from quotients of the integrating factors given on page 24.

62. Show that a differential equation $M\,dx + N\,dy = 0$, which has a solution, has an infinite number of integrating factors.   *Hint:* If $f(x, y) = c$ is a solution, then $\varphi(f) = c$ is a solution.

63. Using $y = \sin x$, an obvious solution, find the complete solution of the Riccati equation $y' = y^2 \cdot \csc^2 x + y \cot x - 1$.

64. The air in a room 25 feet by 30 feet by 10 feet tests .1 per cent carbon dioxide.   How much air containing .04 per cent of carbon dioxide must be admitted into the room per minute in order that 15 minutes later the air in the room test .08 per cent carbon dioxide?

CHAPTER III

Equations of the First Order, but Not of the First Degree

17. Introduction. As explained in Chapter I, a differential equation of the first order is a relation of the form

$$F(x, y, p) = 0, \tag{1}$$

where, for convenience, we use the symbol p to represent $\dfrac{dy}{dx}$. If this function F is not of the first degree in p, Equation (1) may be satisfied by a plurality of values of p for a pair of values (x, y). Geometrically, this indicates a corresponding plurality of integral curves through the point (x, y).

18. Equations solvable for p. If (1) is solvable for p, we may write the several values in the form

$$p = f_1(x, y), \ p = f_2(x, y), \ \cdots .$$

Each of these equations, being of the first order and first degree, may be treated by the methods of Chapter II.

As a very simple example, let us consider the equation

$$p^2 - p = 0, \tag{2}$$

which is satisfied by $p = 0$ or $p = 1$. These readily lead to the solutions $y = c_1$ and $y - x = c_2$. Geometrically, these represent, respectively, the system of all lines parallel to the x-axis, and the system of all lines having the inclination $\dfrac{\pi}{4}$. Since each of the equations $y - c_1 = 0$ and $y - x - c_2 = 0$ satisfies (2) independently, certainly the equation

$$(y - c_1)(y - x - c_2) = 0 \tag{3}$$

satisfies (2), regardless of the values of the arbitrary constants c_1 and c_2. Now, looking upon (3) as the equation of all lines represented by either of the equations

$$y - c_1 = 0, \ y - x - c_2 = 0, \tag{4}$$

55

we see that (3) is no more inclusive than the equation

$$(y - c)(y - x - c) = 0, \tag{5}$$

which likewise gives all lines represented by either of equations (4). We may evidently display the complete solution of (2) by any of the methods (3), (4), or (5).   Of these, (4) is to be preferred, since it conveys a more vivid picture of the situation.

Exercises

Solve the following equations by the above method:

1. $p^2 - (2x + 3y)p + 6xy = 0$.

2. $x^2p^2 - 3x^2y^3p + 2p - 6y^3 = 0$.

3. $p^2x^2(x^2 - 4) = 1$.

4. $p^2 + \dfrac{2x}{y} p - 9 = 0$.

5. $\left(\dfrac{dr}{d\theta}\right)^2 + 2r\left(\dfrac{dr}{d\theta}\right)\tan\theta - r^2 \sin^2\theta = r^2(\cos^2\theta - \sec^2\theta)$.

6. $p^3 - (x^2 + xy^2 + y^4)p^2 + (x^3y^2 + x^2y^4 + xy^6)p - x^3y^6 = 0$.

7. $pxy^2(p^2 + 2) = 2p^2y^3 + px^3$.

8. $p^2 - px - 2py + 2xy = 0$.

9. $p^2 \cos 2y + p(\sin 2y - \sin 2x \cos 2y) = \sin 2x \sin 2y$.

19. Equations solvable for y.   Suppose, now, that equation (1) is solvable for y, giving one or more expressions of the form

$$y = f(x, p). \tag{6}$$

Upon differentiating this with respect to x we obtain

$$p = f_x(x, p) + f_p(x, p)\frac{dp}{dx}.$$

This is a differential equation of the first order and first degree in x and p.   A solution may be found in the form

$$\varphi(x, p, c) = 0. \tag{7}$$

Between (6) and (7) we may eliminate p to obtain the desired solution of (1).

As an example of this method, let us take the equation

$$y = p^{-2}. \tag{8}$$

Differentiating with respect to x, we obtain

$$p = -2p^{-3}\frac{dp}{dx},$$

which can be written

$$dx = -2p^{-4}dp.$$

The general solution of this is

$$x = \frac{2}{3}p^{-3} + c,$$

or

$$3p^3(x - c) - 2 = 0. \tag{9}$$

If we eliminate p between (9) and (8), we obtain the result

$$4y^3 - 9(x - c)^2 = 0,$$

the general solution of (8).

Exercises

Solve the following by the above method:

1. $y = 2p + 3p^2$.
2. $p^2 - 3px + 3y = 0$.
3. $(1 - x^2)p + xy - 5 = 0$.
4. $2yp^2 - (4x - 5)p + 2y = 0$.
5. $y - px = x\sqrt{n^2 + p^2}$.
6. $4x^2(y - px) = 9yp^2$.
7. $(2x + py)^2 = p^2(y^2 + 2x)$.
8. $y - 5x = 3\cos^{-1}p$.
9. $2px - y + 2\log p - \log 4 = 0$.
10. $y = 2px + p$.
11. $xy = p^2$.

20. Equations solvable for x.   Following a process analogous to the above, we may arrive at a solution of (1) by solving for x and differentiating with respect to y.   It will suffice to study an example, say

$$16y^2p^3 + 2px - y = 0. \tag{10}$$

Solving for x, we have

$$x = \frac{y - 16y^2p^3}{2p}.$$

Upon differentiating with respect to y and noting that $\dfrac{dx}{dy} = \dfrac{1}{p}$, we obtain

$$\frac{1}{p} = \frac{2p\left(1 - 32yp^3 - 48y^2p^2\dfrac{dp}{dy}\right) - 2(y - 16y^2p^3)\dfrac{dp}{dy}}{4p^2}.$$

This equation may be factored into the form

$$2(1 + 32yp^3)(p\,dy + y\,dp) = 0,$$

which can be satisfied only if

$$1 + 32yp^3 = 0 \tag{11}$$

or

$$p\,dy + y\,dp = 0.$$

The last equation, which is exact, has the solution

$$yp = \frac{c}{2}, \tag{12}$$

where, for convenience, the constant of integration has been called $\frac{c}{2}$. If we eliminate p between (12) and (10), we obtain

$$y^2 = c(x + 2c^2), \tag{13}$$

the general solution of (10).

If we return to (11) and eliminate p between it and (10), we obtain

$$27y^4 + 2x^3 = 0. \tag{14}$$

Since the relation (14) cannot be recovered from (13) by choice of the arbitrary constant in the latter, we write

$$y^2 = c(x + 2c^2),\ 27y^4 + 2x^3 = 0$$

as the complete solution of (14).   The student should verify that (14) satisfies the given equation.

Exercises

Solve the following by the above method:

1. $4p^2 + \dfrac{2x}{y}\,p - 1 = 0.$ **4.** $y^{-2/3}p^2 - 3xp + 9y = 0.$

2. $x = 2p - p^2.$ **5.** $p = \arccos{(x - p)}.$

3. $p^3 - 8xyp + 16y^2 = 0.$ **6.** $x = \dfrac{p}{y} + \log p - \log y.$

7. $\tan y \sec^4 y\ p^2 + 2xp \sec^2 y - \tan y = 0.$

8. $x = p^2 + y.$

9. $x = py + p^2.$

21. Clairaut's equation. Among the differential equations which can be solved by differentiation are those reducible to the especially interesting type

$$y = px + \varphi(p),\tag{15}$$

called *Clairaut's equation* in honor of the French astronomer and mathematician, Alexis Claude Clairaut (1713–1765). If to this equation we apply the method of Section 19, we obtain

$$p = p + [x + \varphi'(p)]\frac{dp}{dx}.$$

This evidently can be satisfied only if

$$x = -\varphi'(p)\tag{16}$$

or

$$\frac{dp}{dx} = 0.$$

The latter equation leads to the result

$$p = c,$$

and combination of this with (15) yields the solution

$$y = cx + \varphi(c).\tag{17}$$

Turning now to Equation (16), we see that by means of it (15) can be reduced to the form

$$y = -p\varphi'(p) + \varphi(p).\tag{18}$$

We may regard (16) and (18) as parametric equations of a curve that is evidently an integral curve of the differential equation (15).

To make clear the relation between the general solution (17) and the special solution represented parametrically by (16) and (18), let us consider the example

$$y = px + p^2 - 2p + 1.\tag{19}$$

The solution corresponding to (17), *viz.*, the general solution, is

$$y = cx + c^2 - 2c + 1,\tag{20}$$

while the special solution is given by the relations

$$x = -2p + 2, \; y = -p^2 + 1.$$

If between these we eliminate the parameter p, we obtain

$$(x - 2)^2 + 4(y - 1) = 0.\tag{21}$$

Considered geometrically, (20) represents a system of straight lines with slope c and y-intercept $(c - 1)^2$. Several lines of the system are shown in Figure 1. It appears, from this figure, that through certain points (x, y) of the plane, pass two lines of the system, and that through other points passes none. Let us investigate this observation by employing the fact that each line of the system is identified with a value of c. If we solve equation (20) for c, we obtain

$$c = \frac{2 - x \pm \sqrt{(x - 2)^2 + 4(y - 1)}}{2}.$$

Thus we see that a given point (x, y) determines two values of c; or, what is the same, two lines of the system (20). These two

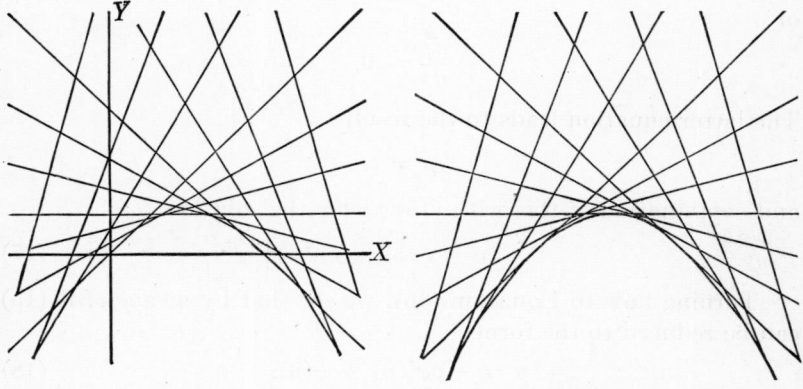

Fig. 1.   Fig. 2.

values of c, and hence the two lines determined, are real and distinct when $(x - 2)^2 + 4(y - 1)$ is positive; imaginary when that quantity is negative; and, what is of special interest, real and the same when $(x - 2)^2 + 4(y - 1) = 0$. This last, we observe, is Equation (21), which has already been discovered as a special solution of the differential equation (19). The equation represents a parabola, which, when superimposed on Figure 1, appears as in Figure 2, where the coördinate axes have been omitted. In the light of the above discussion we have found that through points above this parabola pass two distinct real lines of the system (20); through points below it passes no real line of the system; while through points on the parabola pass two coincident lines of the system.

Referring again to Figure 2, we observe that each line of (20) seems to be tangent to the parabola (21), a fact which we could easily verify by solving (20) and (21) simultaneously. Rather than do that, however, let us return to the differential equation (19) in order to draw the conclusion. If we solve (19) for p, we obtain

$$p = \frac{2 - x \pm \sqrt{(x - 2)^2 + 4(y - 1)}}{2},$$

which defines two distinct real slopes for points (x, y) above the parabola, no real slope for points below the parabola, and two equal real slopes for points on the parabola. If a curve is to be an integral curve of the differential equation (19), then at each of its points it must have a direction which will satisfy (19). That the lines of (20) do have points in common with the parabola, we know because we have shown that points on the parabola determine one, and only one, real value of c satisfying (20). That every real line of (20) passes through one point of the parabola we readily see, since, for points on the parabola,

$$c = \frac{2 - x}{2},$$

and as x is made to range over all real values, c will range over all real values. Finally, since (20) and (21) both define integral curves of (19), and since the direction of an integral curve through points of the parabola is unique, each line of (20) has the same direction as the parabola (21) at their common point, and hence is tangent to the parabola at that point.

22. Singular solutions. The above case of a parabola tangent to every line of a one-parameter system of lines is an illustration of the *envelope** of a system of curves. If the curves of a system

$$f(x, y, c) = 0 \tag{22}$$

are integral curves for a given differential equation

$$\varphi(x, y, p) = 0, \tag{23}$$

each curve possesses, at every one of its points, one of the directions required by (23). The envelope of the system (22), being tangent, at each of its points, to one of the curves (22), also possesses, at each of its points, one of the directions required by (23). It is

---

* See Wilson's *Advanced Calculus*, page 135, for definition and discussion.

therefore an integral curve of (23), and its equation is ordinarily a singular solution. Equation (10) of Section 20 has the singular solution (14), and Equation (19) of Section 21 has the singular solution (21).

The system of curves (22) may or may not have an envelope. If it has an envelope, the latter may or may not be a particular curve of the system. In the last case we are confronted with the problem of finding the equation of the envelope as the singular solution of (23).

23. The c-discriminant. Certain properties of the envelope are manifest in the illustrative problem of Section 21. When the equation (20) was solved for c, we obtained

$$c = \frac{2 - x \pm \sqrt{x^2 - 4x + 4y}}{2}.$$

This expression for c has two distinct values, excepting in the case of points on the envelope

$$x^2 - 4x + 4y = 0,$$

where the two values both become

$$c = \frac{2 - x}{2}.$$

Since c is a double root of (20), with (x, y) on the parabola (21), it is to be expected that this same c is a simple root of the equation*

$$x + 2c - 2 = 0, \tag{24}$$

obtained by differentiating (20) partially with respect to c. This is proved at once by substituting $\frac{2 - x}{2}$ in place of c in (24). The values of x and y which cause (20) to have double values of c, and, hence, which cause (24) to have values of c common with the values in (20), may be found by eliminating c between (20) and (24). Performing this elimination, we obtain (21), which is the parabola previously determined as the singular solution.

Similarly, we may expect to find the envelope of the system of curves (22) by eliminating c between (22) and

$$f_c(x, y, c) = 0. \tag{25}$$

---

* See Dickson's *Theory of Equations*, page 61.

As another example, let us find the envelope of the system of ellipses

$$100x^2 + c^4y^2 - 100c^2 = 0. \tag{26}$$

Partial differentiation with respect to the quantity c gives

$$4c^3y^2 - 200c = 0,$$

which corresponds to (25). Elimination of c between this and (26) gives

$$x^2y^2 = 25.$$

The student will do well to plot this curve and several of the ellipses of (26) in order to observe the envelope property.

For a fuller proof that this process of finding the equation of the envelope of a given one-parameter system of curves is correct, the student may consult Wilson's *Advanced Calculus.*

The equation

$$\psi(x, y) = 0,$$

obtained by eliminating c between (22) and (25), is called the *c-discriminant relation,* and its left-hand member, $\psi(x, y)$, is called the *c-discriminant* of (22). The former may be satisfied by points on curves other than the envelope. The student should factor the discriminant, if possible, and keep only those factors which, when equated to zero, satisfy the differential equation.

24. The p-discriminant. The student may note that if (19) is differentiated partially with respect to p, the result takes the form

$$0 = x + 2p - 2,$$

or

$$p = \frac{2 - x}{2}.$$

This value of p is exactly that defined by solving (19) for p, *viz.,*

$$p = \frac{2 - x \pm \sqrt{(x - 2)^2 + 4(y - 1)}}{2},$$

and imposing the condition that the point (x, y) be a point on the singular solution $(x - 2)^2 + 4(y - 1) = 0$.

This observation may be generalized, to the effect that if the integral curves of an equation of the type (23) have an envelope, then (23) will determine multiple values of p for points on that envelope. Therefore, these values of p will also satisfy the equation

$$\varphi_p(x, y, p) = 0, \tag{27}$$

when (x, y) is the same point of the envelope.

Hence, we may expect the points of the envelope of (22) to satisfy the equation

$$\psi(x, y) = 0, \tag{28}$$

obtained by eliminating p between (23) and (27). This equation expresses the condition on x and y that (23) and (27) should be satisfied by common values of p; $i.\ e.$, that (23) should have multiple roots. Its left-hand member is called the p-*discriminant* of (23), and we shall call the equation the p-*discriminant relation*. The graph of the equation contains the envelope of the system of integral curves of (23), if there is one. Like the c-discriminant, the p-discriminant may be factorable, and the equations expressing the vanishing of some factors may fail to satisfy the differential equation. Each factor of the p-discriminant relation should be tested by substitution into the given equation, and those which fail to satisfy discarded as extraneous.

Exercises

1. Solve the following Clairaut equations:

(a) $y = px + \dfrac{a^2}{p}.$

(b) $y = px + 2p^2 - p.$

(c) $y = px + \sqrt{p^3 - p^2 + p - 1}.$

(d) $y = (x - 5)p + p^2.$

(e) $y = px + \log p.$

(f) $(y - px)(3p - 1) = 5p^2.$

(g) $e^{y-px} = p^2.$

(h) $y^2 \log y = pxy + p^2.$ *Hint:* Set $u = \log y$.

2. A differential equation has, as general solution, the relation $y^2 - 2xyc + (1 + x^2)c^2 - 4 = 0.$ Find the singular solution.

3. Find the singular solution of $y = px + \dfrac{1}{p^2}.$

4. The equations $y = \dfrac{c}{2}(x - c)^2$, where c is any constant, satisfy the differential equation $p^3 - 2xyp + 4y^2 = 0.$ Find the singular solution.

5. Find the singular solution of the equation $p^2 - xp + y = 0$.

6. The general solution of a differential equation is

$$x \cos c + y \sin c = 5.$$

Find the singular solution.

7. Corresponding to each real value of the constant c is a circle whose center has the coördinates $(5 \cos c, 5 \sin c)$, and whose radius equals unity. Find the equation of the system of circles, its differential equation, and the singular solution of the differential equation.

8. Find the singular solution of the differential equation

$$p^2 - 3xp + y^2 = 0.$$

9. Find the singular solution of $p^2 - pxy + y^2 \log 3y = 0$.

10. Find the singular solution of $xp = y \log y$.

11. Find the singular solution of $p^3 - 2xyp + 4y^2 = 0$.

12. The equation $(1 - x^2)p + xy - 10 = 0$ is satisfied by $y = 10x$. Is the latter a particular solution or a singular solution?

13. Is $y = 0$ a singular solution or a particular solution of

$$12xp^2 - 12yp + 4y = 0?$$

14. Find the singular solution of $3p^2y^2 - 2pxy + 4y^2 - x^2 = 0$.

15. Verify that $y = -p\varphi(p) + \varphi(p)$, $x = -\varphi'(p)$, as given in Equations (16) and (18) of the text, form a solution of the Clairaut equation $y = px + \varphi(p)$.

16. Prove that if an equation $F(x, y, p) = 0$ which is homogeneous in x and y be treated by the method of Section 19, then the variables x and p in the resulting equation are separable.

17. Solve $yp + 2x = \pm \sqrt{(y^2 + 4x^2)(1 + p^2)}$.

18. Solve $y - px = ax\sqrt{1 + p^2}$.

19. Solve $x^3p^2 + 4x^2py - 5xy^2 = 0$.

20. Solve $(px - y)(px + y) = y(x - y)$.

21. Solve $x^n p^t - y^n = 0$.

22. Solve Equation 12 of this chapter; that is, $py = \dfrac{c}{2}$. Substitute the result, $y^2 = cx + k$, in the differential equation (10) to find k in terms of c. Compare the results with Equation (13) of the text.

23. The equation $p^2(3x + 1) - 3p(y + 2) + 9 = 0$ has the general solution $2cy + c^2(y - 3x) - 4 = 0$, and the singular solution $y^2 + 4y - 12x = 0$. Show that the relation $y - 3x = 0$ is also a solution, and that it is not given by the general solution. It is the limiting relation approached as the constant c increases beyond all bound. Such a solution is sometimes called an *infinite* solution.

24. If we set $px - y$ equal to a new variable Y, and differentiate, we obtain

$$dY = p \, dx + x \, dp - dy = (p - y') \, dx + x \, dp = x \, dp.$$

If, now, X is so chosen that $dX = dp$, say $X = p$, then we have

$$P \equiv \frac{dY}{dX} = x.$$

Hence, show that any differential equation of the first order

$$f(x, y, p) = 0$$

becomes

$$f(P, PX - Y, X) = 0,$$

which is likewise of the first order.

25. Show that if the change of variable described in Exercise 24, known as a *transformation of Legendre*, be applied twice, then the result is the original equation.

26. Solve the following equations by applying the transformation of Legendre and solving the resulting differential equation. This gives a relation of the form $F(X, Y, c) = 0$. To return to the original variables, put $X = p$, $Y = px - y$, and obtain $F(p, px - y, c) = 0$. Eliminate p between this and the original equation.

(a) $4p^2x = 3$.

(b) $y = \sqrt{p^2 + (px - y)^2}$.

(c) $xp^2 + 4p - 2y = 0$.

(d) $x = 5p + \sqrt{1 + 4p^2}$.

(e) $p^2x = 1 - x$.

(f) $(y - px)x = y$.

27. Examine the solutions of Exercise 1, above, for infinite solutions.

28. Solve the following by any method, showing all solutions:

(a) $y^2 + 2xyp - (1 - x^2)p^2 = 0$.

(b) $(x^2 - 9)p^2 - 2xyp + y^2 - 9 = 0$.

(c) $px \pm \sqrt{1 + p^2} = 0.$

(d) $x^2(1 + p^3)^2 - a^2 = 0.$

(e) $y = -2p + \sqrt{9 + p^2}.$

(f) $3p^2 + 2px^3 - 4x^2y = 0.$

(g) $y = px + (p - r)(p - s),$ where r and s are constants.

(h) $y = px + \sqrt{a^2 + p^2}.$

(i) $x^2p^2 - (2xy - 1)p + y^2 = 0.$

(j) $(y - px)(3p - 5) = 15p.$

(k) $2x - \log (yp^2) = 0.$

(l) $2y = p^2 + p^3.$

(m) $y = px + x \sqrt{a^2 + p^2}.$

(n) $y^2 \log^2 y + p^2 = y^2.$ *Hint:* Let $y = e^z.$

(o) $\dfrac{(ax - 1)^2}{-a^2x^2 + 2ax} = -1 - p^2.$

(p) $p^2 - xp + y = 0.$

(q) $xp^2 - 2yp + 9x = 0.$

(r) $5 \left(\dfrac{ds}{dt}\right)^5 + \left(\dfrac{ds}{dt}\right)^2 - s = 0.$

(s) $\sin (y - px) = \dfrac{1}{\pm \sqrt{1 + p^2}}.$

(t) $\left(\dfrac{dr}{d\theta}\right)^3 - (\sin \theta - \csc \theta + r) \left(\dfrac{dr}{d\theta}\right)^2 + (r \sin \theta -$

$r \csc \theta - 1) \dfrac{dr}{d\theta} + r = 0.$

(u) $e^{2x}(y^2 \log y - py) = p^2.$ *Hint:* Set $v = \log y, u = e^x.$

29. Is $y = 0$ a singular solution or a particular solution of $y = px$?

30. Show that a family of confocal and coaxial parabolas is self orthogonal.

31. Show that a system of confocal central conics is self orthogonal.

32. Find the system of curves such that the subnormal of any curve at any point equals its subtangent at the same point, multiplied by x^2.

33. The product of the intercepts of a line tangent to a curve is a constant k. Find the curve.

34. Find the curves whose tangents are a constant distance from the point (a, b)

35. The portion of the tangent to a curve cut off by the axes is equal to k.   Find the equation of the curve.

36. A circle of radius a rolls on the inside of a circle of radius $4a$ whose center is at the origin.   A fixed diameter of the moving circle generates a system of straight lines.   Find the singular solution of the differential equation of the system of lines.

37. Express in the form of a Clairaut equation the differential equation whose solutions represent the lines tangent to the curve $x^2 = y^3$.

38. Find the equation of the curve for which $OP = 2 \tan \alpha$, where O is the origin, P is the point where an arbitrary tangent meets OX, and α is the inclination of the tangent.

39. The sum of the x- and y-intercepts of an arbitrary tangent to a curve is 3.   Find the equation of the curve.

CHAPTER IV
Linear Differential Equations

25. General properties. We propose in this chapter to treat of a most important class of differential equations, *viz.*, the linear.

The student has already met with it, among the first order equations in Chapter II, Section 12. We now define it for any order, as an equation of the form

$$P_0\frac{d^ny}{dx^n} + P_1\frac{d^{n-1}y}{dx^{n-1}} + P_2\frac{d^{n-2}y}{dx^{n-2}} + \cdots + P_{n-1}\frac{dy}{dx} + P_ny = Q, \quad (1)$$

where $P_0, P_1, \cdots, P_n$ and Q are functions of x alone or constants, with P_0 not identically zero and n a positive integer.

We shall begin by studying the left-hand member,

$$P_0\frac{d^ny}{dx^n} + P_1\frac{d^{n-1}y}{dx^{n-1}} + P_2\frac{d^{n-2}y}{dx^{n-2}} + \cdots + P_{n-1}\frac{dy}{dx} + P_ny. \quad (2)$$

From the form of this left-hand member follow the properties of the linear differential equation.

From the fact, well known to students of calculus, that $\dfrac{d^n[cf(x)]}{dx^n} = c\dfrac{d^nf(x)}{dx^n}$, where c is constant, and that $\dfrac{d^n[f(x) + g(x)]}{dx^n} = \dfrac{d^nf(x)}{dx^n} + \dfrac{d^ng(x)}{dx^n}$, it follows that the expression (2) has the following properties:

PROPERTY 1. *If the expression* (2) *reduces to* F(x) *when y is replaced by* f(x), *then it reduces to* cF(x) *when y is replaced by* cf(x), *where* c *is a constant.*

PROPERTY 2. *If the expression* (2) *reduces to* F(x) *when y is replaced by* f(x) *and to* G(x) *when y is replaced by* g(x), *then it reduces to* F(x) + G(x) *when y is replaced by* f(x) + g(x).

These properties occasion the use of the adjective, *linear*, in connection with equations of the form (1).

26. General solution. It can be readily observed, in view of the above properties, that if the expression (2) reduces to $Q(x)$ when

69

y is replaced by $q(x)$, and to zero when y is replaced by any one of the functions $f_1(x), f_2(x), \cdots , f_n(x)$, then it reduces to $Q(x)$ when y is replaced by $q(x) + c_1 f_1(x) + c_2 f_2(x) + \cdots + c_n f_n(x)$ where the c's are arbitrary constants. This amounts to saying that if

$$y = q(x)$$

satisfies the linear differential equation (1) and if

$$y = f_1(x),\ y = f_2(x),\ \cdots ,\ y = f_n(x)$$

all satisfy the linear differential equation

$$P_0 \frac{d^n y}{dx^n} + P_1 \frac{d^{n-1} y}{dx^{n-1}} + P_2 \frac{d^{n-2} y}{dx^{n-2}} + \cdots + P_{n-1} \frac{dy}{dx} + P_n y = 0, \quad (3)$$

then

$$y = q(x) + c_1 f_1(x) + c_2 f_2(x) + \cdots + c_n f_n(x)$$

satisfies the differential equation (1).

The equation (3) obtained from (1) by replacing $Q(x)$ by 0 is called the *reduced* or *homogeneous* equation corresponding to (1). In the solution just displayed, the function $q(x)$ is known as a *particular integral* of (1) while the expression $c_1 f_1(x) + c_2 f_2(x) + \cdots + c_n f_n(x)$ is called the *complementary function*.

Illustration

Let us examine the third-order linear differential equation

$$(x^2 - 2x + 2)y''' - x^2 y'' + 2xy' - 2y = 12 - 12x + 6x^2 - 2x^3. \quad (4)$$

The left-hand part of the table below shows four functions, x^3, e^x, x, and x^2 and their first, second, and third derivatives.

Function	x^3	e^x	x	x^2	-2
First derivative	$3x^2$	e^x	1	$2x$	$2x$
Second derivative	$6x$	e^x	0	2	$-x^2$
Third derivative	6	e^x	0	0	$x^2 - 2x + 2$

The right-hand part of the table gives the coefficients of y, y', y'', and y''' as they occur in the left-hand member of (4). If we multiply the functions in any one column of the left-hand part of the table by the respective coefficient as taken from the right-hand part of the table, and add, we get the result of substituting the function at the top of that column into the left-hand member of equation (4) with the following results:

The column for x^3 gives

$$-2x^3 + 6x^3 - 6x^3 + 6x^2 - 12x + 12, \text{ or } 12 - 12x + 6x^2 - 2x^3.$$

The column for e^x gives

$$-2e^x + 2xe^x - x^2e^x + (x^2 - 2x + 2)e^x, \text{ or } 0.$$

The column for x gives

$$-2x + 2x - x^2 \cdot 0 + (x^2 - 2x + 2) \cdot 0, \text{ or } 0.$$

The column for x^2 gives

$$-2x^2 + 4x^2 - 2x^2 + (x^2 - 2x + 2) \cdot 0, \text{ or } 0.$$

We note, therefore, that

$$y = x^3$$

is a solution of the given equation (4), while

$$y = e^x, y = x, \text{ and } y = x^2$$

are all solutions of the corresponding reduced equation

$$(x^2 - 2x + 2)y''' - x^2y'' + 2xy' - 2y = 0.$$

Therefore

$$y = x^3 + c_1e^x + c_2x + c_3x^2 \tag{5}$$

satisfies (4) and is a solution.

We recall now, from the discussion in Chapter I, that the general solution of a third-order ordinary differential equation must contain exactly three arbitrary constants.   Solution (5) appears to have exactly three.   But so does the solution

$$y = x^3 + k_1e^x + k_2x + k_3(e^x + x), \tag{6}$$

which clearly satisfies (4) because it is what we get out of (5) by assigning $c_1 = k_1 + k_3$, $c_2 = k_2 + k_3$, $c_3 = 0$.   Also, evidently, the equation

$$y = x^3 + x^2$$

is a solution of (4), since it follows from (5) with $c_1 = 0$, $c_2 = 0$, $c_3 = 1$, but it cannot be recovered from (6) by assigning constant values to the k's.   Hence (6) is certainly not the general solution of (4), although it is a solution apparently involving exactly three arbitrary constants.

The trouble with (6), as general solution of (4), lies in the functions e^x, x, and $e^x + x$ which we used as basis for the complementary function, in that they are linearly dependent. What we mean by this is described in the following definitions:

DEFINITION 1.   *The* n *functions of a set,* $f_1(x), f_2(x), \cdots, f_n(x)$ *are said to be linearly dependent if a set of* n *constants* $c_1, c_2, \cdots, c_n$ *not all of which are zero, exist such that*

$$c_1 f_1(x) + c_2 f_2(x) + \cdots + c_n f_n(x) \equiv 0.$$

DEFINITION 2.   *The functions of the set* $f_1(x), f_2(x), \cdots, f_n(x)$ *are said to be linearly independent if the identity*

$$c_1 f_1(x) + c_2 f_2(x) + \cdots + c_n f_n(x) \equiv 0$$

is impossible with the c*'s constant, unless all the* c*'s are zero.*

That the functions e^x, x, and $e^x + x$ are linearly dependent, is clear from the identity

$$e^x + x - (e^x + x) \equiv 0.$$

On the other hand, the three functions e^x, x, and x^2 are linearly independent for, if

$$c_1 e^x + c_2 x + c_3 x^2 \equiv 0;$$

then

$$c_1 e^x + c_2 + 2c_3 x \equiv 0,$$
$$c_1 e^x + 2c_3 \equiv 0,$$
$$c_1 e^x \equiv 0,$$

where the three new identities are obtained from the first by differentiation. From these we see first that $c_1 = 0$, next that $c_3 = 0$ and, finally that $c_2 = 0$. To determine, in general, whether or not the functions $f_1(x), f_2(x), \cdots, f_n(x)$ are linearly dependent, suppose that the identity of Definition 1 holds with all the c's constant. By $n - 1$ successive differentiations we then have the system of identities

$$
\begin{aligned}
c_1 f_1(x) + c_2 f_2(x) &+ \cdots + c_n f_n(x) \equiv 0, \\
c_1 f_1'(x) + c_2 f_2'(x) &+ \cdots + c_n f_n'(x) \equiv 0, \\
c_1 f_1''(x) + c_2 f_2''(x) &+ \cdots + c_n f_n''(x) \equiv 0, \\
&\ \ \vdots \\
c_1 f_1^{(n-1)}(x) + c_2 f_2^{(n-1)}(x) &+ \cdots + c_n f_n^{(n-1)}(x) \equiv 0.
\end{aligned}
\tag{7}
$$

The problem becomes one of determining whether or not this system has a solution with the c's not all zero. It is known from algebra[*] that if the determinant of coefficients of the c's,

$$\begin{vmatrix} f_1(x) & f_2(x) & \cdots & f_n(x) \\ f_1'(x) & f_2'(x) & \cdots & f_n'(x) \\ f_1''(x) & f_2''(x) & \cdots & f_n''(x) \\ \cdot & \cdot & \cdots & \cdot \\ \cdot & \cdot & \cdots & \cdot \\ \cdot & \cdot & \cdots & \cdot \\ f_1^{(n-1)}(x) & f_2^{(n-1)}(x) & \cdots & f_n^{(n-1)}(x) \end{vmatrix} \tag{8}$$

is different from zero, the system of equations (7) has no solution other than that in which all the c's are zero. Since this condition holds for every value of x, we conclude that if the c's are not all zero the determinant (8) vanishes for every value of x, that is, it is identically equal to zero. Conversely, it can be shown[†] that if the determinant (8) does vanish identically, then c's exist which are constant and not all zero and which satisfy the equations of the system (7). This makes the functions $f_1(x)$, $f_2(x)$, $\cdots$, $f_n(x)$ linearly dependent.

The determinant displayed as (8) appears frequently in function theory and is called the *Wronskian* (determinant) of the functions $f_1(x)$, $f_2(x)$, $\cdots$, $f_n(x)$ which appear in its first row. We shall employ that language in the following theorem which summarizes the conclusion just drawn.

THEOREM. *The functions of a set are linearly dependent if, and only if, their Wronskian is identically equal to zero.*

In the theory of differential equations, it is proved that the linear differential equation of order n has precisely n linearly independent solutions in a region of the plane where $P_0 \not\equiv 0$ and $P_0, P_1, \cdots, P_n$ are continuous functions of x. By invoking this, we conclude that the solution

$$y = q(x) + c_1 f_1(x) + c_2 f_2(x) + \cdots + c_r f_n(x)$$

is indeed the general solution of (1), provided the expression (2) becomes $Q(x)$ when y is replaced by $q(x)$ and becomes zero when y is replaced by $f_1(x)$, $f_2(x)$, $\cdots$, or $f_n(x)$, while the functions $f_1(x)$, $f_2(x)$, $\cdots$, $f_n(x)$ are linearly independent functions.

---

[*] L. E. Dickson, *First Course in Theory of Equations*, p. 119.

[†] Goursat-Herdick, *Differential Equations*, pp. 103–104.

Exercises

1. Show that $y_1 \equiv x - \sin 2x$ and $y_2 \equiv 3x - 3 \sin 2x$ are linearly dependent. Show that any two functions that differ by a constant factor are linearly dependent.

2. (a) Show that $y_1 \equiv x + e^x$, $y_2 \equiv 1 + \cos x$, $y_3 \equiv 0$ are linearly dependent.

(b) Show that any set of functions is linearly dependent if $y \equiv 0$ is one of the set.

3. (a) Show that a set of functions is linearly dependent if two of the functions are identical.

(b) Show that a set of functions is linearly dependent if one of the functions is a constant multiple of another.

(c) Show that a set of functions is linearly dependent if a subset of those functions is linearly dependent.

4. Verify that $y = 0$ is a solution of (3). If $n - 1$ other solutions are found, are we in a position to write down the general solution?

5. Verify that $y = e^{2x}$ and $y = e^{3x}$ are two linearly independent solutions of $\dfrac{d^2y}{dx^2} - 5\dfrac{dy}{dx} + 6y = 0$. Write down the general solution.

6. Given $y'' - y' - 2y = 2 - 2x$, which we shall call Equation (A). Verify that $y = e^{2x}$ is a solution of the corresponding reduced equation. Now let $y = u \cdot e^{2x}$, and substitute in (A). We obtain

$$\frac{d^2u}{dx^2} + \frac{3du}{dx} = \frac{2 - 2x}{e^{2x}}.$$

Let $\dfrac{du}{dx} = v$, and the last equation becomes $\dfrac{dv}{dx} + 3v = \dfrac{2 - 2x}{e^{2x}}$, a linear equation of the first order. This is solved by the methods of Chapter II, Section 12, and has the general solution

$$v = 2e^{-2x}(2 - x) + ce^{-3x},$$

or

$$\frac{du}{dx} = 2e^{-2x}(2 - x) + ce^{-3x}.$$

This equation has the solution

$$u = -\frac{3}{2}e^{-2x} + xe^{-2x} - \frac{c}{3}e^{-3x} + k;$$

hence,

$$y = -\frac{3}{2} + x - \frac{c}{3}\,e^{-x} + ke^{2x}$$

is the general solution of (A), c and k being arbitrary constants.

27. Homogeneous, with constant coefficients. The student may gather from the foregoing discussion that the problem of finding the general solution of a given linear differential equation divides into two parts; one, that of finding a particular integral, and the other, that of finding the complementary function. We shall study first the complementary function, wh ch is to say, we shall study first the problem of solving the equation (3) or an equation of the form (1) in which $Q(x)$ is zero. Even thus restricted, the problem is too difficult to solve in its general form, and we will restrict, for a time, the functions P_0, P_1, $\cdots$, P_n to represent constants. A linear differential equation, thus restricted, is of the form

$$a_0\frac{d^ny}{dx^n} + a_1\frac{d^{n-1}y}{dx^{n-1}} + a_2\frac{d^{n-2}y}{dx^{n-2}} + \cdots + a_{n-1}\frac{dy}{dx} + a_ny = 0, \quad (9)$$

where n is any positive integer, the a's are real constants and a_0 is not zero.

It is a practice frequently employed in mathematics to express the nth derivative of y with respect to x by the symbol $D_x^n y$. Written in this notation, Equation (9) becomes

$$a_0D_x^n y + a_1D_x^{n-1}y + a_2D_x^{n-2}y + \cdots + a_{n-1}D_xy + a_ny = 0,$$

and, if the independent variable is clearly understood to be x, we might safely drop the subscript, x, from the derivative symbols and write (9) in the form

$$a_0D^n y + a_1D^{n-1}y + a_2D^{n-2}y + \cdots + a_{n-1}Dy + a_ny = 0.$$

It appears as though this could be written in the form

$$[a_0D^n + a_1D^{n-1} + a_2D^{n-2} + \cdots + a_{n-1}D + a_n]y = 0,$$

as, indeed, it can, with suitable understanding as to the meaning of the expression

$$a_0D^n + a_1D^{n-1} + a_2D^{n-2} + \cdots + a_{n-1}D + a_n. \quad (10)$$

That this matter cannot be dismissed lightly may be seen by noticing that the last term, a_n, is a real number while no other term has any meaning whatever when taken alone. If $a_{n-1}D$ is not a number while a_n is a number, what sort of thing is $a_{n-1}D + a_n$?

Such an expression as (10) is called an *operator*.   It has no value alone but, when it is followed by a function of x, the whole takes on meaning.   We define this meaning by means of the equalities:

$$D^m u \equiv \frac{d^m u}{dx^m} \quad (m \text{ any positive integer}), \quad \text{(I)}$$

$$(a_0 D^n + a_1 D^{n-1} + \cdots + a_{n-1} D + a_n)u$$
$$\equiv a_0 D^n u + a_1 D^{n-1}u + \cdots + a_{n-1} Du + a_n u, \quad \text{(II)}$$

where the a's are any real constants and n is a positive integer.

While polynomials in D, such as (10), are not quantities, but merely operators, each of which must be followed by a function of x, nevertheless, these operators obey all of the ordinary laws of algebra. In particular, consider the polynomial in D which we get if we multiply together two polynomials in D, say $f(D)$ and $g(D)$.   The product, by ordinary algebra, considering $f(D)$ and $g(D)$ as polynomials, is

$$[f(D) \cdot g(D)].$$

This operator, $[f(D) \cdot g(D)]$, when applied to u, a function of x, produces a result which may also be obtained by operating on u first with one of the factors, say $g(D)$, and then upon that result with the other factor, $f(D)$.   That is, to operate upon u by a polynomial operator, we may factor the operator and operate with the factors successively.   Stated symbolically, this property takes the form

$$[f(D) \cdot g(D)]u \equiv f(D)[g(D)u],$$

when there are just two factors, and

$$[f_1(D) \cdot f_2(D) \cdot f_3(D) \cdots f_n(D)]u \equiv f_1(D)[f_2(D)[f_3(D)[\cdots$$
$$[f_n(D)u] \cdots]]] \quad \text{(11)}$$

when there are n factors.

To establish (11) we begin with the case of two factors each of which is a "power" of D, $i.\ e.$, we prove that

$$[D^{r+s}]u \equiv D^r[D^s u] \equiv D^s[D^r u].$$

As learned in differential calculus

$$\frac{d^{r+s}u}{dx^{r+s}} \equiv \frac{d^r}{dx^r}\left(\frac{d^s u}{dx^s}\right) \equiv \frac{d^s}{dx^s}\left(\frac{d^r u}{dx^r}\right)$$

which, when put in the operator notation, is the desired result.

We next take the case in which one factor is D^r and the other is the polynomial $a_0 D^n + a_1 D^{n-1} + \cdots + a_{n-1} D + a_n$.   The product of these operators in the algebraic sense is $a_0 D^{n+r} + a_1 D^{n+r-1} + \cdots + a_{n-1} D^{r+1} + a_n D^r$. Operating on u with this gives

$$[a_0 D^{n+r} + a_1 D^{n+r-1} + \cdots + a_{n-1} D^{r+1} + a_n D^r]u.$$

On the other hand, if we operate on u by only the polynomial factor we obtain

$$[a_0 D^n + a_1 D^{n-1} + \cdots + a_{n-1} D + a_n]u,$$

or, by (II),

$$a_0 D^n u + a_1 D^{n-1} u + \cdots + a_{n-1} D u + a_n u.$$

Operating now upon this result by the operator, D^r, we obtain

$$D^r[a_0 D^n u + a_1 D^{n-1} u + \cdots + a_{n-1} D u + a_n u],$$

which is the same as

$$\frac{d^r}{dx^r}\left[a_0 \frac{d^n u}{dx^n} + a_1 \frac{d^{n-1} u}{dx^{n-1}} + \cdots + a_{n-1} \frac{du}{dx} + a_n u \right],$$

which, by ordinary calculus, becomes

$$a_0 \frac{d^{n+r} u}{dx^{n+r}} + a_1 \frac{d^{n+r-1} u}{dx^{n+r-1}} + \cdots + a_{n-1} \frac{d^{r+1} u}{dx^{r+1}} + a_n \frac{d^r u}{dx^r}.$$

When this last result is rewritten in the operator symbols it becomes

$$[a_0 D^{n+r} + a_1 D^{n-1+r} + \cdots + a_{n-1} D^{r+1} + a_n D^r]u,$$

as was to be shown. In like manner the student may show that this same result is obtained if u is operated upon first by D^r and the result of that operated upon by the polynomial operator $a_0 D^n + a_1 D^{n-1} + \cdots + a_{n-1} D + a_n$.

In considering the case of the product of two operators both of which are polynomials in D, let us express the resulting operator as

$$(a_0 D^n + a_1 D^{n-1} + \cdots + a_{n-1} D + a_n)[g(D)],$$

where $g(D)$ is a polynomial in D. When multiplied out, this product becomes

$$[a_0 D^n g(D) + a_1 D^{n-1} g(D) + \cdots + a_{n-1} D g(D) + a_n g(D)],$$

and, operating upon u by it, we obtain

$$[a_0 D^n g(D) + a_1 D^{n-1} g(D) + \cdots + a_{n-1} D g(D) + a_n g(D)]u.$$

If, on the other hand, we operate upon u by the operator $g(D)$ and upon the result by the polynomial operator, we obtain

$$[a_0D^n + a_1D^{n-1} + \cdots + a_{n-1}D + a_n][g(D)u].$$

By the definitions of the operators this becomes

$$a_0D^ng(D)u + a_1D^{n-1}g(D)u + \cdots + a_{n-1}Dg(D)u + a_ng(D)u,$$

which in turn, by the preceding cases, becomes

$$[a_0D^ng(D) + a_1D^{n-1}g(D) + \cdots + a_{n-1}Dg(D) + a_ng(D)]u,$$

the result previously obtained with the product operator. Since, in this demonstration, both factors were polynomials in D, we have, in effect, shown that

$$[f(D) \cdot g(D)]u \equiv f(D)[g(D)u] \equiv g(D)[f(D)u].$$

If a polynomial operator is the product of more than two polynomials in D the truth of (11) may be shown by grouping the factors and applying the rule for two factors.

28. The Complementary function. Written in the operator notation, the linear differential equation (9), which has constant coefficients and right-hand member zero, appears as

$$[a_0D^n + a_1D^{n-1} + \cdots + a_{n-1}D + a_n]y = 0.$$

It is proved in algebra* that any real polynomial of degree, n, and therefore, the polynomial

$$a_0D^n + a_1D^{n-1} + \cdots + a_{n-1}D + a_n,$$

may be factored into the form

$$a_0(D - r_1)(D - r_2) \cdots (D - r_n),$$

where the n numbers, $r_1, r_2, \cdots, r_n$ are not necessarily distinct or real. However, if one of these r's is the complex number $a + bi$, where a and b are real numbers and $i = \sqrt{-1}$, then the conjugate complex number, $viz.$, $a - bi$, is also one of the r's.

By the properties of operators, the above differential equation may now be written in the form

$$a_0[(D - r_1)[(D - r_2)[\cdots [(D - r_n)y] \cdots]]] = 0,$$

---

*L. E. Dickson, *First Course in Theory of Equations*, p. 17.

where the factors, $D - r_1, D - r_2, \cdots D - r_n$ may be arranged in any order whatever. Note, now, that if y is such a function of x that

$$(D - r_n)y = 0,$$

then that value of y is a solution of (9), since the result of operating on zero by other polynomial operators is always zero. By rearranging the order of the factors of the operator, we see that y is a solution of the given differential equation if it is a solution of any one of the first-order equations

$$(D - r_1)y = 0,$$
$$(D - r_2)y = 0,$$

$$\cdot \quad \cdot \quad \cdot$$
$$\cdot \quad \cdot \quad \cdot$$
$$\cdot \quad \cdot \quad \cdot$$

$$(D - r_n)y = 0.$$

Thus the problem of solving the nth order linear differential equation with constant coefficients and right-hand member zero appears to have been reduced to that of solving n first-order equations of the same type.

Each of the first-order equations to which the problem has been reduced is of the form

$$(D - r)y = 0,$$

and, by the methods of Chapter II, Section 12, has a solution of the form

$$y = e^{rx}.$$

We conclude that if the operator

$$a_0D^n + a_1D^{n-1} + \cdots + a_{n-1}D + a_n,$$

when considered as an algebraic polynomial, has the factored form,

$$a_0(D - r_1)(D - r_2) \cdots (D - r_n),$$

then the differential equation

$$(a_0D^n + a_1D^{n-1} + \cdots + a_{n-1}D + a_n)y = 0$$

has the solutions

$$y = e^{r_1x}, y = e^{r_2x}, \cdots, y = e^{r_nx},$$

and, hence, the solution

$$y = c_1e^{r_1x} + c_2e^{r_2x} + \cdots + c_ne^{r_nx}, \tag{12}$$

where the c's are arbitrary constants.

Certain conditions may prevail under which (12) is not the general solution sought. First of all, some of the r's may be complex numbers. Say that r_1 is complex and equals $a + bi$, where a and b are real and $i = \sqrt{-1}$. Then another one of the r's is the complex number $a - bi$ and we find, in our solution, expressions $e^{(a+bi)x}$ and $e^{(a-bi)x}$. Such expressions require examination. If $b \neq 0$, the quantity $e^{(a+bi)x}$ is not real. In such a case the value of y, in the solution (12) will not, in general, be real for real values of x and real values of the c's. This condition is jarring in itself and the solution is most unsatisfactory if the student knows nothing about complex numbers and complex functions. Further discussion on this subject will appear later in this chapter.

If any two of the r's in (12) are equal it will fail to be the general solution, even if all of the r's are real numbers. Discussion of this case is also postponed until a later section.

In the most favorable case, *viz.*, that in which all of the r's are real and distinct, the functions e^{r_1x}, e^{r_2x}, $\cdots$, e^{r_nx} are linearly independent, as the student will be asked to show in a problem, and solution (12) is the general solution of the given differential equation.

Exercises

1. Prove that if r_1, r_2, $\cdots$, r_n are n real distinct numbers, then the functions e^{r_1x}, e^{r_2x}, $\cdots$, e^{r_nx} are linearly independent.

2. Find the general solution of each of the following equations:

(a) $y'' - 2y' - 3y = 0.$
(b) $3y''' - y'' - 2y' = 0.$
(c) $2y''' - 5y'' + 2y' = 0.$
(d) $y'' + 2y' - 8y = 0.$
(e) $y^{iv} - 4y'' + 3y = 0.$
(f) $y''' - by'' = a^2y' - a^2by.$ (a, b real constants)
(g) $y^{iv} - 2y''' - y'' + 2y' = 0.$

29. Reduction of order. In this section we shall derive a property possessed by every linear differential equation, even though, at present, we are concerned primarily with equations having constant coefficients and right-hand member zero.

PROPERTY 3. *If* $y = f(x)$ *is a solution of the linear differential equation*

$$P_0 y^{(n)} + P_1 y^{(n-1)} + \cdots + P_{n-1} y' + P_n y = 0,$$

then the substitution y = vf(x) *into the equation*

$$P_0 y^{(n)} + P_1 y^{(n-1)} + \cdots + P_{n-1} y' + P_n y = Q(x)$$

and the subsequent substitution v' = u, *will yield a differential equation of the form*

$$R_0 u^{(n-1)} + R_1 u^{(n-2)} + \cdots + R_{n-2} u' + R_{n-1} u = Q(x),$$

i. e., an equation of order lower by one than the order of the original equation.

Proof

By hypothesis, $y = f(x)$ satisfies the reduced equation displayed above, *i. e.*,

$$P_0 f^{(n)}(x) + P_1 f^{(n-1)}(x) + \cdots + P_{n-1} f'(x) + P_n f(x) \equiv 0.$$

Now, by repeated differentiation, we obtain

$$y = vf(x),$$
$$y' = vf'(x) + v'f(x),$$
$$y'' = vf''(x) + 2v'f'(x) + v''f(x),$$

. . . .

. . . .

$$y^{(n)} = vf^{(n)}(x) + nv'f^{(n-1)}(x) + \frac{n(n-1)}{2} v''f^{(n-2)}(x) + \cdots + v^{(n)}f(x),$$

which, when substituted into the given equation, give

$$[P_0 f(x)]v^{(n)} + [nP_0 f'(x) + P_1 f(x)]v^{(n-1)}$$
$$+ \left[\frac{n(n-1)}{2} P_0 f''(x) + nP_1 f'(x) + P_2 f(x) \right] v^{(n-2)}$$
$$+ \, . \quad . \quad . \quad . \quad . \quad . \quad . \quad . \quad . \quad . \quad . \quad . \quad .$$
$$+ [nP_0 f^{(n-1)}(x) + (n-1)P_1 f^{(n-2)}(x) + \cdots + P_{n-1} f(x)]v'$$
$$+ [P_0 f^{(n)}(x) + P_1 f^{(n-1)}(x) + \cdots$$
$$+ P_{n-1} f'(x) + P_n f(x)]v = Q(x).$$

The last bracket on the left-hand side contains a quantity which vanishes identically. Hence the substitution $v' = u$ and the consequent relations $v'' = u'$, $v''' = u''$, and so forth, yield a linear differential equation of order $n - 1$ in u. Furthermore, if one is successful in solving this last equation for u, as a function of x, he may reverse the substitutions and find y, being careful to replace v by $\int u \, dx + c$.

It follows at once that, if k linearly independent solutions of the reduced linear equation are known, the process of reducing the order may be applied k times, resulting in a final differential equation of order k less than the order of the original equation. The student may do well to reflect why k known solutions which are not linearly independent, will fail to reduce the order of the equation precisely by k.

Illustration

Consider the equation

$$\left(x - \frac{1}{2}\right)y''' - 4xy' + 4y = \frac{e^{2x}}{2}. \tag{13}$$

Two solutions of the reduced equation are easily seen to be $y_1 \equiv 2x$, and $y_2 \equiv e^{2x}$. Set $y = 2xu$, and (13) becomes

$$u'''(2x^2 - x) + u''(6x - 3) - u' \cdot 8x^2 = \frac{e^{2x}}{2},$$

or

$$v''(2x^2 - x) + v'(6x - 3) - v \cdot 8x^2 = \frac{e^{2x}}{2},$$

where $v \equiv u'$. One known solution of the reduced equation corresponding to this is

$$v_2 = \left(\frac{e^{2x}}{2x}\right)' \equiv e^{2x}\left(\frac{1}{x} - \frac{1}{2x^2}\right).$$

Now set

$$v = ze^{2x}\left(\frac{1}{x} - \frac{1}{2x^2}\right),$$

and the equation in v becomes

$$z'' \cdot e^{2x}\left(2x - 2 + \frac{1}{2x}\right) + z' \cdot e^{2x}\left(8x - 6 + \frac{2}{x} - \frac{1}{2x^2}\right) = \frac{e^{2x}}{2},$$

or

$$w' \cdot \frac{4x^2 - 4x + 1}{2x} + w \cdot \frac{16x^3 - 12x^2 + 4x - 1}{2x^2} = \frac{1}{2},$$

where $w \equiv z'$, or

$$w' + w \cdot \frac{16x^3 - 12x^2 + 4x - 1}{4x^3 - 4x^2 + x} = \frac{x}{(2x - 1)^2}.$$

This may be written

$$w' + w\left(4 + \frac{4}{2x - 1} - \frac{1}{x}\right) = \frac{x}{(2x - 1)^2}.$$

An integrating factor for this is

$$e^{\int\left(4+\frac{4}{2x-1}-\frac{1}{x}\right)dx} \equiv e^{4x+2\,\log\,(2x-1)-\log\,x} \equiv \frac{(2x - 1)^2}{x}\,e^{4x}.$$

By use of the above factor the equation is seen to have the solution

$$w \cdot e^{4x}\frac{(2x - 1)^2}{x} = \int \frac{x \cdot e^{4x}(2x - 1)^2}{(2x - 1)^2 \cdot x}\,dx \equiv \frac{e^{4x}}{4} + c_1,$$

or

$$w = \frac{x}{4(2x - 1)^2} + \frac{c_1 x}{e^{4x}(2x - 1)^2}.$$

From this we may return to the original variables by the equations

$$z = \int w\,dx + c_2,$$

$$v = z \cdot e^{2x}\left(\frac{1}{x} - \frac{1}{2x^2}\right),$$

$$u = \int v\,dx + c_3,$$

and

$$y = 2x \cdot u,$$

which will yield y as the general solution of (13).

Exercises

1. For each of the following linear equations, a known solution of the corresponding reduced equation is enclosed in parentheses. Find the general solution of the complete equation in each case.

(a) $xy'' + y' - \dfrac{1}{x}y = 4x$ $\qquad\qquad\qquad\left(y = \dfrac{2}{x}\right).$

(b) $y'' - y' - \dfrac{1}{x}y = e^x(1 + x)$ $\qquad\qquad (y = xe^x).$

(c) $y'' \cos x + y' \sin x = \cot^2 x$ $\qquad\qquad (y = \sin x).$

2. For each of the following linear equations, two known solutions of the corresponding reduced equations are enclosed in parentheses.   Find the general solution of the complete equation in each case.

(a) $y'''(x + 2) - y''(x + 3) = \dfrac{2(x + 2)^2}{x}$ $(y = x; y = xe^x)$.

(b) $x^2 y''' + 5xy'' + 4y' = \log x$ $\left(y = \dfrac{1}{x}; y = \dfrac{\log x}{x}\right)$.

(c) $4xy''' - 4y'' + \dfrac{4}{x} y' = \dfrac{1}{x^3}$ $(y = x^2; y = x^2 \log x)$.

30. Characteristic equation; equal or complex roots.   We have seen that in case the operator

$$a_0 D^n + a_1 D^{n-1} + \cdots + a_{n-1} D + a_n \tag{14}$$

has the factor $D - r$, one solution of the linear differential equation

$$[a_0 D^n + a_1 D^{n-1} + \cdots + a_{n-1} D + a_n]y = 0 \tag{15}$$

is

$$y = e^{rx}.$$

The number, r, by a well-known theorem in algebra, is a solution of the equation

$$a_0 D^n + a_1 D^{n-1} + \cdots + a_{n-1} D + a_n = 0, \tag{16}$$

considered as an nth degree algebraic equation in the variable, D. This equation (16) is called the *characteristic equation* for the differential equation (15).

If the characteristic equation (16) has real and distinct roots the solution to (15) is completely given by (12) of Section (28). If (16) has a real root, r, of multiplicity, k, the differential equation (15) may be written as

$$[f(D)(D - r)^k]y = 0,$$

and we seek the solution of the portion

$$(D - r)^k y = 0.$$

Noting, now, that $y = e^{rx}$ is a solution of this, we attempt to find other solutions by lowering the order.   In order to do this, we make the substitution

$$y = ve^{rx}.$$

In effecting this substitution, we shall have several occasions to evaluate an operation of the type

$$(D - r)[f(x)e^{rx}],$$

which is readily found to be

$$f'(x)e^{rx} + rf(x)e^{rx} - rf(x)e^{rx},$$

or, simply,

$$f'(x)e^{rx}.$$

Consequently, when $(D - r)$ operates k times upon ve^{rx}, as it does when we substitute $y = ve^{rx}$ in the equation $(D - r)^k y = 0$, we obtain

$$v^{(k)}e^{rx} = 0,$$

or

$$v^{(k)} = 0$$

From this, we get, by integration,

$$v = c_1 x^{k-1} + c_2 x^{k-2} + c_3 x^{k-3} + \cdots + c_{k-1}x + c_k,$$

and the solution we seek is

$$y = e^{rx}[c_1 x^{k-1} + c_2 x^{k-2} + c_3 x^{k-3} + \cdots + c_{k-1}x + c_k].$$

It is left to the student to show that the k functions, $1, x, \cdots, x^{k-1}$, are linearly independent and, hence, that this represents the general solution of the equation

$$(D - r)^k y = 0.$$

If the characteristic equation

$$a_0 D^n + a_1 D^{n-1} + \cdots + a_{n-1}D + a_n = 0$$

of the linear differential equation

$$[a_0 D^n + a_1 D^{n-1} + \cdots + a_{n-1}D + a_n]y = 0$$

has a pair of complex roots, $a \pm bi$, the differential equation may be rewritten as

$$f(D)[\{(D - a)^2 + b^2\}y] = 0.$$

The problem is to solve the portion

$$\{(D - a)^2 + b^2\}y = 0.$$

The method employed for real roots, when applied to this equation, yields the expression

$$y = c_1 e^{(a+bi)x} + c_2 e^{(a-bi)x},$$

which has been previously cited as unsatisfactory.   Assuming that the ordinary laws of exponents hold for complex exponents, we write this as

$$y = e^{ax}[c_1 e^{bix} + c_2 e^{-bix}].$$

We shall use the result only as a hint, so that the validity of the law of exponents need not be questioned. This expression for y has a real factor, e^{ax}, and suggests the substitution

$$y = v e^{ax}.$$

From this we obtain

$$(D - a)^2 y = v'' e^{ax},$$
$$b^2 y = b^2 v e^{ax},$$

and, hence, the equation

$$[(D - a)^2 + b^2]y = 0$$

becomes

$$v'' + b^2 v = 0.$$

This equation is seen, by inspection, to be satisfied by $v = \cos bx$ and $v = \sin bx$. Its general solution is, then,

$$v = c_1 \cos bx + c_2 \sin bx,$$

and, therefore, the general solution of the equation

$$[(D - a)^2 + b^2]y = 0$$

is

$$y = e^{ax}[c_1 \cos bx + c_2 \sin bx].$$

We now know how to handle complex roots, provided they are not multiple roots, and real roots whether distinct or not. Let us fix the ideas by an illustration.

To solve the differential equation

$$[(D - 1)(D + 2)(D - 2)^2(D + 1)^3\{(D - 3)^2 + 16\}]y = 0, \quad (17)$$

we consider the equation to be broken into fragments

$$(D - 1)y = 0,$$
$$(D + 2)y = 0,$$
$$(D - 2)^2 y = 0,$$
$$(D + 1)^3 y = 0,$$
$$[(D - 3)^2 + 16]y = 0.$$

Upon solving all of these and recognizing that the various arbitrary constants involved are all independent, we may write down the general solution of (17) as

$$y = c_1 e^x + c_2 e^{-2x} + (c_3 + c_4 x)e^{2x} + (c_5 + c_6 x + c_7 x^2)e^{-x}$$
$$+ (c_8 \cos 4x + c_9 \sin 4x)e^{3x}.$$

We now turn our attention to the case in which the characteristic equation has a multiple complex root or, rather, a pair of multiple complex roots. We may solve this case by a surmise, followed by verification. Note, first, that the general solution of the equation

$$(D - r)^k y = 0$$

turned out to be a polynomial in x, with arbitrary coefficients and degree $k - 1$, multiplied by a solution of the equation

$$(D - r)y = 0.$$

If the same sort of thing were to hold for the complex case we would expect the general solution of the equation

$$[(D - a)^2 + b^2]^k y = 0 \tag{18}$$

to be a polynomial in x, with arbitrary coefficients and degree $k - 1$, times a solution of the equation

$$[(D - a)^2 + b^2]y = 0.$$

But this equation has two linearly independent solutions, viz., $e^{ax} \cos bx$ and $e^{ax} \sin bx$. This, together with the fact that the general solution of (18) should have $2k$ arbitrary constants, leads us to examine the expression

$$
\begin{aligned}
y = {}& (c_1 + c_2 x + c_3 x^2 + \cdots + c_{k-1} x^{k-2} + c_k x^{k-1}) e^{ax} \cos bx \\
& + (k_1 + k_2 x + k_3 x^2 + \cdots + k_{k-1} x^{k-2} + k_k x^{k-1}) e^{ax} \sin bx. \tag{19}
\end{aligned}
$$

To prove that this is the correct general solution of (18), we need to show that it satisfies (18) and that the $2k$ terms involved are linearly independent.

To show that (19) satisfies (18), let us examine the result of operating upon a function of the type

$$e^{ax}[cv \cos bx + gu \sin bx],$$

where c and g are constants and v and u are functions of x, with the operator $[(D - a)^2 + b^2]$. From a foregoing formula,

$$
\begin{aligned}
(D - a)^2 & [(cv \cos bx + gu \sin bx)e^{ax}] \\
& \equiv e^{ax} \frac{d^2}{dx^2} [cv \cos bx + gu \sin bx] \\
& \equiv e^{ax}[cv'' \cos bx + gu'' \sin bx - 2cbv' \sin bx + 2gbu' \cos bx \\
& \qquad\qquad\qquad\qquad\quad - cb^2 v \cos bx - gb^2 u \sin bx].
\end{aligned}
$$

Hence,

$$[(D - a)^2 + b^2][(cv \cos bx + gu \sin bx)e^{ax}]$$
$$\equiv e^{ax}[(cv'' + 2gbu') \cos bx + (gu'' - 2cbv') \sin bx].$$

If, now, v and u are polynomials in x of the same degree, the expressions $cv'' + 2gbu'$ and $gu'' - 2cbv'$ are polynomials of one lower degree. Hence the result of operating on (19) k times in succession by the operator $[(D - a)^2 + b^2]$ is to give an expression of the same sort in which the degree of the polynomials in x forming the coefficients of $e^{ax} \cos bx$ and $e^{ax} \sin bx$ has been reduced by k units. Since the degree is only $k - 1$ to start with, the coefficients become identically zero at the close of the process. Hence (19) is a solution of (18) regardless of the $2k$ arbitrary constants.

We leave it as an exercise for the student to show that the $2k$ terms of (19) are linearly independent functions.

Illustration

To write the general solution of the linear differential equation

$$(D + 2)(D - 4)^3[(D - 4)^2 + 9][(D - 1)^2 + 4]^2 y = 0,$$

note that the root, -2, is simple, that the root, 4, has the multiplicity 3, the roots $4 \pm 3i$ are simple, while the roots $1 \pm 2i$ have the multiplicity 2. Hence, the general solution is

$$y = c_1 e^{-2x} + (c_2 + c_3 x + c_4 x^2)e^{4x} + e^{4x}(c_5 \cos 3x + c_6 \sin 3x)$$
$$+ e^x[(c_7 + c_8 x) \cos 2x + (c_9 + c_{10} x) \sin 2x].$$

Exercises

1. Solve the following:

(a) $\dfrac{d^3y}{dx^3} + 2\dfrac{d^2y}{dx^2} = 0.$

(b) $y'' - 4y' + 13y = 0.$

(c) $y''' + 6y'' + 10y' = 0.$

(d) $y^{iv} - 2y''' + y'' = 0.$

(e) $y^v - 3y^{iv} + 2y''' = 0.$

(f) $\dfrac{d^4y}{dx^4} + 2\dfrac{d^3y}{dx^3} - 3\dfrac{d^2y}{dx^2} - 4\dfrac{dy}{dx} + 4y = 0.$

(g) $\dfrac{d^4y}{dx^4} + \dfrac{d^3y}{dx^3} - 3\dfrac{d^2y}{dx^2} - 5\dfrac{dy}{dx} - 2y = 0.$

(h) $\dfrac{d^4y}{dx^4} - 2\dfrac{d^3y}{dx^3} + 5\dfrac{d^2y}{dx^2} = 0.$

(i) $y''' - 2y'' + y' = 0.$

(j) $y^{vi} + 8y^{iv} + 16y'' = 0.$

(k) $4y^{iv} - 20y''' + 33y'' - 17y' = 0.$

2. Write down the complete solution of the homogeneous linear differential equation with constant coefficients whose characteristic equation has the roots $r = 1$, $r = 1$, $r = 4 + i$, $r = 4 - i$.

3. Show that if the roots of the characteristic equation of a differential equation include the values $a \pm bi$, the solution

$$y = e^{ax}(c_1 \cos bx + c_2 \sin bx),$$

where c_1 and c_2 are arbitrary real constants, can be written in the equivalent form

$$y = k_1 e^{ax}[\sin (bx + k_2)],$$

where k_1 and k_2 are arbitrary real constants. *Hint:*

$$e^{ax}(c_1 \cos bx + c_2 \sin bx)$$

$$= e^{ax} \cdot \sqrt{c_1^2 + c_2^2} \cdot \left[\frac{c_1}{\sqrt{c_1^2 + c_2^2}} \cos bx + \frac{c_2}{\sqrt{c_1^2 + c_2^2}} \sin bx \right].$$

4. Put the solutions of Exercises 1(b), 1(c), and 1(h) in the form discussed in Exercise 3.

5. Show that a result alternative to the one in Exercise 3 is

$$y = k_1 e^{ax}[\cos (bx + k_2)].$$

31. Right-hand side not zero. For the non-homogeneous linear equation

$$\frac{d^n y}{dx^n} + P_1 \frac{d^{n-1} y}{dx^{n-1}} + P_2 \frac{d^{n-2} y}{dx^{n-2}} + \cdots + P_{n-1} \frac{dy}{dx} + P_n y = Q, \quad (20)$$

we need only to find a particular integral and add to it the complementary function which, the student will recall, is the **general** solution of the reduced equation

$$\frac{d^n y}{dx^n} + P_1 \frac{d^{n-1} y}{dx^{n-1}} + P_2 \frac{d^{n-2} y}{dx^{n-2}} + \cdots + P_{n-1} \frac{dy}{dx} + P_n y = 0.$$

Relatively simple methods of finding the particular integral present themselves in certain cases.* Consider, for example, the equation

$$\frac{d^3 y}{dx^3} - 2 \frac{d^2 y}{dx^2} - \frac{dy}{dx} + 2y = 3x^2 - 5x + 2.$$

---

* Throughout the remainder of this section we shall assume the coefficients of the equations to be constants.

The complementary function is easily found to be

$$u(x) \equiv c_1 e^{-x} + c_2 e^x + c_3 e^{2x}.$$

To find a particular integral, observe that

$$v(x) \equiv ax^2 + bx + c,$$

where a, b, and c are constants to be determined, suggests itself readily as a possible particular integral. On this assumption, we get

$$\frac{dv}{dx} \equiv 2ax + b,$$

$$\frac{d^2v}{dx^2} \equiv 2a,$$

$$\frac{d^3v}{dx^3} \equiv 0.$$

Substituting these in the equation, we have

$$\frac{d^3v}{dx^3} - 2\frac{d^2v}{dx^2} - \frac{dv}{dx} + 2v \equiv -4a - 2ax - b + 2ax^2 + 2bx + 2c$$

$$\equiv 3x^2 - 5x + 2.$$

Since this is an identity, we equate coefficients of like powers of x on both sides, and thus obtain

$$\begin{cases} 2a = 3, \\ 2b - 2a = -5, \\ 2c - 4a - b = 2, \end{cases}$$

whence, $a = \dfrac{3}{2}$, $b = -1$, $c = \dfrac{7}{2}$, therefore $v(x) \equiv \dfrac{3}{2}x^2 - x + \dfrac{7}{2}$, and the complete solution is

$$y = c_1 e^{-x} + c_2 e^x + c_3 e^{2x} + \frac{3}{2}x^2 - x + \frac{7}{2}.$$

This example lays the ground for

NOTE I. *If* $Q(x)$ *in* (20) *is a polynomial of degree* m, *assume the particular solution of* (20) *to be* $v(x) \equiv A_0 x^m + A_1 x^{m-1} + \cdots + A_{m-1}x + A_m$, *substitute* v *and its successive derivatives in* (20), *and compute the A's by equating coefficients of like powers on both sides of the equation.* (See Exercise 6, below, for exception.)

Certain other special cases are taken care of by the following two notes:

NOTE II. *If* $Q(x)$ *in* (20) *is of the form* B_0 *sin* $mx + B_1$ *cos* mx, *assume a particular integral* $v \equiv A_0$ *sin* $mx + A_1$ *cos* mx, *and, by substituting for* y, *find the* A's. (See Exercise 14, below, for exception.)

NOTE III. *If* $Q(x)$ *in* (20) *is of the form* Be^{mx}, *assume as a particular integral* $v \equiv Ae^{mx}$, *and, by substituting in* (20) *for* y, *determine* A. (See Exercise 23, below, for exception.)

Exercises

1. Verify that if the right-hand side of (20) is

$$Q \equiv B_0 x^m + B_1 x^{m-1} + \cdots + B_{m-1} x + B_m,$$

the number of equations for finding $A_0, A_1, \cdots, A_m$, as in Note I, will be $m + 1$. This is a partial verification of Note I. Why partial?

2. Solve $\dfrac{d^2y}{dx^2} + \dfrac{dy}{dx} - 2y = 2x^2 - 3x$.

3. Solve $\dfrac{d^3y}{dx^3} - \dfrac{d^2y}{dx^2} - 4\dfrac{dy}{dx} + 4y = x^4 - 3x + 5$.

4. Solve $\dfrac{d^3y}{dx^3} - \dfrac{d^2y}{dx^2} - 9\dfrac{dy}{dx} + 9y = 2x + 3$.

5. Solve $\dfrac{d^3y}{dx^3} + \dfrac{d^2y}{dx^2} - 5\dfrac{dy}{dx} + 3y = x^3 - x + 1$.

6. Let the equation be

$$\frac{d^ny}{dx^n} + a_1\frac{d^{n-1}y}{dx^{n-1}} + \cdots + a_{n-k}\frac{d^ky}{dx^k} = B_0 x^m + B_1 x^{m-1} + \cdots + B_m.$$

Show that if we substitute $v \equiv A_0 x^m + A_1 x^{m-1} + \cdots + A_m$, the left-hand member becomes a polynomial of degree $m - k$, and that hence it cannot identically equal a polynomial of degree m. Show further that the substitution $v \equiv A_0 x^{m+k} + A_1 x^{m+k-1} + \cdots + A_m x^k$ will convert the left-hand member into a polynomial of degree m, so that, by setting it identically equal to $B_0 x^m + B_1 x^{m-1} + \cdots + B_m$, we can compute the A's.

7. Solve $\dfrac{d^3y}{dx^3} - 3\dfrac{d^2y}{dx^2} + 2\dfrac{dy}{dx} = 2x^2 - 3x + 1$. *Hint:* See Exercise 6.

8. Solve $\dfrac{d^3y}{dx^3} - \dfrac{d^2y}{dx^2} = 2x + 3$.

9. Solve $\dfrac{d^3y}{dx^3} - 2\dfrac{d^2y}{dx^2} - 3\dfrac{dy}{dx} = x^2 - 5$.

10. Verify Note II for the case in which $c_1 \cos mx$, $c_2 \sin mx$ are not terms of the complementary function.

11. Solve $\dfrac{d^3y}{dx^3} - 2\dfrac{d^2y}{dx^2} - 3\dfrac{dy}{dx} = 3 \sin x$.

12. Solve $\dfrac{d^4y}{dx^4} - y = -2 \sin 2x + \cos 2x$.

13. Solve $\dfrac{d^4y}{dx^4} + 4\dfrac{d^2y}{dx^2} = \sin x - 2 \cos 3x$.

14. (a) Prove that the equation

$$\frac{d^ny}{dx^n} + a_1\frac{d^{n-1}y}{dx^{n-1}} + \cdots + a_{n-1}\frac{dy}{dx} + a_ny = B_0 \sin mx + B_1 \cos mx$$

can have no particular integral of the form $v \equiv A_0 \sin mx + A_1 \cos mx$ if its characteristic equation

$$f(r) \equiv r^n + a_1r^{n-1} + \cdots + a_{n-1}r + a_n = 0$$

has the roots $r = \pm mi$.   *Hint:* In that case, v is a solution of the reduced equation.

   (b) Prove that the equation of part (a) can have no particular integral of the form

$$v \equiv A_0x^h \sin mx + A_1x^h \cos mx \quad (k > h, \text{ a positive integer}),$$

if its characteristic equation has the roots $r = \pm mi$, of multiplicity k.   In this case the equation has a particular integral of the form specified, but with $h = k$.

15. Find a particular integral of $\dfrac{d^3y}{dx^3} + 9\dfrac{dy}{dx} = 2 \cos 3x$.   *Hint:* The characteristic equation $r(r^2 + 9) = 0$ has $r = \pm 3i$ as simple roots.   Set $v = x(A_0 \sin 3x + A_1 \cos 3x)$.

16. Find a particular integral of $\dfrac{d^4y}{dx^4} + 2\dfrac{d^2y}{dx^2} + y = -\sin x$.

17. Find a particular integral of $\dfrac{d^4y}{dx^4} + 4\dfrac{d^2y}{dx^2} = -\cos 2x$.

18. Find a particular integral of $\dfrac{d^4y}{dx^4} + 5\dfrac{d^2y}{dx^2} + 4y = \cos x + \sin 3x$.

19. Show that the method of Note III yields the result:

$$A = \frac{B}{m^n + a_1 m^{n-1} + a_2 m^{n-2} + \cdots + a_{n-1}m + a_n}.$$

20. Find a particular integral of $\dfrac{d^2y}{dx^2} - 3\dfrac{dy}{dx} + 5y = 3e^{2x}$.

21. Find a particular integral of $\dfrac{d^3y}{dx^3} + 2\dfrac{d^2y}{dx^2} - \dfrac{dy}{dx} = 4e^{-x}$.

22. Find a particular integral of $\dfrac{d^3y}{dx^3} - 4\dfrac{d^2y}{dx^2} + 3\dfrac{dy}{dx} = x + 2e^x$.

23. (a) Show that the method of Note III fails if m is a root of the characteristic equation.

(b) Show that if $Q(x)$ in (20) is of the form Be^{mx}, while the characteristic equation has the root m of multiplicity k, then (20) can have no particular integral of the form

$$v \equiv A \cdot x^h e^{mx} \quad (h \text{ a positive integer less than } k).$$

In this case the equation has a particular integral of the form specified, but with $h = k$.

24. Find a particular integral of $\dfrac{d^3y}{dx^3} - 6\dfrac{d^2y}{dx^2} + 9\dfrac{dy}{dx} = 2e^{3x}$.

Hint: $r = 3$ is a root of multiplicity $k = 2$ of the characteristic equation $r^3 - 6r^2 + 9r = 0$.

25. Find a particular integral of

(a) $\dfrac{d^2y}{dx^2} - 2\dfrac{dy}{dx} + y = -e^x$.

(b) $\dfrac{d^3y}{dx^3} + \dfrac{d^2y}{dx^2} - 6\dfrac{dy}{dx} = e^x + e^{2x} - 2e^{-3x}$.

26. Find a particular integral of $\dfrac{d^3y}{dx^3} + \dfrac{d^2y}{dx^2} - 6\dfrac{dy}{dx} = e^x + e^{2x} - 2e^{-3x}$.

27. Find a particular integral of $\dfrac{d^2y}{dx^2} + 3\dfrac{dy}{dx} = x^2 e^{2x}$. *Hint:* Set $y = z \cdot e^{2x}$, substitute in the equation, and obtain

$$e^{2x}\left[\frac{d^2z}{dx^2} + 7\frac{dz}{dx} + 10z\right] = x^2 e^{2x},$$

or
$$\frac{d^2z}{dx^2} + 7\frac{dz}{dx} + 10z = x^2.$$

To find an integral of this equation, employ the methods of Note I, and obtain
$$z = .1x^2 - .14x + .078.$$

Hence, a particular integral of the given equation is
$$y = e^{2x}(.1x^2 - .14x + .078).$$

28. Prove that if the right-hand member of the complete differential equation is of the form $Q(x) \equiv e^{mx} \cdot \varphi(x)$, the substitution $y = e^{mx} \cdot z$ will reduce the given equation to one in z, in which the right-hand member is $\varphi(x)$.

29. Find a particular integral of $\dfrac{d^2y}{dx^2} - 2\dfrac{dy}{dx} - y = e^x \cdot \sin x$.

30. Find a particular integral of $\dfrac{d^3y}{dx^3} - 4\dfrac{d^2y}{dx^2} = e^{3x}(x + 2)$.

31. Prove that if the right-hand member of the complete equation is $f_1(x) + f_2(x) + f_3(x) + \cdots$, then $v(x) \equiv v_1(x) + v_2(x) + v_3(x) + \cdots$, is a particular integral, where $v_i(x)$ is a particular integral corresponding to $f_i(x)(i = 1, 2, 3, \cdots)$.

32. Find a particular integral of $\dfrac{d^2y}{dx^2} - 4y = 2e^{3x} + \sin x$.

Hint: Assume as particular integral, $v \equiv Ae^{3x} + B \sin x + C \cos x$.

33. Find a particular integral of $\dfrac{d^3y}{dx^3} - 2\dfrac{d^2y}{dx^2} = 2x - \cos x$.

34. Find a particular integral of $\dfrac{d^3y}{dx^3} - \dfrac{dy}{dx} = e^x(x^2 - \sin x)$.

35. Find a particular integral of
$$\frac{d^2y}{dx^2} - (a + b)\frac{dy}{dx} + aby = e^{ax} + 2e^{bx} + \cos x.$$

32. Inverse operators. What shall we understand by $\dfrac{1}{D - a} \cdot u$? Now, if D is a number, $(D - a)\dfrac{1}{D - a} = 1$. This is consistent with $\left[(D - a) \cdot \dfrac{1}{D - a}\right] u \equiv 1 \cdot u \equiv u$, *i. e.*, with

$(D - a) \left[\dfrac{1}{D - a} \cdot u \right] \equiv u$, if we interpret $\dfrac{1}{D - a} \cdot u$ as that quantity which, operated on by $D - a$, produces u. In other words, the relation $\dfrac{1}{D - a} \cdot u \equiv v$ is equivalent to the relation $(D - a)v \equiv u$.

We write $\dfrac{1}{D - a} \cdot u$, if we wish to, as $(D - a)^{-1}u$, and the law of exponents $(D - a)(D - a)^{-1}u \equiv (D - a)^0 u$ is satisfied for the operator $D - a$. Higher negative powers of $D - a$ are defined directly as

$$(D - a)^{-2}u \equiv \frac{1}{(D - a)^2} u \equiv \frac{1}{D - a} \left[\frac{1}{D - a} \cdot u \right],$$
$$(D - a)^{-3}u \equiv \frac{1}{(D - a)^3} u \equiv \frac{1}{D - a} \left[\frac{1}{(D - a)^2} u \right], \text{ etc.}$$

We are now in a position to apply these ideas to the solution of a linear differential equation with constant coefficients.

Illustration

To solve the equation

$$\frac{d^2y}{dx^2} - \frac{dy}{dx} - 2y = 2x,$$

write

$$(D^2 - D - 2)y = 2x$$
$$(D + 1)(D - 2)y = 2x$$
$$(D + 1)v = 2x$$

where

$$v \equiv (D - 2)y.$$

We have seen that $\dfrac{1}{D - a} \cdot u = v$ is equivalent to $(D - a)v \equiv \dfrac{dv}{dx} - av = u$. This is a linear equation of the first order in v, and by the methods of Section 12, Chapter II, we get the solution

$$v = e^{ax} \int u \cdot e^{-ax} \, dx + ce^{ax},$$

where c is an arbitrary constant. We embody this in the formula

$$\frac{1}{D - a} \cdot u = e^{ax} \int ue^{-ax} \, dx + ce^{ax}, \tag{21}$$

which the student will have frequent occasion to use.   Returning to our illustration, we have, putting $a = -1$, and $u = 2x$,

$$v = \frac{1}{D+1} \cdot 2x = e^{-x} \int 2xe^x \, dx + c_1e^{-x}.$$

Hence,

$$(D - 2)y = e^{-x} \int 2xe^x \, dx + c_1e^{-x}$$
$$\equiv 2e^{-x}(xe^x - e^x) + c_1e^{-x}$$
$$\equiv 2x - 2 + c_1e^{-x}.$$

Operating on both sides of this equation with the operator $\dfrac{1}{D-2}$, and employing formula (21) (with $a = 2$, $u \equiv 2x - 2 + c_1e^{-x}$), we have

$$y = \frac{1}{D-2}[2x - 2 + c_1e^{-x}]$$
$$\equiv e^{2x} \int (2x - 2 + c_1e^{-x})e^{-2x} \, dx + c_2e^{2x}$$
$$\equiv e^{2x}\left[\frac{e^{-2x}}{2}(-2x - 1) + e^{-2x} - \frac{c_1}{3}e^{-3x} \right] + c_2e^{2x}$$
$$\equiv -x - \frac{1}{2} + 1 - \frac{c_1}{3}e^{-x} + c_2e^{2x}$$
$$\equiv c_1e^{-x} + c_2e^{2x} + \frac{1}{2} - x,$$

where, in the last line, c_1 has been written in place of $-\dfrac{c_1}{3}$, both

c_1 and c_2 being arbitrary constants.   The student will identify this result as the sum of the complementary function and a particular integral, as defined in Section 26.

The generality of the process should now be clear.   Given the equation

$$\frac{d^ny}{dx^n} + a_1\frac{d^{n-1}y}{dx^{n-1}} + \cdots + a_{n-1}\frac{dy}{dx} + a_ny = Q(x),$$

write it as

$$(D^n + a_1D^{n-1} + \cdots + a_{n-1}D + a_n)y \equiv [f(D)]y.$$

To fix the ideas, let

$$f(D) \equiv (D - \alpha)(D - \beta)(D - \gamma),$$

where the real roots α, β, γ, of the characteristic equation $f(r) = 0$ may or may not be distinct. We have, then,

$$(D - \alpha)(D - \beta)(D - \gamma)y = Q(x),$$

or

$$(D - \alpha)u = Q(x),$$

where

$$u \equiv (D - \beta)(D - \gamma)y.$$

Hence,

$$u = e^{\alpha x} \int Q \cdot e^{-\alpha x}dx + c_1 e^{\alpha x}.$$

Thus, u is determined, and the equation becomes

$$(D - \beta)v = u,$$

where

$$v \equiv (D - \gamma)y.$$

Hence,

$$v = e^{\beta x} \int u \cdot e^{-\beta x}dx + c_2 e^{\beta x}.$$

Thus, v is determined, and the equation becomes

$$(D - \gamma)y = v,$$

from which we may determine y as

$$y = e^{\gamma x} \int v \cdot e^{-\gamma x}dx + c_3 e^{\gamma x}.$$

The distinction between the homogeneous and non-homogeneous equation is not essential in this process. In the last example, had $Q(x)$ been zero, we should simply have had, as our first step in the solution, $u = c_1 e^{\alpha x}$.

In contrast with the methods of the above examples, the student may find it advantageous to omit the various constants of integration* and thus to obtain the particular integral only. The complementary function is easily obtained by inspection, as explained in Sections 28 and 30. Thus, in the first illustration, in solving

$$(D + 1)v = 2x,$$

---

* That is, use formula (21) as

$$\frac{1}{D - a} \cdot u = e^{ax} \int u \cdot e^{-ax}dx.$$

we might well have written

$$v = e^{-x} \int 2xe^x dx \equiv 2x - 2,$$

and then

$$y = \frac{1}{D - 2}(2x - 2) \equiv -x + \frac{1}{2}.$$

The complementary function corresponding to the roots $r = -1$ and $r = 2$ of the characteristic equation, is

$$y = c_1 e^{-x} + c_2 e^{2x}.$$

The complete solution of our equation is recovered in this manner as

$$y = c_1 e^{-x} + c_2 e^{2x} - x + \frac{1}{2}.$$

33. The use of partial fractions. If D is thought of as an algebraic quantity, the equality

$$\frac{1}{D^2 - a^2} \equiv \frac{1}{2a}\left(\frac{1}{D - a} - \frac{1}{D + a}\right)$$

holds for all values of D for which either member of the equation is defined. We now inquire into the validity of replacing the operator $\frac{1}{D^2 - a^2}$ by the operator $\frac{1}{2a}\left(\frac{1}{D - a} - \frac{1}{D + a}\right)$. To this end consider

$$(D^2 - a^2) \cdot \left[\frac{1}{2a}\left(\frac{1}{D - a} - \frac{1}{D + a}\right) \cdot Q\right].$$

It obviously reduces to

$$(D^2 - a^2)\left(\frac{1}{2a} \cdot \frac{1}{D - a} Q\right) - (D^2 - a^2)\left(\frac{1}{2a} \cdot \frac{1}{D + a} Q\right)$$

$$\equiv \frac{1}{2a}(D + a)(D - a)\left(\frac{1}{D - a} \cdot Q\right) - \frac{1}{2a}(D - a)(D + a)\left(\frac{1}{D + a} \cdot Q\right)$$

$$\equiv \frac{1}{2a}(D + a)\left[(D - a)\frac{1}{D - a}Q\right] - \frac{1}{2a}(D - a)\left[(D + a)\frac{1}{D + a}Q\right]$$

$$\equiv \frac{1}{2a}(D + a)Q - \frac{1}{2a}(D - a)Q \equiv \frac{1}{2a}[(D + a)Q - (D - a)Q]$$

$$\equiv \frac{1}{2a}[(D + a) - (D - a)]Q \equiv \frac{1}{2a}[2a]Q \equiv Q.$$

Now a quantity which, when operated upon by $D^2 - a^2$, becomes Q, is $\dfrac{1}{D^2 - a^2} \cdot Q$, by definition of the symbol, and the equality

$$\frac{1}{D^2 - a^2} \cdot Q \equiv \frac{1}{2a} \left[\frac{1}{D - a} - \frac{1}{D + a} \right] \cdot Q$$

is thus verified. The student will observe that the identity

$$\frac{1}{D^2 - a^2} \equiv \frac{1}{2a} \left[\frac{1}{D - a} - \frac{1}{D + a} \right]$$

still holds if D is regarded as a quantity, fixed or variable, instead of as a symbol of operation. It is, indeed, precisely the identity the student would derive if he set out to reduce $\dfrac{1}{D^2 - a^2}$ to the sum of partial fractions.

We are now prepared to generalize as follows: Let the given equation be

$$[f(D)]y = Q,$$

where

$$f(D) \equiv (D - a)(D - b)(D - c) \cdots$$

with $a, b, c \cdots$ all distinct and real, and let

$$\frac{1}{f(D)} \equiv \frac{1}{(D - a)(D - b)(D - c) \cdots}$$
$$\equiv \frac{A}{D - a} + \frac{B}{D - b} + \frac{C}{D - c} + \cdots .$$

Then,

$$y = \frac{1}{f(D)} \cdot Q$$

$$\equiv \frac{1}{(D - a)(D - b)(D - c) \cdots} \cdot Q$$

$$\equiv \left(\frac{A}{D - a} + \frac{B}{D - b} + \frac{C}{D - c} + \cdots \right) Q$$

$$\equiv A \left(\frac{1}{D - a} \cdot Q \right) + B \left(\frac{1}{D - b} \cdot Q \right) + C \left(\frac{1}{D - c} \cdot Q \right) + \cdots .$$

$$(22)$$

We leave it to the student to go through the details of the argument. His method should be to operate on the final member of (22) by $(D - a)(D - b)(D - c) \cdots$, and to show that it reduces to Q.

In case the characteristic equation, $f(r) = 0$, has a root r of multiplicity, say k, so that

$$f(D) \equiv (D - r)^k (D - a) \cdots ,$$

then, as taught in the theory of partial fractions,

$$\frac{1}{f(D)} \equiv \frac{R_1}{D - r} + \frac{R_2}{(D - r)^2} + \cdots + \frac{R_k}{(D - r)^k} + \frac{A}{D - a} + \cdots ,$$

and all the expressions equated in formula (22) are modified accordingly.   Thus, in that case,

$$y = \frac{1}{f(D)} \cdot Q$$

$$\equiv \frac{1}{(D - r)^k (D - a) \cdots} \cdot Q$$

$$\equiv \left(\frac{R_1}{D - r} + \frac{R_2}{(D - r)^2} + \cdots + \frac{R_k}{(D - r)^k} + \frac{A}{D - a} + \cdots \right) Q$$

$$\equiv R_1 \left(\frac{1}{D - r} \cdot Q \right) + R_2 \left(\frac{1}{(D - r)^2} \cdot Q \right) + \cdots$$

$$+ R_k \left(\frac{1}{(D - r)^k} \cdot Q \right) + A \left(\frac{1}{D - a} \cdot Q \right) + \cdots . \quad (23)$$

The significance of formulas (22) and (23) will be perceived at once.   For it is evidently simpler to operate on $Q(x)$ *separately* by $\dfrac{A}{D - a}, \dfrac{B}{D - b}, \cdots$ and to add the results, than it is to operate on it *successively* by such operators.

As an illustration, consider:

$$\frac{d^2 y}{dx^2} - \frac{dy}{dx} - 2y = 2x.$$

(This equation has been solved in the preceding section, to illustrate the method of successive application of the operator.)   From

$$(D^2 - D - 2)y \equiv (D + 1)(D - 2)y = 2x$$

we get at once

$$y = \frac{1}{(D + 1)(D - 2)} \cdot 2x.$$

Let the student reduce

$$\frac{1}{(D + 1)(D - 2)}$$

to

$$\frac{-\frac{1}{3}}{D+1} + \frac{\frac{1}{3}}{D-2} \equiv \frac{1}{3}\left(\frac{1}{D-2} - \frac{1}{D+1}\right).$$

Hence,

$$
\begin{aligned}
y &= \frac{1}{3}\left(\frac{1}{D-2}\cdot 2x - \frac{1}{D+1}\cdot 2x\right) \\
&\equiv \frac{1}{3}\left[e^{2x}\int 2xe^{-2x}\,dx - e^{-x}\int 2xe^{x}\,dx\right] \\
&\equiv \frac{1}{3}\left[2e^{2x}\cdot\frac{e^{-2x}}{4}(-2x-1) - 2e^{-x}\cdot e^{x}(x-1)\right] \\
&\equiv \frac{1}{3}\left[\frac{-2x-1}{2} - 2x + 2\right] \equiv -x + \frac{1}{2}.
\end{aligned}
$$

(We concern ourselves here with the particular integral only and omit the constants of integration.)

Exercises

1. By the method of Section 32, find the complete solutions of:

(a) $\dfrac{d^2y}{dx^2} - 2\dfrac{dy}{dx} = \cos x.$

(b) $\dfrac{d^3y}{dx^3} + 2\dfrac{d^2y}{dx^2} - 3\dfrac{dy}{dx} = x + 2.$

(c) $\dfrac{d^2y}{dx^2} - a\dfrac{dy}{dx} + b\dfrac{dy}{dx} - aby = 2e^{3x}.$

(d) $\dfrac{d^3y}{dx^3} - 2\dfrac{d^2y}{dx^2} - \dfrac{dy}{dx} + 2y = -xe^{x}.$

(e) $\dfrac{d^3y}{dx^3} - 4\dfrac{d^2y}{dx^2} + 4\dfrac{dy}{dx} = e^{x} - \sin 2x.$

2. Show that the solution of $[(D-a)(D-b)(D-c)]y = Q(x)$ can be displayed in the form

$$y = e^{cx}\int\left\{e^{bx}\int\left[e^{ax}\int Q\cdot e^{-ax}dx\right]e^{-bx}dx\right\}e^{-cx}dx.$$

3. By the method of this section, show that the complete solution of $(D-a)^k y = 0$ is $y = e^{ax}(c_1 + c_2 x + c_3 x^2 + \cdots + c_k x^{k-1}).$

4. Verify that

$$
\begin{aligned}
[f(D)]e^{rx} &\equiv (D^n + a_1 D^{n-1} + a_2 D^{n-2} + \cdots + a_{n-1}D + a_n)e^{rx} \\
&\equiv e^{rx}(r^n + a_1 r^{n-1} + \cdots + a_{n-1}r + a_n) \\
&\equiv e^{rx}\cdot f(r).
\end{aligned}
$$

5. Solve the following by applying the method of partial fractions:

(a) $\dfrac{d^3y}{dx^3} + 2\dfrac{d^2y}{dx^2} - 8\dfrac{dy}{dx} = \cos^2 x.$

(b) $\dfrac{d^4y}{dx^4} + 6\dfrac{d^3y}{dx^3} + 9\dfrac{d^2y}{dx^2} = \sin 2x - xe^x.$

(c) $\dfrac{d^3y}{dx^3} - a\dfrac{d^2y}{dx^2} + 4\dfrac{d^2y}{dx^2} - 4a\dfrac{dy}{dx} = 3x^2 + \dfrac{x}{a}.$

(d) $\dfrac{d^3y}{dx^3} + 3\dfrac{d^2y}{dx^2} = 3x^2 - 1.$

(e) Exercises 1(a), 1(b), 1(c), and 1(d) above.

34. Method of variation of parameters. In this section we take up a method of finding a particular integral of a linear differential equation applicable not only to the equation with constant coefficients but also to any linear differential equation for which the complementary function has been found. It is called the method of variation of parameters (sometimes called the method of variation of constants), due to Lagrange.* The student has already seen the method at work in the case of first order linear equations treated in Section 12, Chapter II. We may now apply it to the linear equation of any order, n.

Let the equation be

$$\frac{d^n y}{dx^n} + P_1 \frac{d^{n-1}y}{dx^{n-1}} + P_2 \frac{d^{n-2}y}{dx^{n-2}} + \cdots + P_{n-1}\frac{dy}{dx} + P_n y = Q(x), \quad (24)$$

and let the reduced equation have the complete solution

$$y = c_1 y_1 + c_2 y_2 + \cdots + c_n y_n. \quad (25)$$

The method consists in seeking to modify the c's in such a manner that (25) becomes a solution of (24). For that purpose, let us think of the c's as functions of x, to be determined presently. From (25), by differentiation, we have

$$y' = (c_1 y_1' + c_2 y_2' + \cdots + c_n y_n') + (c_1' y_1 + c_2' y_2 + \cdots + c_n' y_n),$$

and we impose, as one condition on the c's, that

$$c_1' y_1 + c_2' y_2 + \cdots + c_n' y_n \equiv 0,$$

so that

$$y' = c_1 y_1' + c_2 y_2' + \cdots + c_n y_n',$$

---

* (1736–1813); one of the greatest mathematicians of all time.

and hence,

$$y'' = (c_1 y_1'' + c_2 y_2'' + \cdots + c_n y_n'') + (c_1' y_1' + c_2' y_2' + \cdots + c_n' y_n').$$

We now impose a second condition, that

$$c_1' y_1' + c_2' y_2' + \cdots + c_n' y_n' \equiv 0,$$

which gives

$$y'' = c_1 y_1'' + c_2 y_2'' + \cdots + c_n y_n''.$$

Differentiating again, we obtain

$$y''' = (c_1 y_1''' + c_2 y_2''' + \cdots + c_n y_n''') + (c_1' y_1'' + c_2' y_2'' + \cdots \\ + c_n' y_n''),$$

and again imposing the condition

$$c_1' y_1'' + c_2' y_2'' + \cdots + c_n' y_n'' \equiv 0,$$

we have

$$y''' = c_1 y_1''' + c_2 y_2''' + \cdots + c_n y_n'''.$$

Continuing in this manner, we arrive, finally, at

$$y^{(n)} = (c_1 y_1^{(n)} + c_2 y_2^{(n)} + \cdots + c_n y_n^{(n)}) + (c_1' y_1^{(n-1)} + c_2' y_2^{(n-1)} \\ + \cdots + c_n' y_n^{(n-1)}).$$

We now set the last parenthesis equal to $Q(x)$.

The conditions thus imposed on the c's form a linear system of n equations in the n variables $c_1', c_2', \cdots, c_n'$, displayed as follows:

$$\begin{cases} c_1' y_1 & + c_2' y_2 & + \cdots + c_n' y_n & \equiv 0 \\ c_1' y_1' & + c_2' y_2' & + \cdots + c_n' y_n' & \equiv 0 \\ c_1' y_1'' & + c_2' y_2'' & + \cdots + c_n' y_n'' & \equiv 0 \\ \cdot & \cdot & \cdots \cdot & \cdot \\ \cdot & \cdot & \cdots \cdot & \cdot \\ c_1' y_1^{(n-2)} & + c_2' y_2^{(n-2)} & + \cdots + c_n' y_n^{(n-2)} & \equiv 0 \\ c_1' y_1^{(n-1)} & + c_2' y_2^{(n-1)} & + \cdots + c_n' y_n^{(n-1)} & \equiv Q(x). \end{cases} \quad (26)$$

The determinant of this system is

$$\begin{vmatrix} y_1 & y_2 & \cdots & y_n \\ y_1' & y_2' & \cdots & y_n' \\ y_1'' & y_2'' & \cdots & y_n'' \\ \cdot & \cdot & \cdots & \\ \cdot & \cdot & \cdots & \\ y_1^{(n-2)} & y_2^{(n-2)} & \cdots & y_n^{(n-2)} \\ y_1^{(n-1)} & y_2^{(n-1)} & \cdots & y_n^{(n-1)} \end{vmatrix},$$

the Wronskian of y_1, y_2, $\cdots$, y_n, and is not identically zero, by virtue of the hypothesis that these y's are linearly independent (Section 26, page 73). Hence, the system of equations (26) can be solved for c_i', and the expressions for the c's may be found by quadratures.

We still have to show that (25) is a solution of (24), if the c's satisfy (26). Now if we substitute

$$\begin{cases} y &= c_1y_1 &+ c_2y_2 &+ \cdots + c_ny_n \\ y' &= c_1y_1' &+ c_2y_2' &+ \cdots + c_ny_n' \\ y'' &= c_1y_1'' &+ c_2y_2'' &+ \cdots + c_ny_n'' \\ \quad \cdot & \quad \cdot & \quad \cdot & \qquad \cdot \\ \quad \cdot & \quad \cdot & \quad \cdot & \qquad \cdot \\ y^{(n-1)} &= c_1y_1^{(n-1)} &+ c_2y_2^{(n-1)} &+ \cdots + c_ny_n^{(n-1)} \\ y^{(n)} &= c_1y_1^{(n)} &+ c_2y_2^{(n)} &+ \cdots + c_ny_n^{(n)} + Q(x) \end{cases}$$

in (24), the left-hand side becomes

$$c_1[y_1^{(n)} + P_1y_1^{(n-1)} + \cdots + P_{n-1}y_1' + P_ny_1] + c_2[y_2^{(n)} + P_1y_2^{(n-1)}$$
$$+ \cdots + P_{n-1}y_2' + P_ny_2] + \cdots + c_n[y_n^{(n)} + P_1y_n^{(n-1)} + \cdots$$
$$+ P_{n-1}y_n' + P_ny_n] + Q(x),$$

and hence, it is identically equal to $Q(x)$, since each y_i is, by hypothesis, a solution of the reduced equation, and therefore each bracket equals zero identically. Thus (25), with the c's in the form determined, is indeed a solution of (24).

The actual task of solving (26) for c_i', and then performing the quadratures for finding the c's, may, of course, become too laborious to be effectively used in solving (24). The application of the method, nevertheless, is wide.

Consider as an illustration:

$$\frac{d^3y}{dx^3} - \frac{1}{2}\frac{d^2y}{dx^2} = e^{-\frac{1}{2}x}.$$

The complete solution of the reduced equation is, obviously, $y = c_1 + c_2x + c_3e^{\frac{1}{2}x}$. Differentiate, and obtain

$$y' = c_2 + \frac{c_3}{2}e^{x/2} + (c_1' + c_2'x + c_3'e^{x/2}),$$

and set $c_1' + c_2'x + c_3'e^{x/2} \equiv 0$,   (a)

$$y'' = \frac{c_3}{4}e^{x/2} + \left(c_2' + \frac{c_3'}{2}e^{x/2}\right),$$

and set $c_2' + \frac{c_3'}{2}e^{x/2} \equiv 0$,   (b)

$$y''' = \frac{c_3}{8} e^{x/2} + \left(\frac{c_3'}{4} e^{x/2}\right),$$

and set $\dfrac{c_3'}{4} e^{x/2} \equiv e^{-\frac{1}{2}x}$. (c)

From (a), (b), and (c) we obtain:

$$c_3' \equiv 4e^{-x}, \qquad \text{hence } c_3 \equiv -4e^{-x},$$
$$c_2' \equiv -2e^{-x/2}, \qquad \text{hence } c_2 \equiv 4e^{-x/2},$$
$$c_1' \equiv 2xe^{-x/2} - 4e^{-x/2}, \text{ hence } c_1 \equiv -4xe^{-x/2},$$

and a solution of the equation (a particular integral) is

$$y = -4xe^{-x/2} + 4e^{-x/2} \cdot x - 4e^{-x} \cdot e^{x/2} \equiv -4e^{-x/2}.$$

The complete solution is, therefore,

$$y = c_1 + c_2 x + c_3 e^{x/2} - 4e^{-x/2}.$$

Exercises

1. Solve by the method of variation of parameters:

(a) $\dfrac{d^2y}{dx^2} + a^2 y = \cot ax.$

(c) $\dfrac{d^2y}{dx^2} + \dfrac{dy}{dx} - 12y = x - \sin x.$

(b) $\dfrac{d^3y}{dx^3} - a^2 \dfrac{dy}{dx} = e^{2ax} \sin^2 x.$

(d) $\dfrac{d^3y}{dx^3} + \dfrac{dy}{dx} = e^x + 2x - 1.$

2. Verify that $y = x$ and $y = x^2$ are solutions of $\dfrac{d^2y}{dx^2} - \dfrac{2}{x}\dfrac{dy}{dx} + \dfrac{2}{x^2} y = 0$, and, hence, that the complete solution is $y = c_1 x + c_2 x^2$. Find, by the method of variation of parameters, a particular solution of $\dfrac{d^2y}{dx^2} - \dfrac{2}{x}\dfrac{dy}{dx} + \dfrac{2}{x^2} y = x^3 \log x.$

3. Verify that $y = x$ is a solution of $x^2 \dfrac{d^2y}{dx^2} - x\dfrac{dy}{dx} + y = 0$. Set $y = xu$ in the given equation, and obtain, as a solution of the resulting equation in u, $u = c_1 \log x + c_2$. (Hence, $y = c_1 x \log x + c_2 x$ is the general solution.) By variation of parameters, find next a particular solution of

$$x^2 \dfrac{d^2y}{dx^2} - x\dfrac{dy}{dx} + y = \dfrac{(\log x)^3}{x}.$$

4. Show how the discussion in the preceding text establishes the theorem: "The general solution of the reduced equation being

known, the integration of the complete linear differential equation of order n is effected by n quadratures."

35. Inverse operators corresponding to complex roots. We now inquire into the meaning of the operator $\dfrac{1}{(D-a)^2 + b^2}$. If we operate on $Q(x)$ by it and call the result, y, we have

$$y = \frac{1}{(D-a)^2 + b^2} Q(x),$$

and, operating on both sides of this with the operator $[(D-a)^2 + b^2]$ we have

$$[(D-a)^2 + b^2]y = Q(x).$$

This second-order linear differential equation has the complementary function

$$y = e^{ax}(c_1 \cos bx + c_2 \sin bx). \tag{27}$$

Let us find a particular integral by the method of variation of parameters. The process gives

$$y = e^{ax}(c_1 \cos bx + c_2 \sin bx),$$
$$y' = e^{ax}[c_1(a \cos bx - b \sin bx) + c_2(a \sin bx + b \cos bx)],$$
$$y'' = e^{ax}[c_1(a^2 \cos bx - 2ab \sin bx - b^2 \cos bx)$$
$$\qquad\qquad + c_2(a^2 \sin bx + 2ab \cos bx - b^2 \sin bx)],$$

and the identities

$$\begin{cases} c_1'e^{ax} \cos bx & + c_2'e^{ax} \sin bx & \equiv 0 \\ c_1'e^{ax}[a \cos bx - b \sin bx] + c_2'e^{ax}[a \sin bx + b \cos bx] \equiv Q. \end{cases} \tag{28}$$

Solving the identities (28) for c_1' and c_2', we obtain

$$c_1' = -\frac{1}{b} e^{-ax} \sin bx \cdot Q, \; c_2' = \frac{1}{b} e^{-ax} \cos bx \cdot Q,$$

whence

$$c_1 = -\frac{1}{b} \int e^{-ax} \sin bx \cdot Q \cdot dx, \; c_2 = \frac{1}{b} \int e^{-ax} \cos bx \cdot Q \cdot dx.$$

Replacing c_1 and c_2 in (27) by these values, we have the result

$$\frac{1}{(D-a)^2 + b^2} Q(x) = \frac{e^{ax}}{b} \left[\sin bx \int Q e^{-ax} \cos bx \, dx - \right.$$
$$\left. \cos bx \int Q e^{-ax} \sin bx \, dx \right]. \tag{29}$$

Application of the above result to the example

$$\frac{d^2y}{dx^2} + 4y = x^2$$

or to

$$(D^2 + 4)y = x^2$$

gives

$$y = \frac{1}{D^2 + 4} \cdot x^2$$

$$\equiv \frac{1}{2}\left[\sin 2x \int x^2 \cos 2x \, dx - \cos 2x \int x^2 \sin 2x \, dx \right]$$

by use of (29) with $a = 0$, $b = 2$, $Q \equiv x^2$.

Exercises

1. Solve the following equations by the above method:

(a) $\dfrac{d^2y}{dx^2} + y = \cos 2x \cdot \cos 3x.$

(b) $\dfrac{d^3y}{dx^3} - 2\dfrac{d^2y}{dx^2} + 2\dfrac{dy}{dx} = \cos^2 x.$

(c) $\dfrac{d^4y}{dx^4} + 8\dfrac{d^2y}{dx^2} + 16y = e^x.$

2. Verify formula (29) directly; that is, by operating upon both sides by $(D - a)^2 + b^2$.

3. Verify that an analogue to formula (29) is

$$\frac{1}{(D - a)^2 - b^2} Q$$

$$= \frac{e^{ax}}{b}\left[\sinh bx \int Qe^{-ax} \cosh bx \, dx - \cosh bx \int Qe^{-ax} \sinh bx \, dx \right].$$

36. The linear equation with variable coefficients. When the linear differential equation has constant coefficients, its treatment is complete, inasmuch as its integration reduces to solving a certain algebraic equation, *viz.*, the characteristic equation. The difficulties that may arise in solving that algebraic equation are of no interest as far as the subject of differential equations is concerned. The case is different when the coefficients in the equation are variable. There is then no general method available for its integration. We do take note, however, of certainly highly special types for which methods of integration are at hand, *viz.*, the so-called *Cauchy* linear equation, and the *exact* linear equation.

37. Cauchy's linear equation.   The Cauchy equation[*] is defined as one of the type

$$x^n \frac{d^n y}{dx^n} + a_1 x^{n-1} \frac{d^{n-1}y}{dx^{n-1}} + \cdots + a_{n-1}x \frac{dy}{dx} + a_n y = Q(x), \quad (30)$$

where the a's are constants.

The substitution $x = e^t$ will transform any Cauchy linear differential equation of order n into a linear differential equation of order n in which the coefficients are constants.   To see that this is so, note that

$$x \frac{dy}{dx} = \frac{dy}{dt} = Dy,$$

$$x^2 \frac{d^2 y}{dx^2} = \frac{d^2 y}{dt^2} - \frac{dy}{dt} = D(D-1)y,$$

$$x^3 \frac{d^3 y}{dx^3} = \frac{d^3 y}{dt^3} - 3\frac{d^2 y}{dt^2} + 2\frac{dy}{dt} = D(D-1)(D-2)y,$$

$$\cdot \quad \cdot \quad \cdot \quad \cdot \quad \cdot \quad \cdot \quad \cdot \quad \cdot \quad \cdot \quad \cdot \quad \cdot$$

$$\cdot \quad \cdot \quad \cdot \quad \cdot \quad \cdot \quad \cdot \quad \cdot \quad \cdot \quad \cdot \quad \cdot \quad \cdot$$

$$x^n \frac{d^n y}{dx^n} = D(D-1)(D-2) \cdots (D-n+1)y,$$

where D is now understood to represent differentiation with respect to t.   When these expressions are placed in (30), the latter becomes

$$[D(D-1)(D-2) \cdots (D-n+1) + a_1 D(D-1)(D-2) \cdots$$
$$(D-n+2) + \cdots + a_{n-1}D + a_n]y = Q(e^t).$$

This equation has constant coefficients and is readily solved by the methods already described for such equations.

Illustration

To solve the differential equation

$$x^2 \frac{d^2 y}{dx^2} - 3x \frac{dy}{dx} - 5y = 0, \quad (31)$$

we make the substitution $x = e^t$ and the consequent substitutions

---

[*] So called after Augustin Louis Cauchy (1789–1857).   Also called the Euler equation; also, by others, the homogeneous linear equation.   The last term is obviously undesirable, as the term "homogeneous" has already been used in a different sense.

$x^2 \dfrac{d^2y}{dx^2} = D(D-1)y$, $x\dfrac{dy}{dx} = Dy$, and obtain the new equation

$$[D(D-1) - 3D - 5]y = 0,$$

or

$$[D^2 - 4D - 5]y = 0. \qquad (D-5)(D+1)$$

The characteristic equation for this having the roots 5 and -1, the general solution is written down at once as

$$y = c_1 e^{5t} + c_2 e^{-t}.$$

Transformed back in terms of x, this gives,

$$y = c_1 x^5 + c_2 x^{-1}$$

as the general solution of (31).

Exercises

1. Solve by the above method:

(a) $x^2 \dfrac{d^2y}{dx^2} - 4x\dfrac{dy}{dx} + 6y = 0.$

(b) $x^2 \dfrac{d^2y}{dx^2} - 5x\dfrac{dy}{dx} + 8y = x^3 \sinh x.$

(c) $x^3 \dfrac{d^3y}{dx^3} + 2x^2\dfrac{d^2y}{dx^2} - 6x\dfrac{dy}{dx} = 0.$

(d) $x^3 \dfrac{d^3y}{dx^3} + 3x^2\dfrac{d^2y}{dx^2} + x\dfrac{dy}{dx} = a^2x\dfrac{dy}{dx}.$

(e) $x^3 \dfrac{d^3y}{dx^3} - 2x^2\dfrac{d^2y}{dx^2} = 2x^3 - x.$

2. Show that the equation

$$(a+bx)^n \frac{d^ny}{dx^n} + a_1(a+bx)^{n-1}\frac{d^{n-1}y}{dx^{n-1}} + \cdots + a_{n-1}(a+bx)\frac{dy}{dx}$$

$$+ a_n y = Q(x)$$

can be solved by the substitution $a + bx = e^t$.

3. Solve by the method of Exercise 2.

(a) $(2-x)^2 \dfrac{d^2y}{dx^2} + (2-x)\dfrac{dy}{dx} - 15y = 0.$

(b) $(1+2x)^2 \dfrac{d^2y}{dx^2} - (2+4x)\dfrac{dy}{dx} - 12y = 3x + 1.$

4. Solve the equation $x^2 \dfrac{d^2y}{dx^2} - 3x \dfrac{dy}{dx} - 5y = 0$ by using the substitution $y = x^r$. *Hint:* Note that the equation becomes a quadratic algebraic equation in r whose two solutions give two linearly independent solutions of the original differential equation.

5. Solve by the method of Exercise 4:

(a) $x^2 \dfrac{d^2y}{dx^2} + 3x \dfrac{dy}{dx} + y = 0.$

(b) $x^3 \dfrac{d^3y}{dx^3} + 3x^2 \dfrac{d^2y}{dx^2} + x \dfrac{dy}{dx} = 0.$

(c) $x^3 \dfrac{d^3y}{dx^3} - 2x \dfrac{dy}{dx} = 0.$

6. Solve:

(a) $x^2 \dfrac{d^2y}{dx^2} - x \dfrac{dy}{dx} + 10y = 0.$

(b) $x^2 \dfrac{d^2y}{dx^2} + x \dfrac{dy}{dx} + 4y = 0.$

(c) $(1 - 3x)^2 \dfrac{d^2y}{dx^2} - 3(1 - 3x) \dfrac{dy}{dx} - 9y = [\log (1 - 3x)]^2.$

(d) $(3 + x)^3 \dfrac{d^3y}{dx^3} + 3(3 + x)^2 \dfrac{d^2y}{dx^2} + (6 + 2x) \dfrac{dy}{dx} = 0.$

38. Exact linear equations. If we differentiate the linear equation

$$R_0 y^{(n-1)} + R_1 y^{(n-2)} + \cdots + R_{n-2} y' + R_{n-1} y = S(x) + c, \quad (32)$$

where the R_i are functions of x, we obtain another linear equation

$$P_0 y^{(n)} + P_1 y^{(n-1)} + \cdots + P_{n-2} y'' + P_{n-1} y' + P_n y = Q(x), \quad (33)$$

where the P_i are functions of x such that

$$
\begin{cases}
Q(x) \equiv S'(x) \\
P_0 \quad \equiv R_0 \\
P_1 \quad \equiv R_0' \ + R_1 \\
P_2 \quad \equiv R_1' \ + R_2 \\
\quad . \qquad . \qquad . \\
\quad . \qquad . \qquad . \\
\quad . \qquad . \qquad . \\
P_{n-1} \equiv R_{n-2}' + R_{n-1} \\
P_n \quad \equiv R_{n-1}'
\end{cases}
\quad (34)
$$

and hence,

$$
\begin{cases}
S(x) \equiv \displaystyle\int Q(x)dx + c \\
R_0 \quad \equiv P_0 \\
R_1 \quad \equiv P_1 - P'_0 \\
R_2 \quad \equiv P_2 - P'_1 + P''_0 \\
\cdot \qquad \cdot \qquad \cdot \qquad \cdot \\
\cdot \qquad \cdot \qquad \cdot \qquad \cdot \\
R_{n-2} \equiv P_{n-2} - P'_{n-3} + P''_{n-4} - \cdots + (-1)^{n-2}P_0^{(n-2)} \\
R_{n-1} \equiv P_{n-1} - P'_{n-2} + P''_{n-3} - \cdots + (-1)^{n-1}P_0^{(n-1)}.
\end{cases}
\tag{35}
$$

Under these circumstances Equation (33) is said to be *exact* and to have (32) as its *first integral.**

From the last equation in (34) and the last in (35), it is seen that

$$
P_n - R'_{n-1} \equiv P_n - P'_{n-1} + P''_{n-2} - P'''_{n-3} + \cdots \\
+ (-1)^n P_0^{(n)} \equiv 0. \quad (36)
$$

Thus, this relation is a necessary condition for the exactness of (33). It is also clearly sufficient, for whenever it is satisfied we can build the functions R_i and $S(x)$ by formulas (35), and (34) will be satisfied.

To illustrate, let us consider the linear equation

$$
(x^2 + 1)y'' + 4xy' + 2y = 2 \cos x - 2x,
$$

of the form (33), with $n = 2$, $P_0 \equiv x^2 + 1$, $P_1 \equiv 4x$, $P_2 \equiv 2$. Setting up (36), we obtain

$$
P_2 - P'_1 + P''_0 \equiv 2 - 4 + 2 = 0;
$$

therefore the relation holds, the given equation is exact, and its first integral is

$$
R_0 y' + R_1 y = \int (2 \cos x - 2x)dx + c_1,
$$

where

$$
R_0 \equiv P_0 \equiv x^2 + 1, \\
R_1 \equiv P_1 - P'_0 \equiv 4x - 2x \equiv 2x;
$$

---

* The notion of exactness is also applicable to other than linear equations. Thus, any equation $f(x, y, y', y'', \cdots, y^{(n)}) = 0$ is said to be *exact* if a function $\varphi(x, y, y', y'', \cdots, y^{(n-1)})$ exists such that $\dfrac{d\varphi}{dx} \equiv f$. The differential equation $\varphi(x, y, y', y'', \cdots, y^{(n-1)}) = c$ is then defined as the *first integral* of $f(x, y, y', y'', \cdots, y^{(n)}) = 0$. However, in the general case, no test for exactness is available, and no formula for the first integral exists.

that is,
$$(x^2 + 1)y' + 2xy = 2 \sin x - x^2 + c_1.$$

This first integral happens to be exact also, since, for it, $P_0 \equiv x^2 + 1$, $P_1 \equiv 2x$, and $P_1 - P_0' \equiv 0$, and its first integral is

$$R_0 y = \int (2 \sin x - x^2 + c_1)dx + c_2,$$

where $R_0 \equiv P_0 \equiv x^2 + 1$; that is,

$$(x^2 + 1)y = -2 \cos x - \frac{x^3}{3} + c_1 x + c_2.$$

In this example we have arrived at a complete solution of the equation proposed. But such will not always be the case, for the first integral of an exact equation is not always itself exact, and all we may expect of (33), in general, when (36) is satisfied, is that it be replaced by its first integral, *i. e.*, by a linear equation of next lower order.

In the particular case, however, in which the given linear equation is exact and of order two, its first integral is linear and of order one, and, consequently, it can be integrated, whether or not it is exact.

Exercises

1. (a) Show that $(2x - 1)y''' + (4 + x)y'' + 2y' = 0$ is exact, and find its first integral.

(b) Show that the first integral of the equation in (a) is also exact, and derive its first integral as

$$(2x - 1)y' + xy = c_1 x + c_2.$$

(c) Show that the last equation is not exact. Obtain its solution (and hence the solution of the original equation in (a)).

2. Solve:

(a) $(x + \sin x)y''' + 3(1 + \cos x)y'' - 3 \sin x \cdot y'$
$$- \cos x \cdot y = - \sin x.$$

(b) $(e^x + 2x)y^{iv} + 4(e^x + 2)y''' + 6e^x y'' + 4e^x y' + e^x y$
$$= \frac{1}{x^5}.$$

(c) $\sin x \cdot y''' + (2 \cos x + 1)y'' - \sin x \cdot y' = \cos x.$

(d) $(x^2 + 1)y''' + 8xy'' + 10y' = 3 - \frac{1}{x^2} + 2 \log x.$

(e) $(x + 2)^2 y''' - y' = \frac{-8}{x^3} - \frac{8}{x^2} - \frac{1}{x} - 1.$

3. (a) Show that the linear equation with constant coefficients,

$$y^{(n)} + a_1 y^{(n-1)} + a_2 y^{(n-2)} + \cdots + a_{n-2} y'' + a_{n-1} y' + a_n y = Q(x),$$

is exact if, and only if, $a_n = 0$. What is its first integral in that case?

(b) State the condition that must be satisfied by the coefficients of the Cauchy linear equation

$$a_0 x^n y^{(n)} + a_1 x^{n-1} y^{(n-1)} + \cdots + a_{n-1} x y' + a_n y = Q(x)$$

if it is to be exact. Show that, in case the condition is satisfied, the first integral is reducible to a Cauchy linear equation.

(c) Show that if a second order linear equation

$$P_0 y'' + P_1 y' + P_2 y = Q(x)$$

is exact and its first integral lacks the term in y, then $P_2 = 0$. State the converse proposition.

4. (a) Show that a necessary and sufficient condition that $\mu(x)$ be an integrating factor of

$$P_0 y^{(n)} + P_1 y^{(n-1)} + \cdots + P_{n-2} y'' + P_{n-1} y' + P_n y = 0, \quad \text{(A)}$$

is that it satisfy the equation,

$$\mu P_n - (\mu P_{n-1})' + (\mu P_{n-2})'' - \cdots + (-1)^n (\mu P_0)^{(n)} = 0, \quad \text{(B)}$$

called the *adjoint equation* of (A). Note that it is a linear differential equation in μ, and of order n.

(b) Find the adjoint equation of

$$x^3 y''' + x y' - y = 0. \tag{C}$$

The result is found to be $\qquad -\mu + (x\mu)' + (x^3\mu)''' = -\mu + \mu' + x\mu' + x^3\mu'''$
$$+ 9x^2\mu'' + 1\cdot$$

$$x^3 \mu''' + 9x^2 \mu'' + 19x \mu' + 8\mu = 0. \tag{D}$$

(c) Obtain $\mu = x^{-2}$ as one solution of (D). Verify that its use will make (C) exact and yield a first integral

$$xy'' - y' + \frac{y}{x} = c_1.$$

(d) Find the adjoint equation of (D), *i. e.*, the equation satisfied by ν, where ν is an integrating factor of (D). The result is

$$x^3 \nu''' + x \nu' - \nu = 0. \tag{E}$$

Note that (E) and (C) are identical equations. This result is general and is embodied in the following

$$\left(-x^2\mu\right) - (\mu)' + (x\mu)'' = -x^2u - u' + u' + u' + xu''$$
$$= -x^2u + u' + xu''$$

THEOREM. *Every integral of the adjoint equation is an integrating factor of the given equation; likewise, every integral of a given homogeneous linear equation is an integrating factor of its adjoint equation.*

(e) Prove the second statement in the above theorem.

(f) Find the adjoint equation of $xy'' + y' - x^2y = 0$.

39. Simultaneous linear equations. We bring this chapter to a close by considering a system of two equations in two dependent variables, both functions of the same independent variable. Such a system is called *linear* if the dependent variables and their derivatives enter to the first degree in each of the equations. Thus,

$$\begin{cases} P_0x^{(m)} + P_1x^{(m-1)} + \cdots + P_mx + Q_0y^{(n)} + Q_1y^{(n-1)} \\ \qquad\qquad\qquad\qquad + \cdots + Q_ny = T_1(t), \\ R_0x^{(u)} + R_1x^{(u-1)} + \cdots + R_ux + S_0y^{(v)} + S_1y^{(v-1)} \\ \qquad\qquad\qquad\qquad + \cdots + S_vy = T_2(t), \end{cases} \quad (37)$$

is such a system, if the derivatives are with respect to t and $P_0 \cdots$, P_m; $Q_0, \cdots, Q_n$; $R_0, \cdots, R_u$; $S_0, \cdots, S_v$ are functions of t alone.

A pair of functions, $x = f(t)$, $y = g(t)$, that satisfies each of the two equations identically is said to be a solution of the system.*

We shall restrict ourselves to a system with constant coefficients, *i. e.*, one of the type

$$\begin{cases} [f_1(D)]x + [g_1(D)]y = T_1(t), \\ [f_2(D)]x + [g_2(D)]y = T_2(t), \end{cases} \quad (38)$$

where D is an operator denoting differentiation with respect to t, while $f_i(D)$ and $g_i(D)$ $(i = 1, 2)$ are polynomials in D with constant coefficients. We illustrate the method of treating such a pair of equations by the following example.

Let the given system be

$$\begin{cases} \dfrac{d^2x}{dt^2} - 9x + \dfrac{dy}{dt} + 3y = \sin 2t, \\ \dfrac{dx}{dt} + x - \dfrac{dy}{dt} = 2t, \end{cases}$$

---

* It is proved in the theory of differential equations that such a system of n linear equations in n dependent variables, functions of the same independent variable, has a unique solution for the range of values of the independent variable t, $a \le t \le b$, if in that range $P_0(t) \not\equiv 0$; $Q_0(t) \not\equiv 0$; $R_0(t) \not\equiv 0$; $S_0(t) \not\equiv 0$; $\cdots$ and $\dfrac{P_1}{P_0}, \cdots, \dfrac{P_m}{P_0}; \dfrac{Q_1}{Q_0}, \cdots, \dfrac{Q_n}{Q_0}; \dfrac{R_1}{R_0}, \cdots, \dfrac{R_u}{R_0}; \dfrac{S_1}{S_0}, \cdots, \dfrac{S_v}{S_0}$, are continuous functions of t.

or

$$\begin{cases} (D^2 - 9)x + (D + 3)y = \sin 2t, \\ (D + 1)x - Dy = 2t. \end{cases}$$

To eliminate one of the variables, say y, operate on the first equation by D, and on the second by $(D + 3)$, obtaining

$$\begin{cases} (D^3 - 9D)x + D(D + 3)y = 2\cos 2t, \\ (D^2 + 4D + 3)x - D(D + 3)y = 6t + 2. \end{cases}$$

Adding the two, we get

$$(D^3 + D^2 - 5D + 3)x = 2\cos 2t + 6t + 2.$$

a linear equation in x alone.

By the methods of the preceding sections, we obtain as the complementary function, *i. e.*, the solution of the reduced equation,

$$x = c_1 e^t + c_2 t e^t + c_3 e^{-3t}.$$

For a particular integral, we use the method of Section 31 and assume

$$\begin{aligned} x &= A \sin 2t + B \cos 2t + Et + F, \\ \therefore \quad Dx &= 2A \cos 2t - 2B \sin 2t + E, \\ D^2 x &= -4A \sin 2t - 4B \cos 2t, \\ D^3 x &= -8A \cos 2t + 8B \sin 2t, \end{aligned}$$

so that

$$\begin{aligned} (D^3 + D^2 - 5D + 3)x &= (18B - A) \sin 2t - (18A + B) \cos 2t \\ &\qquad + 3Et + (3F - 5E) \\ &\equiv 2 \cos 2t + 6t + 2, \end{aligned}$$

whence,

$$\begin{aligned} 18B - A &= 0, \\ 18A + B &= -2, \\ 3E &= 6, \\ 3F - 5E &= 2, \end{aligned}$$

so that

$$A = \frac{-36}{325}, \; B = \frac{-2}{325}, \; E = 2, \; F = 4,$$

and the complete solution is

$$x = c_1 e^t + c_2 t e^t + c_3 e^{-3t} - \frac{36}{325} \sin 2t - \frac{2}{325} \cos 2t + 2t + 4.$$

We now have the choice of either substituting this value of x into one of the given equations and solving for y, or repeating the above process in order to eliminate x from the given pair of equations. By the first plan, we get from the second of the given equations

$$Dy = (D + 1)x - 2t$$

$$= (D + 1)\left(c_1 e^t + c_2 t e^t + c_3 e^{-3t} - \frac{36}{325}\sin 2t - \frac{2}{325}\cos 2t + 2t + 4\right) - 2t$$

$$= (2c_1 + c_2)e^t + 2c_2 t e^t - 2c_3 e^{-3t} - \frac{32}{325}\sin 2t - \frac{74}{325}\cos 2t + 6,$$

whence,

$$y = (2c_1 + c_2)e^t + 2c_2 e^t(t - 1) + \frac{2}{3}c_3 e^{-3t} + \frac{16}{325}\cos 2t - \frac{37}{325}\sin 2t + 6t + c_4.$$

These expressions for x and y are solutions of the system of equations only if they satisfy both equations simultaneously. If we substitute them into the first of the two given equations, we have

$$(D^2 - 9)\left(c_1 e^t + c_2 t e^t + c_3 e^{-3t} - \frac{36}{325}\sin 2t - \frac{2}{325}\cos 2t + 2t + 4\right)$$

$$+ (D + 3)\left[(2c_1 - c_2)e^t + 2c_2 t e^t + \frac{2}{3}c_3 e^{-3t} + \frac{16}{325}\cos 2t - \frac{37}{325}\sin 2t + 6t + c_4\right] \equiv \sin 2t,$$

which reduces to

$$\sin 2t - 30 + 3c_4 \equiv \sin 2t,$$

whence, $c_4 = 10$. The complete solution of the system is thus

$$x = c_1 e^t + c_2 t e^t + c_3 e^{-3t} - \frac{36}{325}\sin 2t - \frac{2}{325}\cos 2t + 2t + 4,$$

$$y = (2c_1 - c_2)e^t + 2c_2 t e^t + \frac{2}{3}c_3 e^{-3t} + \frac{16}{325}\cos 2t - \frac{37}{325}\sin 2t + 6t + 10.$$

To proceed by the second method, we operate on the two given equations by $(D + 1)$ and $(D^2 - 9)$, respectively, obtaining

$$\begin{cases} (D + 1)(D^2 - 9)x + (D^2 + 4D + 3)y = \sin 2t + 2\cos 2t, \\ (D + 1)(D^2 - 9)x - (D^3 - 9D)y = -18t, \end{cases}$$

and, by subtracting

$$(D^3 + D^2 - 5D + 3)y^* = \sin 2t + 2\cos 2t + 18t,$$

---

* The operator in the left-hand member of this equation is the same as in the equation for x. Let the student operate on (38) and convince himself that this is generally true.

so that the complementary function is $y = k_1 e^t + k_2 t e^t + k_3 e^{-3t}$, and a particular integral turns up (using again the method of Section 31 if we choose), as

$$y = -\frac{37}{325} \sin 2t + \frac{16}{325} \cos 2t + 6t + 10.$$

We obtain as the complete solution

$$y = k_1 e^t + k_2 t e^t + k_3 e^{-3t} - \frac{37}{325} \sin 2t + \frac{16}{325} \cos 2t + 6t + 10.$$

Obviously, we have no reason to assume k_1, k_2, k_3 identical with c_1, c_2, c_3; hence, it remains to find how these constants are related. To that end, substitute the values of x and y already found into either of the given equations. We choose the second, as the simpler one, and obtain

$$\left[(2c_1 + c_2)e^t + 2c_2 t e^t - 2c_3 e^{-3t} - \frac{32}{325} \sin 2t - \frac{74}{325} \cos 2t + 6 + 2t \right]$$
$$- \left[k_1 e^t + k_2 t e^t + k_2 e^t - 3k_3 e^{-3t} - \frac{74}{325} \cos 2t - \frac{32}{325} \sin 2t + 6 \right]$$
$$\equiv 2t,$$

or

$$(2c_1 + c_2 - k_1 - k_2)e^t + (2c_2 - k_2)t e^t - (2c_3 - 3k_3)e^{-3t} + 2t \equiv 2t.$$

For this to be an identity, we must have

$$\begin{cases} k_1 + k_2 = 2c_1 + c_2, \\ k_2 = 2c_2, \\ 3k_3 = 2c_3, \end{cases} \text{whence,} \quad \begin{cases} k_1 = 2c_1 - c_2, \\ k_2 = 2c_2, \\ k_3 = \frac{2}{3} c_3. \end{cases}$$

With these values of k_1, k_2, and k_3, we obtain

$$y = (2c_1 - c_2)e^t + 2c_2 t e^t + \frac{2}{3} c_3 e^{-3t} + \frac{16}{325} \cos 2t - \frac{37}{325} \sin 2t$$
$$+ 6t + 10,$$

as above.*

---

* In the system of equations solved here, one was of order two, and the other was of order one, while the number of arbitrary constants in the solution turned out to be three. This is in consonance with the so-called Existence Theorem, which asserts the existence and uniqueness of the solution of a system of linear differential equations, under the conditions stated in the preceding footnote. The theorem also asserts that the number of arbitrary constants in the general solution equals (at most) the sum of the orders of the several equations of the system.

Exercises

1. Solve the following systems of equations:

(a) $$\begin{cases} \dfrac{dx}{dt} + \dfrac{dy}{dt} - y = e^t, \\[2mm] 2\dfrac{dx}{dt} + \dfrac{dy}{dt} + 2y = \cos t. \end{cases}$$

(b) $\dfrac{dx}{dt} + 2x - y = \dfrac{dy}{dt} - x + 3y = 0.$

(c) $\dfrac{dx}{3t - 2y} = \dfrac{dy}{4 + 2x} = dt.$

(d) $\dfrac{dx}{dt} + \dfrac{dy}{dt} - 3y = \dfrac{d^2x}{dt^2} + \dfrac{dy}{dt} = 0.$

(e) $$\begin{cases} \dfrac{d^2x}{dt^2} + \dfrac{d^2y}{dt^2} + \dfrac{dy}{dt} = \sinh 2t, \\[2mm] 2\dfrac{d^2x}{dt^2} + \dfrac{d^2y}{dt^2} = 2t. \end{cases}$$

(f) $$\begin{cases} \dfrac{d^2x}{dt^2} - \dfrac{x}{4} - \dfrac{dy}{dt} = e^{2t} + 1, \\[2mm] \dfrac{dy}{dt} - y = t - 2. \end{cases}$$

(g) $$\begin{cases} \dfrac{d^2x}{dt^2} - \dfrac{dx}{dt} + \dfrac{dy}{dt} = 0, \\[2mm] \dfrac{d^2x}{dt^2} - x + \dfrac{d^2y}{dt^2} = 0. \end{cases}$$

(h) $$\begin{cases} \dfrac{d^2x}{dt^2} - \dfrac{dy}{dt} = -2e^{2t}, \\[2mm] \dfrac{d^3x}{dt^3} + 2\dfrac{dx}{dt} = 12e^{2t} - \sin t. \end{cases}$$

2. Prove that if $\begin{Bmatrix} x = f_1(t) \\ y = g_1(t) \end{Bmatrix}$ and $\begin{Bmatrix} x = f_2(t) \\ y = g_2(t) \end{Bmatrix}$ are two solutions of the homogeneous system

$$\begin{cases} [F_1(D)]x + [G_1(D)]y = 0 \\ [F_2(D)]x + [G_2(D)]y = 0 \end{cases},$$

then

$$\begin{cases} x = c_1 f_1(t) + c_2 f_2(t) \\ y = c_1 g_1(t) + c_2 g_2(t) \end{cases},$$

where c_1 and c_2 are arbitrary constants, is also a solution.

3. Solve the system

$$\begin{cases} \dfrac{dx}{dt} = x + 2y \\[2mm] \dfrac{dy}{dt} = 3x + 2y \end{cases}$$

by assuming as a solution

$$\begin{cases} x = Ae^{mt}, \\ y = Be^{mt}. \end{cases}$$

Hint: The substitution will yield

$$\begin{cases} A(1 - m) + 2B = 0, \\ 3A + (2 - m)B = 0, \end{cases}$$

and this pair of equations will be satisfied by values of A and B other than $A = B = 0$ if and only if

$$\begin{vmatrix} 1 - m & 2 \\ 3 & 2 - m \end{vmatrix} = 0.$$

This is called the characteristic equation of the given system. It is satisfied by $m = -1$ and $m = 4$. The equations in A and B yield $B = -A$ when $m = -1$, and $B = \dfrac{3A}{2}$ when $m = 4$, with A arbitrary. Hence, the solutions of the system are

and

$$\begin{cases} x = A_1 e^{-t} \\ y = -A_1 e^{-t} \end{cases}$$

$$\begin{cases} x = A_2 e^{4t} \\ y = \dfrac{3A_2}{2} e^{4t} \end{cases}.$$

By Exercise 2,

$$\begin{cases} x = A_1 e^{-t} + A_2 e^{4t} \\ y = -A_1 e^{-t} + \dfrac{3A_2}{2} e^{4t} \end{cases}$$

is also a solution. It is the general solution, since it has two arbitrary constants.

4. Solve by the method of Exercise 3:

(a) $$\begin{cases} \dfrac{dx}{dt} = 4x + 2y, \\[2mm] \dfrac{dy}{dt} = -x + y. \end{cases}$$
(b) $$\begin{cases} \dfrac{dx}{dt} = -3y, \\[2mm] \dfrac{dy}{dt} = -x + 2y. \end{cases}$$

5. Verify that if the characteristic equation of

$$\begin{cases} \dfrac{dx}{dt} = ax + by, \\[2mm] \dfrac{dy}{dt} = cx + dy, \end{cases} \tag{I}$$

$viz.,$ $\begin{vmatrix} a - m & b \\ c & d - m \end{vmatrix} = 0$, has a double root m, then

$$\begin{cases} x = A_1 e^{mt} + A_2 t e^{mt}, \\ y = B_1 e^{mt} + B_2 t e^{mt}, \end{cases}$$

is the complete solution of (I), where A_1 and A_2 are arbitrary constants and B_1 and B_2 are determined by A_1 and A_2.

6. Solve by using Exercise 5:

(a) $\begin{cases} \dfrac{dx}{dt} = 4x - y, \\[2mm] \dfrac{dy}{dt} = x + 2y. \end{cases}$ (b) $\begin{cases} \dfrac{dx}{dt} = x + y, \\[2mm] \dfrac{dy}{dt} = -x + 3y. \end{cases}$

7. Verify that if the characteristic equation of the system (I) of Exercise 5 has the complex roots $p \pm qi$ (p, q, real), then the complete solution is

$$\begin{cases} x = e^{pt}(A_1 \sin qt + A_2 \cos qt), \\ y = e^{pt}(B_1 \sin qt + B_2 \cos qt), \end{cases}$$

where A_1 and A_2 are arbitrary, while B_1 and B_2 are determined by A_1 and A_2.

8. Solve, using Exercise 7:

(a) $\begin{cases} \dfrac{dx}{dt} = 2x - y, \\[2mm] \dfrac{dy}{dt} = x + 2y. \end{cases}$ (b) $\begin{cases} \dfrac{dx}{dt} = 4x - 5y, \\[2mm] \dfrac{dy}{dt} = x + 2y. \end{cases}$

9. Extend the method of Exercise 3 to the system:

$$\begin{cases} \dfrac{dx}{dt} = 2x, \\[2mm] \dfrac{dy}{dt} = 3x - 2y, \\[2mm] \dfrac{dz}{dt} = 2y + 3z. \end{cases}$$

Solution: Assume $x = Ae^{mt}$, $y = Be^{mt}$, $z = Ce^{mt}$. Substitution yields

$$\begin{aligned}(2-m)A &= 0,\\ 3A - (2+m)B &= 0,\\ 2B + (3-m)C &= 0.\end{aligned}$$

Hence, the characteristic equation of the system is

$$\begin{vmatrix} 2-m & 0 & 0 \\ 3 & -2-m & 0 \\ 0 & 2 & 3-m \end{vmatrix} = 0,$$

satisfied by $m = 2$, $m = -2$, and $m = 3$. For $m = 2$, we have

$$B = \frac{3A}{4}, \ C = -\frac{3A}{2}, \ A \text{ undetermined};$$

for $m = -2$, we have

$$A = 0, \ C = -\frac{2B}{5}, \ B \text{ undetermined};$$

while for $m = 3$, we have

$$A = 0, \ B = 0, \ C \text{ undetermined}.$$

Hence, three distinct solutions are

$$\begin{cases} x = Ae^{2t}, \\ y = \dfrac{3A}{4}\,e^{2t}, \\ z = -\dfrac{3A}{2}\,e^{2t}, \end{cases} \quad \begin{cases} x = 0, \\ y = Be^{-2t}, \\ z = -\dfrac{2B}{5}\,e^{-2t}, \end{cases} \quad \begin{cases} x = 0, \\ y = 0, \\ z = Ce^{3t}. \end{cases}$$

The theorem of Exercise 2 is also applicable to a homogeneous system of more than two equations, and thus

$$\begin{cases} x = Ae^{2t}, \\ y = \dfrac{3A}{4}\,e^{2t} + Be^{-2t}, \\ z = -\dfrac{3A}{2}\,e^{2t} - \dfrac{2B}{5}\,e^{-2t} + Ce^{3t}, \end{cases}$$

is a solution. This is, in fact, the complete solution, since it has three arbitrary constants.

10. Solve, as in Exercise 9:

$$\text{(a)}\begin{cases}\dfrac{dx}{dt} = -3x + 48y - 28z,\\[2mm]\dfrac{dy}{dt} = -4x + 40y - 22z,\\[2mm]\dfrac{dz}{dt} = -6x + 57y - 31z.\end{cases}\quad\text{(b)}\begin{cases}\dfrac{dx}{dt} = 6x - 72y + 44z,\\[2mm]\dfrac{dy}{dt} = 4x - 43y + 26z,\\[2mm]\dfrac{dz}{dt} = 6x - 63y + 38z.\end{cases}$$

11. The x-component of the velocity of a moving particle equals the sum of its coördinates, the y-component of its velocity is twice its abscissa. Find its path, if at the start of its motion it is at $(1, 0)$.

40. Miscellaneous exercises on Chapter IV.

1. Solve the following:

(a) $y''' - y' = 0.$

(b) $y''' + 3y' - 4y = 0.$

(c) $y^{iv} - 2ay''' + a^2y'' = x^2 - 1.$

(d) $y''' + 2y'' - 4y' - 8y = e^{3x} + 2.$

(e) $y^{iv} - 3y''' + \dfrac{11}{4}y'' - \dfrac{3}{4}y' = \cos x.$

(f) $y''' - 2y'' - 3y' + 10y = 0.$

(g) $y^{iv} - 8y''' + 20y'' = x^2 + e^{3x}.$

(h) $y^{iv} + 2y''' - 3y'' - 4y' + 4y = 32\sin 2x - 24\cos 2x.$

(i) $y''' - 2y'' - a^2y' + 2a^2y = \sinh x.$

(j) $4y''' - 8y'' - 11y' - 3y + 18e^x = 0.$

(k) $y''' - 3ay'' + 3a^2y' - a^3y = e^{ax}.$

(l) $y^{iv} + 2a^2y'' + a^4y = \cosh ax.$

(m) $\cdot x^2y'' - 4xy' + 6y = x^4 - x^2.$

(n) $y''' + \dfrac{3}{x}y'' - \dfrac{2}{x^2}y' + \dfrac{2}{x^3}y = 6x\log x - 6\log x$

$$- x - 8.$$

(o) $(2 - x)^2y'' + (2 - x)y' - 3y = 0.$

(p) $\dfrac{y''}{x} - \dfrac{3y'}{x^2} + \dfrac{4y}{x^3} = \dfrac{5}{x^2}.$

(q) $(3 + 2x)^3y''' + 2(3 + 2x)^2y'' + 4(3 + 2x)y' = 0$

(r) $y''' - y'' - 2y' = x^3 \cdot e^{2x}.$

2. In each of the following, find the particular solution satisfying the conditions stated:

(a) $y'' - 6y' + 13y = 0$; $y = 0$, $y' = 4e^{3\pi}$, when $x = \pi$.

(b) $y''' + y'' - 10y' + 8y = 16x - 20$; $y = 0$, $y' = 7$, $y'' = -15$, when $x = 0$.

(c) $x^2y'' - 5xy' + 13y = 0$; $y = 2$, $y' = 4$, when $x = 1$.

3. Show the following equations to be exact; integrate them as far as possible:

(a) $(x^2 + 3x)y'' + (3x - 1)y' + y = (20x + 30)(x^2 + 3x)^{\frac{2}{3}}$.

(b) $y''' - \sin x \cdot y'' - 2 \cos x \cdot y' + y \sin x = \log x$.

(c) $xy''' + \log x \cdot y'' + \dfrac{2}{x} y' - \dfrac{1}{x^2} y = 2x$.

(d) $xy^{iv} + 5y''' = 24$.

(e) $y^{iv} \sin x + 4y''' \cos x - 6y'' \sin x - 4y' \cos x + y \sin x = 6 \csc^4 x \cdot \cot x$.

4. (a) Find the adjoint equation of $xy'' + 2y' - xy = e^x$. Show that e^x and e^{-x} are solutions of the adjoint equation, and, employing them as integrating factors of the given equation, find its general solution.

(b) Find integrating factors of $x^2y'' + 6xy' + 6y = 0$, by solving its adjoint equation.

(c) Show that the equation $(x^2 + x)y'' + (2x + 1)y' + 2y = 0$ is self-adjoint, i. e., is identical with the adjoint equation.

5. In the exercises below, known solutions of the reduced equation are enclosed in parentheses; solve or reduce to an equation of lower order:

(a) $y'' \sin 2x - y' \cos 2x + 2y \sin 2x = \cos 2x \sqrt{\sin 2x}$; $(y = \cos 2x)$.

(b) $y'' \cdot x^2 \cos x + y'(x^2 \sin x - 2x \cos x) + y(2 \cos x - x \sin x) = \dfrac{x^3}{\sec x}$; $(y = x \sin x)$.

(c) $(1 - \log x)y'' + \dfrac{y'}{x} - \dfrac{y}{x^2} = \dfrac{1 - \log x}{\log x}$; $(y = \log x)$.

(d) $xy'' - y' + \dfrac{y}{x} = 3x^2$; $(y = x; y = x \log x)$.

(e) $(x^2 - 2x)y''' + y''(2x - x^2) - 2y' + 2y = 0$; $(y = e^x; y = x^2)$.

6. (a) Show that the homogeneous linear equation whose solutions are $y = y_1(x)$, $y = y_2(x)$, $y = y_3(x)$, is

$$\begin{vmatrix} y & y' & y'' & y''' \\ y_1 & y_1' & y_1'' & y_1''' \\ y_2 & y_2' & y_2'' & y_2''' \\ y_3 & y_3' & y_3'' & y_3''' \end{vmatrix} = 0.$$

(b) Write down the homogeneous linear equation whose solutions are $y = y_1(x)$, $y = y_2(x)$, $y = y_3(x)$, and $y = y_4(x)$.

(c) Write down the homogeneous linear equation whose solutions are $y = x^2$, and $y = 2x$.

(d) Write down the homogeneous linear equation whose solutions are $y = e^x$, $y = x$, $y = x^2$.

7. Show that the second order linear equation

$$y'' + Py' + Qy = R$$

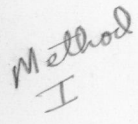

may be changed to one of the form

$$u'' + Su = T,$$

and find S and T in terms of P, Q, and R.   *Hint:* Set $y = u \cdot v$, and reduce the equation to

$$u'' \cdot v + u'(2v' + vP) + u(v'' + v'P + vQ) = R.$$

Now define v by

$$2v' + vP = 0 \ (\therefore v = e^{-\frac{1}{2}\int P\,dx}),$$

and obtain the desired result.

8. Solve the following by applying the method of Exercise 7:

(a) $y'' + y' \cot x - \dfrac{17 + \csc^2 x}{4} y = 0.$

(b) $y'' + \dfrac{y'}{x} - \dfrac{4x^2 + 1}{4x^2} y = \dfrac{e^x}{\sqrt{x}}.$

(c) $x^2 y'' + 4x^3 y' + (4x^4 + 2x^2 + 1)y = 0.$

(d) $y'' + y' \log x + \left(\dfrac{x-4}{2x^2} + \dfrac{\log^2 x}{4}\right) y = \sqrt{\dfrac{e^x}{x^x}}.$

9. Show that the second order linear equation

$$y'' + Py' + Qy = R$$

may, by a change of independent variable from x to z

Method II

$\left(i. \ e., \text{ by } y' = \dfrac{dy}{dz} \cdot z', \ y'' = \dfrac{dy}{dz} \cdot z'' + \dfrac{d^2 y}{dz^2} \cdot z'^2\right)$ be transformed into

$$\dfrac{d^2 y}{dz^2} + \dfrac{Pz' + z''}{z'^2} \cdot \dfrac{dy}{dz} + \dfrac{Q}{z'^2} y = \dfrac{R}{z'^2}.$$

Note: We may make the coefficient of y constant by defining z by $z'^2 = \pm Q$ (choosing the sign which will make z' real). If it happens that this choice of z renders the coefficient of $\dfrac{dy}{dz}$ also constant, the new equation will have all its coefficients constant and will be readily integrable. Thus, in the case of the equation $y'' + \dfrac{4x^2 - 1}{x}\,y'$ $-\,4x^2y = 4x^4$, we try $z'^2 = 4x^2$ ($\therefore z' = 2x$, $z'' = 2$, $z = x^2$); then $\dfrac{Pz' + z''}{z'^2} = 2$, and the transformed equation is $\dfrac{d^2y}{dz^2} + 2\,\dfrac{dy}{dz}$ $-\,y = z$, with the solution

$$y = c_1e^{(-1+\sqrt{2})z} + c_2e^{(-1-\sqrt{2})z} - z - 2.$$

The solution of the original equation is, therefore,

$$y = c_1e^{(-1+\sqrt{2})x^2} + c_2e^{(-1-\sqrt{2})x^2} - x^2 - 2.$$

10. Solve the following by applying the method of Exercise 9:

(a) $y'' - (2e^x + 1)y' + e^{2x} \cdot y = e^{3x}$.

(b) $y'' + (\sin x - \cot x)y' + y \sin^2 x = 0$.

(c) $y'' - \left(3 \tan x + \dfrac{1}{\sin x \cos x}\right) y' - y \cdot \tan^2 x = 0$.

11. Test the following for the applicability of either the method of Exercise 7 or that of Exercise 9, and solve:

(a) $y'' - 4xy' - (1 - 4x^2)y = e^{x^2}$.

(b) $y'' + \dfrac{5}{4x}\,y' - \dfrac{1}{4x^2}\,y = \dfrac{\log x}{4x^2}$.

(c) $y'' - \dfrac{y'}{x \log x} - y \log^2 x = 0$.

(d) $y'' + y' \tan x + \left(\dfrac{1}{2} + \dfrac{3 \tan^2 x}{4} - \dfrac{6}{x^2}\right) y = \sqrt{\cos x}$.

(e) $y'' + y' \sqrt{x} + y\left(\dfrac{x}{4} + \dfrac{1}{4\sqrt{x}} - 9\right) = xe^{-\frac{1}{3}x^{3/2}}$.

12. (a) Prove that the Riccati equation $y' = P + Qy + Ry^2$, where P, Q, and R are functions of x alone, is transformed by the substitution $y = -\dfrac{1}{R} \cdot \dfrac{du/dx}{u}$ into the linear equation

$$u'' - u'\left(Q + \dfrac{dR/dx}{R}\right) + u \cdot PR = 0,$$

if R is not identically zero.

(b) Apply the above substitution to

$$y' = -\frac{3}{x^3} + \left(2 - \frac{3}{x}\right) y + x^3 y^2,$$

and obtain

$$u'' - 2u' - 3u = 0.$$

Solve this for u, and from the solution derive

$$y = -\frac{1}{x^3} \cdot \frac{3c_1 e^{3x} - c_2 e^{-x}}{c_1 e^{3x} + c_2 e^{-x}} = -\frac{1}{x^3} \cdot \frac{3e^{3x} - ce^{-x}}{e^{3x} + ce^{-x}}.$$

where $c = \dfrac{c_2}{c_1}$.

(c) Solve $y' = -\dfrac{20}{x^3} - \dfrac{y}{x} + xy^2$.

(d) Solve $y' = \dfrac{\log^2 x}{x} + \dfrac{2 \log^2 x + 1}{x \log x} y + \dfrac{y^2}{x}$.

(e) Solve $y' = -4 \csc x + (3 - \cot x) y + y^2 \sin x$.

(f) Prove that if three solutions, $y = y_1$, $y = y_2$, $y = y_3$, of a Riccati equation are known, the equation is given by

$$\begin{vmatrix} y' & 1 & y & y^2 \\ y_1' & 1 & y_1 & y_1^2 \\ y_2' & 1 & y_2 & y_2^2 \\ y_3' & 1 & y_2 & y_3^2 \end{vmatrix} = 0.$$

(g) Write down the Riccati equation whose three solutions are $y = \log x$, $y = x$, $y = 1$.

13. Solve the following systems of equations:

(a) $\begin{cases} \dfrac{dx}{dt} = 4x + 3y, \\ \dfrac{dy}{dt} = 8x + 2y. \end{cases}$

(b) $\begin{cases} \dfrac{du}{dx} + 13v = 3u, \\ \dfrac{dv}{dx} + 9v = 4u. \end{cases}$

(c) $\dfrac{dx}{dt} - 6x + 2y = \dfrac{dy}{dt} - 2x - 2y = 0.$

(d) $\begin{cases} \dfrac{du}{dx} = u - 4y + z, \\ \dfrac{dy}{dx} = -2y + z, \\ \dfrac{dz}{dx} = 4z. \end{cases}$

(e) $\begin{cases} \dfrac{dx}{dt} + y = t^2 + 6t + 1, \\ x - \dfrac{dy}{dt} = 3t^2 - 3t - 1. \end{cases}$

(f) $\begin{cases} \dfrac{dx}{dt} + \dfrac{dy}{dt} + 2x + y = e^{2t} + t, \\[2mm] \dfrac{dx}{dt} + \dfrac{dy}{dt} - x + 3y = e^{-t} - 1. \end{cases}$

(g) $x - \dfrac{dx}{dt} - 2y = \dfrac{d^2x}{dt^2} - 2\dfrac{dy}{dt} - 2t + \cos 2t = 0.$

(h) $\dfrac{d^2x}{dt^2} - \dfrac{dx}{dt} + \dfrac{dy}{dt} = \dfrac{dx}{dt} + \dfrac{d^2y}{dt^2} + \dfrac{dy}{dt} = 0.$

(i) $\dfrac{d^2x}{dt^2} + 6x + 7y = 0 = \dfrac{d^2y}{dt^2} + 3x + 2y - 2t.$

14. A particle moving on a straight line is said to be in simple harmonic motion if its acceleration is proportional to its distance from a fixed point on the line and is directed toward that point. Denoting the distance of the particle from that point at the time t by s, show that the differential equation of its motion is $\dfrac{d^2s}{dt^2} = -k^2s$. Solve this equation on the basis that at $t = 0$, $s = h$, and $v = 0$. Show that the motion is periodic, and of period $\dfrac{2\pi}{k}$; also that the amplitude is h.

Note: The differential equation of this Exercise is of the form $\dfrac{d^2s}{dt^2} = f(s)$. A possible method of integrating such an equation is to multiply it by $2\dfrac{ds}{dt}$, obtaining $2\dfrac{ds}{dt} \cdot \dfrac{d^2s}{dt^2} = 2f(s)\dfrac{ds}{dt}$, or $\left(\dfrac{ds}{dt}\right)^2 = \displaystyle\int 2f(s) \cdot ds \equiv \varphi(s) + c_1$; whence, $\dfrac{ds}{\sqrt{\varphi(s) + c_1}} = \pm dt$, and the variables are separated.

Let the student work out the given equation by this method.

15. If the acceleration of a particle under the force of gravity is inversely proportional to the square of its distance from the center of the earth, and is directed toward the center, find the velocity at the surface of the earth of a particle falling from an infinite distance. *Hint:* Show that the equation of its motion is $\dfrac{d^2s}{dt^2} = -\dfrac{k^2}{s^2}$. Use the method of the above note. (This equation is non-linear.) Also use the initial conditions: $(s = \infty, \ v = 0)$ and $\left(s = R, \dfrac{d^2s}{dt^2} = -g\right)$, where R is the radius of the earth.

16. A particle moves on a straight line in a resisting medium, and the resistance is proportional to the velocity. Assuming that the particle starts with a velocity v_0 from a position $s = s_0$, show that as time goes on the particle approaches the position $s = s_0 + \dfrac{v_0}{k^2}$, where $(-k^2)$ is the constant of proportionality.

17. A particle moves on a straight line in a resisting medium, under an attraction proportional to its distance from a fixed center on the line; the attraction is directed toward the center, and the resistance is proportional to the speed. Assuming the constants of proportionality to be 25 and 6, respectively, also that the particle starts from the center with a velocity of 8 ft. per sec., show that the particle will have an infinite number of oscillations and will approach a state of rest at the center. Find the period of the vibrations. This is a case of *damped vibrations* in mechanics.

18. (a) A pendulum of length l is suspended from a fixed point and is constrained to move in a vertical plane through the point of suspension. Assume that the weight is concentrated at a point in the bob (hence the string weightless), and that there is no resistance; show that the motion is represented by the equation

$$l \frac{d^2\theta}{dt^2} = -g \sin \theta,$$

where θ is the angle that the string makes with the vertical at the time t. Use the method of the note to Exercise 14, and obtain

$$\frac{d\theta}{\sqrt{c_1 l + 2g \cos \theta}} = \pm \frac{dt}{\sqrt{l}}.$$

This integral cannot be expressed in terms of elementary functions.

(b) Solve the equation in (a), modified to the case in which θ remains tolerably small throughout the motion, so that $\sin \theta$ is approximately equal to θ. Find the period. Note that the equation is now of the same form as that in Exercise 14, and the motion represented by it is simple harmonic motion.

19. A particle moves in a plane in such a manner that its velocity component in the direction of each coördinate axis is equal to the other coördinate. Find its possible paths.

20. A beam of length l feet is supported at both ends, and is loaded at the center by a weight of w tons. Find the deflection of the beam at any point, and the maximum deflection. *Hint:* It is proved in mechanics that the bending moment at any cross-section (defined as the algebraic sum of the moments, about the center of the section, of all forces acting on one side of the section) is equal to $\dfrac{EI}{R}$, where E is the modulus of elasticity for the material of the beam, I is the moment of inertia of the cross-section about a horizontal axis through its center, and R is the radius of curvature, at the cross-section, of the curve into which the beam is bent.

Now, $R = \dfrac{(1 + y'^2)^{3/2}}{y''}$, as the student will recall from his elementary calculus, and hence the bending moment is

$$\frac{EI}{R} = EIy''(1 + y'^2)^{-3/2} = EIy''\left[1 - \frac{3}{2}y'^2 + \frac{15}{8}y'^4 - \cdots\right].$$

If the bending is slight, the slope y' is very small, and we may neglect y'^2 and higher powers and obtain EIy'' for the right-hand member.

The differential equation of the curve assumed by the beam is thus obtained by equating the bending moment at a distance x from a suitably assumed origin, to EIy''.

For the problem stated, take the origin at the lowest point of the (deflected) beam, which, by symmetry, is its mid-point, and the y-axis at right angles to the beam. The bending moment at any

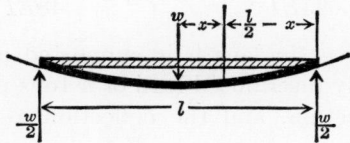

Fig. 3.

section for which x is positive is $\dfrac{w}{2}\left(\dfrac{l}{2} - x\right)$; hence, the differential equation of the curve is

$$EIy'' = \frac{w}{2}\left(\frac{l}{2} - x\right),$$

whence, by direct integration,

$$EIy' = \frac{w}{2}\left(\frac{lx}{2} - \frac{x^2}{2}\right) + c_1,$$

where $c_1 = 0$, since $y' = 0$ at $x = 0$, and from this

$$EIy = \frac{w}{2}\left(\frac{lx^2}{4} - \frac{x^3}{6}\right) + c_2,$$

where $c_2 = 0$, since $y = 0$ at $x = 0$, and we have

$$y = \frac{w}{24EI}\,(3lx^2 - 2x^3).$$

Since we have imposed the restriction, above, that x be positive, we must repreat the process with the contrary assumption, i. e., the assumption that x is negative.   The result thus obtained will be

$$y = \frac{w}{24EI}\,(3lx^2 + 2x^3),$$

and therefore we see that the two results may be combined into the one equation

$$y = \frac{w}{24EI}\,(3lx^2 - 2|x|^3).$$

The maximum value of y obviously corresponds to $x = \pm\dfrac{l}{2}$, at which it has the value $Y = \dfrac{w}{48EI}\,l^3$, and the deflection at any cross-section is

$$Y - y = \frac{w}{48EI}\,l^3 - \frac{w}{24EI}\,(3lx^2 - 2|x|^3) = \frac{w}{48EI}\,(l^3 - 6lx^2 + 4|x|^3).$$

21. A beam l feet in length is supported at the ends and is carrying a uniformly distributed load of w tons per foot run.   Find its maximum deflection, and the deflection at any cross-section.

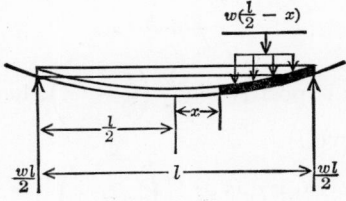

Fig. 4.

Hint: The bending moment at the section indicated is

$$\frac{wl}{2}\left(\frac{l}{2} - x\right) - \frac{w}{2}\left(\frac{l}{2} - x\right)^2 = \frac{w}{2}\left(\frac{l^2}{4} - x^2\right),$$

for the point of application of the force $\dfrac{wl}{2}$ is at a distance $\dfrac{l}{2} - x$ from

the section, and for the force $w\left(\dfrac{l}{2} - x\right)$, the distance is $\dfrac{1}{2}\left(\dfrac{l}{2} - x\right)$;

also, the second force imparts a moment opposite in sign to that imparted by the first.

22. (a) A beam l feet in length is fixed at one end and is carrying a load of w tons at the other end.   Find its maximum deflection, and the deflection at any point.

(b) A beam 30 feet in length is fixed at one end and is carrying a uniformly distributed load of 1 ton per foot run.   Find its maximum deflection, and the deflection at any point.

(c) A beam 40 feet in length is fixed at one end.   It is loaded at the free end with a weight of 2 tons, and is carrying a total weight of 60 tons evenly distributed over the beam.   Find the slope, and the amount of deflection at the free end.

23. A particle is projected upward, and moves against gravity and a resistance which is proportional to the velocity.   If the constant of proportionality is k^2, and if the initial velocity is v_0, show that the particle will come to rest at the instant defined by

$$t = \frac{1}{k^2} \log \frac{v_0 k^2 + g}{g}.$$

24. (a) An electrical circuit contains an inductance of L henries and a condenser of capacity C farads.   The circuit has no outside electromotive force, but a charge of q_0 coulombs is present on the condenser at the time $t = 0$, and an initial current of i_0 amperes is flowing through the circuit.   By equating the total voltage to zero, find the differential equation in q and t.   Solve for q in terms of t.

(b) Under the conditions of (a), set up the equation between i and t.

25. (a) A circuit contains a resistance of R ohms, a condenser of capacity C farads, and an inductance of L henries.   No outside voltage is applied, but at the time $t = 0$ a charge of q_0 is on the condenser, and a current of i_0 amperes is flowing through the circuit.   Find the relation between q and t.

In solving the equation, note the cases: $R^2C > 4L$, $R^2C = 4L$, $R^2C < 4L$.

(b) Under the conditions of (a), find the relation between i and t.

26. (a) A circuit contains a condenser of capacity C farads, an inductance of L henries, and a constant electromotive force of V volts. If the initial charge and current are q_0 and i_0, respectively, express q in terms of t.

(b) Under the conditions of (a), express i in terms of t.

27. (a) If the electromotive force of Exercise 26 is changed from the constant V to a variable $v = E \sin \omega t$ (E and ω constant), express q in terms of t.

(b) Under the conditions of (a), express i in terms of t.

28. If a variable electromotive force $v = E \sin \omega t$ (E and ω constant) is inserted in the circuit of Exercise 25, find i in terms of t. Show that the current approaches the form $i = I \sin \omega t$, and find the value of ω for which I is maximum.

29. The x-component of the acceleration of a moving particle is equal to twice its ordinate, the y-component of its acceleration equals one-half its abscissa. Find the equation of its path, if at the time $t = 0$, the particle is at the origin and the x- and y-components of its velocity are each equal to 1.

30. The force exerted by a spring is proportional to the amount it is stretched beyond its natural length. A nine-pound weight hanging at rest at the end of a spring stretches it 2 inches. The weight is drawn down another 2 inches and released. Find the equation of the ensuing motion, also its period and amplitude.

31. Solve Exercise 30 under the modifying condition that the motion is retarded by a force which, measured in pounds, equals $\frac{1}{75}$ of the absolute value of the velocity of the weight, measured in feet per second.

32. A cylindrical spar buoy 2 feet in diameter and weighing 720 pounds stands vertically in water weighing 62.5 pounds per cubic foot. It is slightly depressed and then released. Find the period of the resulting motion.

33. The sole force acting on a particle moving in a plane is the force of attraction to a fixed point, O, in that plane, the force being inversely proportional to the square of the distance of the particle from O. Show that the locus of the particle is a conic with O as focus. *Hint:* Show that with the particle at $P(r, \theta)$ the components of the force along and at right angles to OP are, respectively,

$$\frac{d^2r}{dt^2} - r\left(\frac{d\theta}{dt}\right)^2 \text{ and } r\frac{d^2r}{dt^2} + 2\frac{dr}{dt} \cdot \frac{d\theta}{dt}.$$

Hence,

$$\frac{d^2r}{dt^2} - r\left(\frac{d\theta}{dt}\right)^2 = \frac{-k}{r^2}, \tag{A}$$

and

$$r\frac{d^2\theta}{dt^2} + 2\frac{dr}{dt} \cdot \frac{d\theta}{dt} = 0. \tag{B}$$

Equation (B) gives at once

$$r^2\frac{d\theta}{dt} = h \qquad (h \text{ a constant}). \tag{C}$$

Set $r = \dfrac{1}{u}$ and write Equation A in terms of derivatives with respect to θ. making use of (C). The final result is

$$r = \frac{\dfrac{h^2}{k}}{1 + \dfrac{ch^2}{k}\cos(\theta - d)}.$$

CHAPTER V

Numerical Approximation to Solutions

41. Picard's method. Let our problem be to find a particular solution of

$$y' = f(x, y), \tag{1}$$

say, the solution passing through (x_0, y_0). It may well happen that no method is available for integrating (1) formally, in which case resort may be had to some means of finding an approximation to the solution desired.

One such method has been indicated in Exercise 5, page 14, and the student will do well to re-read the discussion of that exercise. To illustrate the method again, let the particular solution of

$$y' = x - y^2 \tag{2}$$

passing through $\left(0, \frac{1}{2}\right)$ be desired. We compute, for $\left(0, \frac{1}{2}\right)$,

$$y' = x - y^2 = -\frac{1}{4},$$

$$y'' = 1 - 2yy' = \frac{5}{4},$$

$$y''' = -2yy'' - 2y'^2 = -\frac{11}{8},$$

$$y^{iv} = -2yy''' - 6y'y'' = \frac{13}{4},$$

$$y^v = -2yy^{iv} - 8y'y''' - 6y''^2 = -\frac{123}{8}, \text{ etc.}$$

The series

$$y = \frac{1}{2} + x\left(-\frac{1}{4}\right) + \frac{x^2}{2!} \cdot \frac{5}{4} + \frac{x^3}{3!}\left(-\frac{11}{8}\right) + \frac{x^4}{4!} \cdot \frac{13}{4}$$
$$+ \frac{x^5}{5!}\left(-\frac{123}{8}\right) + \cdots \tag{3}$$

134

is, indeed, the Taylor expansion, about $\left(0, \dfrac{1}{2}\right)$, of that function

$$y = f(x) \tag{4}$$

which satisfies (2) and for which $y = \dfrac{1}{2}$ when $x = 0$, *i. e.*, it is the Taylor expansion of the particular solution sought.

In general, it is not possible to obtain (4) explicitly from its Taylor expansion; in fact, if it were possible, (1) probably would be readily integrable in the first place.

A finite number of terms of the series (3) will, then, serve as an approximation to (4), and hence if the value of y in (4) is desired, say for $x = .2$, we compute it as

$$y = \frac{1}{2} + (.2)\left(-\frac{1}{4}\right) + \frac{.04}{2}\cdot\frac{5}{4} + \frac{.008}{6}\left(-\frac{11}{8}\right) + \frac{.0016}{24}\cdot\frac{13}{4}$$
$$+ \frac{.00032}{120}\left(-\frac{123}{8}\right) + \cdots = .47334, \text{ approximately.}$$

Let us now turn to another method, due to the eminent French mathematician Émile Picard, and bearing his name.

To solve the problem proposed at the beginning of this section, start with

$$y_1 \equiv y_0 + \int_{x_0}^{x} f(x, y_0)dx.$$

Form, next,

$$y_2 \equiv y_0 + \int_{x_0}^{x} f(x, y_1)dx,$$

then

$$y_3 \equiv y_0 + \int_{x_0}^{x} f(x, y_2)dx,$$

and

$$y_4 \equiv y_0 + \int_{x_0}^{x} f(x, y_3)dx.$$

By continuing this process, we obtain a series of functions of x,

$$y_0, y_1, y_2, y_3, y_4, \cdots,$$

all of which take on the value y_0 at $x = x_0$, and, furthermore, such that

$$\begin{cases} y_1' \equiv f(x, y_0)^* \therefore (y_1')_{x=x_0} = f(x_0, y_0), \\ y_2' \equiv f(x, y_1) \quad \therefore (y_2')_{x=x_0} = f(x_0, y_0), \\ y_3' \equiv f(x, y_2) \quad \therefore (y_3')_{x=x_0} = f(x_0, y_0), \\ y_4' \equiv f(x, y_3) \quad \therefore (y_4')_{x=x_0} = f(x_0, y_0), \text{ etc.} \end{cases} \tag{5}$$

These functions are not themselves solutions of (1), since they do not identically satisfy $y_i' = f(x, y_i)$ $(i = 1, 2, 3, 4, \cdots)$, but it is proved that the successive functions in the sequence form better and better approximations to the solution sought. Indeed, Picard proves that this sequence tends to a limit which is precisely the solution in question.

For the example (2) worked in this section, Picard's method would yield $\left(\text{with } x_0 = 0, \ y_0 = \frac{1}{2}, \text{ and } f(x, y) \equiv x - y^2 \right)$

$$y_1 \equiv \frac{1}{2} + \int_0^x \left(x - \frac{1}{4} \right) dx \equiv \frac{1}{2} - \frac{x}{4} + \frac{x^2}{2},$$

$$y_2 \equiv \frac{1}{2} + \int_0^x \left[x - \left(\frac{1}{2} - \frac{x}{4} + \frac{x^2}{2} \right)^2 \right] dx \equiv \frac{1}{2} - \frac{x}{4} + \frac{5x^2}{8} - \frac{3x^3}{16}$$
$$+ \frac{x^4}{16} - \frac{x^5}{20},$$

$$y_3 \equiv \frac{1}{2} + \int_0^x (x - y_2^2) dx,$$

etc. The value of y for $x = .2$ would be found as

$$(y_1)_{x=.2} = .47$$
$$(y_2)_{x=.2} = .47358,$$

where the second would be a better approximation to the value sought than the first, while $(y_3)_{x=.2}$ would be a still better approximation.

It is evident that the labor involved in performing the successive integrations weakens the effectiveness of the method as a practical means of approximation. It is, however, of great theoretical significance.

Exercises

1. (a) Obtain the approximate solution of $y' = xy$ which passes through $\left(\frac{1}{2}, 1 \right)$, in the form of a Taylor series. Using the

---

* Wood's *Advanced Calculus*, page 141, Equation (1).

first 4 terms of the series, compute the value of y in the above solution for $x = .55$.

(b) Obtain the approximate solution in (a) by Picard's method.   Compute y_2 for $x = .55$.

(c) Compare the results in (a) and (b) with the value of y in the exact solution, for $x = .55$.

2. Obtain the approximate solution of $y' = \log xy$ which passes through $(1, 1)$, in the form of a Taylor series.   Use the first three terms of the series to compute the value of y in the above solution, for $x = 1.1$.

3. By Picard's method, obtain the approximation to the solution of $y' = x - y$ which passes through $(0, 2)$, down to y_4.   Compare each of y_1, y_2, y_3, y_4 with the exact solution.

4. Show that the successive approximations, by Picard's method, to the solution of $y' = -y$ through (x_0, y_0), tend to the limit $y = y_0 e^{x_0 - x}$, i.e., to the exact solution.

5. Show that all the approximations, by Picard's method, to the solution of $y' = x$ through (x_0, y_0) are identical with the exact solution.

6. (a) Obtain the approximate solutions to $y' = x + y^2$ through $(0, 0)$:

   i. By Picard's method.
   ii. As a Taylor series.

(b) Compute the values of y in the two parts of Exercise 6(a) for $x = -.1$.

7. Extend formulas (5) of the text to show that y_i, in the Picard sequence of approximations, has all its x-derivatives up to and including the ith, but not, in general, the $(i + 1)^{\text{st}}$, equal at (x_0, y_0) to its value as determined by $f(x, y)$, where i equals 1, 2, 3, $\cdots$.

8. Obtain, by Picard's method, an approximation to that solution of the system

$$\begin{cases} \dfrac{dy}{dx} = z, \\ \dfrac{dz}{dx} = x - y^2, \end{cases}$$

which is satisfied by $y = 1$ and $z = 2$, when $x = 0$.   *Hint:* Picard's sequence of approximations to a particular solution of

$$\begin{cases} \dfrac{dy}{dx} = f(x, y, z), \\[2mm] \dfrac{dz}{dx} = g(x, y, z), \end{cases}$$

satisfied by (x_0, y_0, z_0), is

$$\begin{cases} y_1 \equiv y_0 + \displaystyle\int_{x_0}^{x} f(x, y_0, z_0)dx, \\[4mm] z_1 \equiv z_0 + \displaystyle\int_{x_0}^{x} g(x, y_0, z_0)dx, \end{cases}$$

$$\begin{cases} y_2 \equiv y_0 + \displaystyle\int_{x_0}^{x} f(x, y_1, z_1)dx, \\[4mm] z_2 \equiv z_0 + \displaystyle\int_{x_0}^{x} g(x, y_1, z_1)dx, \end{cases}$$

etc.

9. Obtain, by Picard's method, a third approximation to that solution of

$$\begin{cases} \dfrac{dy}{dx} = x + z^2, \\[2mm] \dfrac{dz}{dx} = y - x, \end{cases}$$

for which $y = 0$ and $z = 1$, when $x = 0$.

10. Obtain. by Picard's method, a third approximation to that solution of

$$\begin{cases} \dfrac{dy}{dx} = z^2, \\[2mm] \dfrac{dz}{dx} = y + u, \\[2mm] \dfrac{du}{dx} = u - z, \end{cases}$$

for which $y = 1$, $z = 0$, and $u = 1$, when $x = 0$.

11. (a) Obtain an approximation for Exercise 8 as two simultaneous Taylor series. *Hint:* At $(0, 1, 2)$, we have

$$\begin{cases} y' = z = 2, \\ z' = x - y^2 = -1, \end{cases}$$

$$\begin{cases} y'' = z' = -1, \\ z'' = 1 - 2yy' = 1 - 4 = -3, \end{cases}$$

$$\begin{cases} y''' = z'' = -3, \\ z''' = -2yy'' - 2y'^2 = 2 - 8 = -6, \end{cases}$$

etc.

(b) Obtain an approximate solution for Exercise 9 as two simultaneous Taylor series.

(c) Obtain an approximate solution for Exercise 10 as three simultaneous Taylor series.

12. Derive the formulas analogous to formulas (5) of the text for the case of two simultaneous equations, as discussed in Exercise 8.

13. Obtain an approximation to that solution of $y'' = x + y^2 - 2y'$ for which $y = 1$ and $y' = 1$, when $x = 0$:

(a) in the form of a Taylor series;

(b) by Picard's method.

Hint: For (b), replace the given equation by the system

$$\begin{cases} \dfrac{dy}{dx} = z, \\[2mm] \dfrac{dz}{dx} = x + y^2 - 2z. \end{cases}$$

14. Obtain an approximation to that solution of $y'' = x + y - y^2$ for which $y = -1$ and $y' = 1$, when $x = 0$:

(a) in the form of a Taylor series;

(b) by Picard's method.

42. Runge's method. A most effective single formula for the problem treated in this chapter, *viz.*, to find the value of y at $x = x_0 + h$ for the particular integral of

$$y' = f(x, y) \tag{1}$$

through (x_0, y_0), is that due to Runge and published by him in 1895.

The formula makes use of the following quantities:

$$\begin{cases} \Delta' = hf_0, \\[2mm] \Delta'' = hf\left(x_0 + \dfrac{h}{2}, y_0 + \dfrac{1}{2}\Delta'\right), \\[2mm] \Delta''' = hf(x_0 + h, y_0 + \Delta'), \\[2mm] \Delta^{iv} = hf(x_0 + h, y_0 + \Delta'''), \\[2mm] k = \dfrac{\Delta' + 4\Delta'' + \Delta^{iv}}{6}. \end{cases} \tag{6}$$

It may be of interest to the student to note the similarity between the last of (6) and what is known as Simpson's Rule in the Integral Calculus.

To illustrate Runge's method, we consider the value of y corresponding to $x = 1.4$ for the particular integral of $y' = \dfrac{x^3 - y}{x}$ having $y = .5$ when $x = 1$.

Here

(x_0, y_0) is $(1, .5)$; $f_0 = .5$; $h = .4$; and hence $\Delta' = hf_0 = .2$;

$x_0 + \dfrac{h}{2} = 1.2$; $y_0 + \dfrac{1}{2}\Delta' = .6$; $f\left(x_0 + \dfrac{h}{2}, y_0 + \dfrac{\Delta'}{2}\right) = .94$;

$$\therefore \Delta'' = .376;$$

$x_0 + h = 1.4$; $y_0 + \Delta' = .7$; $f(x_0 + h, y_0 + \Delta') = 1.46$; $\therefore \Delta'''$
$$= .584;$$

$y_0 + \Delta''' = 1.084$; $f(x_0 + h, y_0 + \Delta''') = 1.1857$; $\therefore \Delta^{iv} = .47428$;

$$k = \frac{\Delta' + 4\Delta'' + \Delta^{iv}}{6} = .36305;$$

and the value of y sought is, approximately, $y_0 + k = .5 + .36305$ $= .86305$. Now the given equation may be integrated, and the particular integral determined to be $y = \dfrac{x^3}{4} + \dfrac{1}{4x}$, which gives the value of y, when $x = 1.4$, as $.86457$, and hence our approximation is at fault by 2 in the third decimal place.

Let us now apply the formula twice—first, to determine y when $x = 1.2$ (and we shall find $y = .64022$); then, starting with $(1.2, .64022)$ as (x_0, y_0), to determine y as desired. For the first tabulation we have

$$h = .2; f_0 = .5; \therefore \Delta' = .1;$$
$$\Delta'' = .2f(1.1, .55) = .142;$$
$$\Delta''' = .2f(1.2, .6) = .188;$$
$$\Delta^{iv} = .2f(1.2, .688) = .17334;$$

and

$$k = \frac{.1 + 4(.142) + .17334}{6} = .14022.$$

Hence, $y = .5 + .14022 = .64022$. For the second tabulation we have

$$h = .2; f_0 = f(1.2, .64022) = .90648; \therefore \Delta' = .18130;$$
$$\Delta'' = .2f(1.3, .73087) = .22556;$$
$$\Delta''' = .2f(1.4, .82152) = .27464;$$
$$\Delta^{iv} = .2f(1.4, .91486) = .26130;$$

and

$$k = \frac{.18130 + 4(.22556) + .26130}{6} = .22431.$$

Hence, $y = .64022 + .22431 = .86453$, and the accuracy of the result is seen to be much greater here than in the previous case.

Note: In case $|f_0| > 1|$, it is better to write $y' = f(x, y)$ as $\dfrac{dx}{dy} = \dfrac{1}{f(x, y)} \equiv g(x, y) (\therefore |g_0| < 1)$, and interchange the rôles of x and y; *i. e.*, the method will then lend itself to finding x corresponding to $y = y_0 + h$.

Exercises

1. Apply Runge's method to find:

(a) The value of y at $x = .2$ for the particular integral of $y' = x - y^2$ passing through $(0, .5)$.

(b) The value of y at $x = 1.7$ for the particular integral of $y' = \log_{10}\left(y + \dfrac{1}{2x}\right)$ passing through $(1, 2)$:

      i. By applying the method once for the whole interval.

      ii. By applying the method twice (as in the last illustration); say for $h = .3$, and then for $h = .4$.

(c) The value of y at $x = 1.8$ for the particular integral of $y' = \dfrac{y - 2x^2}{x + y}$ passing through $(1, 2.5)$:

      i. By applying the method once.

      ii. By applying the method twice.

(d) The value of y at $x = 1.32$ for the particular integral of $y' = \sqrt[3]{y - 2x}$ having $y = 2.5$ when $x = 1.24$.

(e) The value of x at $y = 3.3$ for the particular integral of $y' = \dfrac{2y - 3x}{x}$ having $y = 3$ when $x = 1$. *Hint:* Re-read the last note in the text. Since $f_0 = 3$, put $\dfrac{dx}{dy} = \dfrac{x}{2y - 3x} \equiv g(x, y)$, and have $g_0 = \dfrac{1}{3}$, $\Delta' = hg_0$, $\Delta'' = hg\left(x_0 + \dfrac{1}{2}\Delta', y_0 + \dfrac{h}{2}\right)$, etc.

Compare the answer obtained with the answer in the exact particular solution.

(f) The value of x at $y = 1.3$ for the particular integral of $y' = x - \sqrt{y}$ having $y = 1$ when $x = 5$.

2. Apply Runge's method to $y' = -y$, and show that for the particular integral through (x_0, y_0) the value of y, when $x = x_0 + h$, is

$$y = y_0 + \frac{h}{6} (3hy_0 - 6y_0 - h^2y_0).$$

Verify that this agrees with the value of y in the exact particular integral as far as the coefficient of h^3.

3. Apply Runge's method to $y' = x^2 - x$, and show that for the particular integral through (x_0, y_0) the value of y, when $x = x_0 + h$, is

$$y = y_0 + \frac{h}{6} (6x_0^2 - 6x_0 + 6hx_0 + 2h^2 - 3h).$$

Show that this is identical with the value of y in the exact particular integral.   Account for this identity.

4. Runge's formula for an approximation to the values of y and z corresponding to $x = x_0 + h$, for the particular integral of

$$\begin{cases} \dfrac{dy}{dx} = f(x, y, z), & \text{for 1 variable} \\[2mm] \dfrac{dz}{dx} = g(x, y, z), \end{cases}$$

having $y = y_0$ and $z = z_0$ when $x = x_0$, is

$$y = y_0 + k,$$
$$z = z_0 + m,$$

where

$$k = \frac{\Delta' + 4\Delta'' + \Delta^{iv}}{6}, \quad m = \frac{\delta' + 4\delta'' + \delta^{iv}}{6}$$

and

$$\Delta' = hf_0,$$
$$\delta' = hg_0;$$
$$\Delta'' = hf\left(x_0 + \frac{h}{2}, y_0 + \frac{\Delta'}{2}, z_0 + \frac{\delta'}{2}\right),$$
$$\delta'' = hg\left(x_0 + \frac{h}{2}, y_0 + \frac{\Delta'}{2}, z_0 + \frac{\delta'}{2}\right);$$
$$\Delta''' = hf(x_0 + h, y_0 + \Delta', z_0 + \delta'),$$
$$\delta''' = hg(x_0 + h, y_0 + \Delta', z_0 + \delta');$$
$$\Delta^{iv} = hf(x_0 + h, y_0 + \Delta''', z_0 + \delta'''),$$
$$\delta^{iv} = hg(x_0 + h, y_0 + \Delta''', z_0 + \delta''').$$

Prove that Runge's value for y agrees as far as the coefficient of h^3 with the Taylor expansion:

$$y = y_0 + hf_0 + \frac{h^2}{2}\left(\frac{df}{dx}\right)_0 + \frac{h^3}{6}\left(\frac{d^2f}{dx^2}\right)_0 + \cdots,$$

and similarly for z.

5. Apply Runge's method (see Exercise 4) to find:

  (a) The values of y and z corresponding to $x = .3$, for the particular integral of

$$\begin{cases} \dfrac{dy}{dx} = y + 2z, \\[2mm] \dfrac{dz}{dx} = x + y^2, \end{cases}$$

having $y = .4$ and $z = .1$, when $x = 0$.

  (b) The values of y and z corresponding to $x = .9$, for the particular integral of

$$\begin{cases} \dfrac{dy}{dx} = \sqrt{1 + z^2 - x}, \\[2mm] \dfrac{dz}{dx} = \sqrt{1 - y^2}, \end{cases}$$

having $y = .6$ and $z = .1$, when $x = .5$.

  (c) The values of y and z corresponding to $x = 2.7$, for the particular integral of

$$\begin{cases} \dfrac{dy}{dx} = 10^{x-y+z}, \\[2mm] \dfrac{dz}{dx} = \log_{10}(x + y + z), \end{cases}$$

having $y = 3$ and $z = 0$, when $x = 2$.   *Suggestion:* Apply the method in two steps, say for $h = .4$, and then for $h = .3$.

6. A modification of Runge's method, due to Kutta, is to take

$$\Delta' = hf_0, \quad \Delta'' = hf\left(x_0 + \frac{h}{3}, y_0 + \frac{\Delta'}{3}\right),$$

$$\Delta''' = hf\left(x_0 + \frac{2h}{3}, y_0 + \Delta'' - \frac{\Delta'}{3}\right),$$

$$\Delta^{iv} = hf(x_0 + h, y_0 + \Delta''' - \Delta'' + \Delta'),$$

$$k = \frac{\Delta' + 3\Delta'' + 3\Delta''' + \Delta^{iv}}{8}.$$

(a) Use this method to find the value of y at $x = 0.6$ for the particular integral of $y' = \dfrac{x + y^2}{2 + x}$ passing through $(0, 1)$.

(b) Use Kutta's method to find the value of y at $x = 0.8$ for the particular integral of $y' = \dfrac{x^2 - 2y}{y + 1}$ passing through $(1, 0)$.

43. Milne's method. A most efficient method of numerical integration is one due to W. E. Milne,* a method of comparative recency.

We turn again to the differential equation

$$y' = f(x, y) \tag{1}$$

with the initial condition $x = x_0$, $y = y_0$. We assume that, by any method whatever, we have found the values of y for $x = x_0 + h$, $x_0 + 2h$, and $x_0 + 3h$. Milne's method consists in finding y for $x = x_0 + 4h$ by the formula

$$y_4 = y_0 + \frac{4h}{3}(2y_1' - y_2' + 2y_3') \tag{7}$$

where $y_4 = y(x_0 + 4h)$, $y_3 = y(x_0 + 3h)$, $y_2 = y(x_0 + 2h)$, and $y_1 = y(x_0 + h)$, while $y_i' = f(x_0 + ih, y_i)$, $i = 1, 2, 3, 4$.

Having the values of y_1, y_2, and y_3, obtained by some other method, as we have previously stated, we compute the values of y_1', y_2', and y_3' by substituting (x_1, y_1), (x_2, y_2), and (x_3, y_3) into (1). Next we find y_4 by (7) and then y_4' by substituting (x_4, y_4) into (1). These values of y_4 and y_4' just found are tentative values of y and y' corresponding to $x = x_4 = x_0 + 4h$. When found, they should be checked by the formula

$$y_4 = y_2 + \frac{h}{3}(y_4' + 4y_3' + y_2'). \tag{8}$$

If the values of y_4, as given by (7) and (8) agree, to the number of places contemplated in the approximation, this value of y_4 is assumed to be correct. Otherwise, compute the value of the expression

$$\tfrac{1}{29} \mid y_4^{(2)} - y_4^{(1)} \mid,$$

---

* "Numerical Integration of Ordinary Differential Equations," *The American Mathematical Society Monthly*, Vol. 33 (1926), pp. 455–460.

where $y_4^{(2)}$ is the value of y_4 given by (8) and $y_4^{(1)}$, that given by (7). If this quantity is negligible to the number of places we wish to retain, we may assume that the value of y_4 given by (8) is correct. Otherwise a smaller value of h must be employed.

Illustration

Given the differential equation

$$y' = 2y - x \tag{9}$$

and four points, $(1, 1)$, $(1.1, 1.1054)$, $(1.2, 1.2229)$ and $(1.3, 1.3554)$ on the same integral curve of it, let us find, by Milne's method, the values of y corresponding to $x = 1.4$, 1.5, and 1.6.

The given values, as well as the results obtained, are shown in Table 1. The calculation of $y(1.4)$ is made by Formula (7) as

x	y	y'
1	1	1
1.1	1.1054	1.1108
1.2	1.2229	1.2458
1.3	1.3554	1.4108
1.4	1.5063	1.6126
1.5	1.6794	1.8588
1.6	1.8799	2.1598

Table 1.

$$y(1.4) = 1 + \frac{4(.1)}{3} [2(1.4108)$$
$$- 1.2458 + 2(1.1108)]$$
$$= 1.5063.$$

By (9) we find

$$y'(1.4) = 2(1.5063) - 1.4 = 1.6126.$$

Then, by (8)

$$y(1.4) = 1.2229 + \frac{.1}{3} [1.6126 + 4(1.4108) + 1.2458] = 1.5063,$$

a value which agrees with the value previously obtained. Hence we assume that it is correct and enter it in Table 1. The method is repeated to add other rows to the table, as follows.

$$y(1.5) = 1.1054 + \frac{.4}{3} [2(1.6126) - 1.4108 + 2(1.2458)] = 1.6795, \quad \text{eq. 7}$$
$$y'(1.5) = 2(1.6795) - 1.5 = 1.8590, \quad \text{eq. 9}$$
$$y(1.5) = 1.3554 + \frac{.1}{3} [1.8590 + 4(1.6126) + 1.4108] = 1.6794. \quad \text{eq. 8}$$

$$y(1.6) = 1.2229 + \frac{.4}{3} [2(1.8588) - 1.6126 + 2(1.4108)] = 1.8798, \quad \text{eq. 7}$$
$$y'(1.6) = 2(1.8798) - 1.6 = 2.1596, \quad \text{eq. 9}$$
$$y(1.6) = 1.5063 + \frac{.1}{3} [2.1596 + 4(1.8588) + 1.6126] = 1.8799. \quad \text{eq. 8}$$

The fact that the check value of y has not differed from the tentative value more than one unit in the fourth decimal place suggests that we might be able to increase the value of h to .2. To this end we draw up Table 2, taking alternate rows from Table 1. From this table, using (7) we obtain

x	y	y'
1	1	1
1.2	1.2229	1.2458
1.4	1.5063	1.6126
1.6	1.8799	2.1598

Table 2.

$$y(1.8) = 1 + \frac{4(.2)}{3}\,[2(2.1598) - 1.6126$$
$$+ 2(1.2458)] = 2.3863,$$

$$y'(1.8) = 2(2.3863) - 1.8 = 2.9726,$$

$$y(1.8) = 1.5063 + \frac{.2}{3}\,[2.9726 + 4(2.1598) + 1.6126] = 2.3879.$$

Thus, the check value of $y(1.8)$ differs from the tentative value by 0.0016. One 29th part of this difference is not negligible, since we are keeping four decimal places. We conclude that $h = .2$ is too large and if we want to extend the integral curve further than the points of table 1 we shall have to go back to $h = .1$.

Exercises

1. In each of the following cases fill in the blanks in the given table which lists sets of points on an integral curve to the corresponding differential equation.

(a) $\dfrac{dy}{dx} = x + y$,

x	0	0.1	0.2	0.3	0.4	0.5
y	1	1.1103	1.2428	1.3997		

(b) $\dfrac{dy}{dx} = \dfrac{y - x}{y + x}$,

x	0	0.1	0.2	0.3	0.4	0.5
y	1	1.091	1.168	1.233		

(c) $\dfrac{dy}{dx} = y - xy$,

x	1	1.2	1.4	1.6	1.8	2.0	2.2
y	1	0.9802	0.9231	0.8353			

2. For the following differential equations, find by any method three more points on the integral curve through the point given and then proceed to the value x given, by the method of Milne.

(a) Find y at $x = 1.5$ on the integral curve of $xy' = y - 3x$ through (1, 2.000).

(b) Find y at $x = 0.50$ on the integral curve of $y' = \sin x + \cos y$ through (0.00, 0.00).

CHAPTER VI

Integration in Series

44. Equations of the first order. We propose, in this chapter, to study the problem of approximating to the general solution of an ordinary differential equation by means of a power series.

We begin with an illustration, given

$$y' = x + \frac{1}{y}, \tag{1}$$

let us assume its solution to be

$$y = A_0 + A_1 x + A_2 x^2 + A_3 x^3 + A_4 x^4 + \cdots, \tag{2}$$

the coefficients in the series to be determined presently, in such a manner that (2) satisfies (1) formally.

Now, since the right-hand side of (1) has the properties of continuity, single-valuedness, etc., demanded in the Existence Theorem, we know that for any point $(0, A_0)$ (with the exception of $(0, 0)$, where the conditions of the Theorem fail to be met), there exists a unique solution

$$y = f(x) \tag{3}$$

which is continuous for some range of values of x in the neighborhood of $x = 0$, and which takes on the value A_0 at $x = 0$. Again, the series in (2) converges for some range of values of x in the neighborhood of $x = 0$,* and hence represents some continuous function which takes on the value A_0 at $x = 0$. After (2) has been made to satisfy (1) formally by the proper choice of coefficients, the function represented by it must be identical with (3), by the uniqueness of the solution. (It is not to be expected, however, that the explicit form of (3) will be in evidence from its expansion (2). In fact, if such is the case the equation is usually integrable directly,

---

* That a power series like (2) converges over some interval about $x = 0$, is proved in the Theory of Functions of a Real Variable. To be sure, the length of the interval may be zero in the case of some series, *i. e.*, $x = 0$ may be the only value of x for which the series converges.

and no recourse to integration in series is necessary.) We now differentiate (2) to obtain

$$y' = A_1 + 2A_2x + 3A_3x^2 + 4A_4x^3 + 5A_5x^4 + \cdots .* \qquad (4)$$

Hence, by (1), or, what is the same, by

$$yy' - xy - 1 = 0, \qquad (5)$$

$$(A_0 + A_1x + A_2x^2 + A_3x^3 + \cdots)(A_1 + 2A_2x + 3A_3x^2 + 4A_4x^3$$
$$+ \cdots) - (A_0x + A_1x^2 + A_2x^3 + A_3x^4 + \cdots) - 1 \equiv 0.$$

Hence,†

$$A_0A_1 + (2A_0A_2 + A_1^2)x + (3A_0A_3 + 3A_1A_2)x^2 + (4A_0A_4$$
$$+ 4A_1A_3 + 2A_2^2)x^3 + (5A_0A_5 + 5A_1A_4 + 5A_2A_3)x^4 + \cdots$$
$$- (A_0x + A_1x^2 + A_2x^3 + A_3x^4 + \cdots) - 1 \equiv 0. \qquad (6)$$

Since (6) is to be an identity, the coefficients of every power of x on the left-hand side must equal zero. Whence,

$$\begin{cases} A_0A_1 - 1 = 0, \\ 2A_0A_2 + A_1^2 - A_0 = 0, \\ 3A_0A_3 + 3A_1A_2 - A_1 = 0, \\ 4A_0A_4 + 4A_1A_3 + 2A_2^2 - A_2 = 0, \\ 5A_0A_5 + 5A_1A_5 + 5A_2A_3 - A_3 = 0, \text{ etc.;} \end{cases} \qquad (7)$$

and

$$\begin{cases} A_1 = \dfrac{1}{A_0}, \\[2mm] A_2 = \dfrac{A_0 - A_1^2}{2A_0} = \dfrac{A_0^3 - 1}{2A_0^3}, \\[2mm] A_3 = \dfrac{A_1 - 3A_1A_2}{3A_0} = \dfrac{3 - A_0^3}{6A_0^5}, \\[2mm] A_4 = \dfrac{A_2 - 2A_2^2 - 4A_1A_3}{4A_0} = \dfrac{7A_0^3 - 15}{24A_0^7}, \text{ etc.} \end{cases} \qquad (8)$$

The equalities (7), and hence (8), may be extended as far as desired, and it is thus possible to find as many coefficients of (2) as desired in

---

* A power series may be differentiated term by term within its interval of convergence, and the resulting series will converge to the derivative of the function represented by the original series.

† Two power series $B_0 + B_1x + B_2x^2 + B_3x^3 + \cdots$ and $C_0 + C_1x + C_2x^2 + C_3x^3 + \cdots$ may be multiplied within their common interval of convergence, and the product is the series $B_0C_0 + (B_0C_1 + B_1C_0)x + (B_0C_2 + B_1C_1 + B_2C_0)x^2 + (B_0C_3 + B_1C_2 + B_2C_1 + B_3C_0)x^3 + \cdots$.

terms of A_0, while A_0 itself remains arbitrary. Substituting from (8) into (2), we obtain as the general solution of (1) the infinite series

$$y = A_0 + \frac{1}{A_0} x + \frac{A_0^3 - 1}{2A_0^3} x^2 + \frac{3 - A_0^3}{6A_0^5} x_3 + \frac{7A_0^3 - 15}{24A_0^7} x^4 + \cdots \quad (9)$$

The student may satisfy himself that by extending the set of equalities (7), any coefficient A_m may be found in terms of A_0, A_1, $\cdots$, A_{m-1}, and hence in terms of A_0; therefore, precisely one arbitrary constant will enter in (9), as was, of course, to be expected from the order of (1).

Since every function of x cannot be developed as a power series in $x\left(e.\ g.,\ \log x, \frac{1}{x}\right)$, we need not expect to be able to approximate to the general solution of every equation

$$y' = F(x, y) \quad (10)$$

by means of a series (2).* The solution may in such a case be obtained as a power series in $x - a(a \neq 0)$. See Exercise 6 below.

Exercises

1. Integrate in series

$$y' = x^2 + x + \frac{y}{x}.$$

Show that the solution is a finite power series: $y = Ax + x^2 + \frac{x^3}{2}$ (A arbitrary). Integrate the equation directly, and compare results.

2. Integrate in series

$$y' = xe^x + \frac{y}{x}.$$

(*Hint:* Replace e^x by its development as a power series.) Show that the solution is

$$y = A_1 x + x^2 + \frac{x^3}{2!} + \frac{x^4}{3!} + \frac{x^5}{4!} + \cdots \qquad (A_1 \text{ arbitrary})$$

$$= (A_1 - 1)x + x\left(1 + x + \frac{x^2}{2!} + \frac{x^3}{3!} + \frac{x^4}{4!} + \cdots\right)$$

$$= Ax + xe^x \qquad (A \text{ arbitrary}).$$

Integrate the equation directly, and compare results.

---

* Such an impossibility will show up in the list of equalities corresponding to (7) of the text, since the coefficients of (2) will fail to be determined by them.

3. Integrate in series:

(a) $y' = \dfrac{x^2 + y}{x}.$ (b) $y' = x + 2xy.$

(c) $(x + 1)(y' - e^x) + y = 0.$

4. Integrate in series:

(a) $y' = \dfrac{y}{1 + xy}.$ (c) $y' = \dfrac{x + y}{1 + y}.$

(b) $y' = x - y^2.$ (d) $y' = \dfrac{x}{x^2 - y}.$

5. Integrate in series: $y' = \dfrac{y}{x - y}.$ In working this problem, the student will note that the first equality in the set analogous to (7) of the text is $A_0(1 + A_1) = 0$. By assuming A_0 arbitrary and $A_1 = -1$, we obtain the series representing the general solution. If we assume $A_0 = 0$, the succeeding equalities in the set will make all the coefficients equal to zero, and will thus lead to the finite series $y = 0$.

This is a singular solution. Obtain it also directly from the differential equation.

6. (a) Show that $y' = \dfrac{x + y}{x}$ cannot be solved for y as a power series in x.

(b) Solve $y' = \dfrac{x + y}{x}$ for y as a power series in $x - 1$. *Hint:* Set

$$x - 1 = z \left(\therefore \frac{dy}{dz} = \frac{dy}{dx} \right).$$

The equation becomes

$$\frac{dy}{dz} = \frac{z + 1 + y}{z + 1}.$$

Assume

$$y = A_0 + A_1 z + A_2 z^2 + A_3 z^3 + \cdots,$$

and obtain

$$y = A_0 + (1 + A_0)z + \frac{1}{2} z^2 - \frac{1}{6} z^3 + \frac{1}{12} z^4 - \frac{1}{20} z^5 + \cdots$$

$$= A_0 x + (x - 1) + \frac{1}{2} (x - 1)^2 - \frac{1}{6} (x - 1)^3 + \frac{1}{12} (x - 1)^4$$

$$- \frac{1}{20} (x - 1)^5 + \cdots.$$

This result may be put in a simpler form by noting that

$$y' = A_0 + 1 + (x - 1) - \frac{(x - 1)^2}{2} + \frac{(x - 1)^3}{3} - \frac{(x - 1)^4}{4} + \cdots$$
$$= A_0 + 1 + \log x$$

$\left(\text{verify that the coefficient of } (x-1)^n \text{ in the last expansion is } \dfrac{(-1)^{n-1}}{n}\right)$,
whence, $y = A_0 x + x \log x$ (the constant of the last integration being zero by $x = 1$, $y = A_0$) is the general solution. Integrate the given equation directly, and compare the results.

7. Integrate in series:

(a) $y' = \dfrac{x^2 + x + y}{x + 1}$.   (b) $y' = \dfrac{x^2 - x + y}{x}$.

45. Linear equations of the second order. Consider the linear equation

$$P_0 y'' + P_1 y' + P_2 y = 0. \tag{11}$$

Let the functions $P_i (i = 0, 1, 2)$ be such that the substitution $y = x^m$ transforms the left-hand member of (11) into an expression containing a finite number of distinct powers of x. (This will certainly be the case if P_i are polynomials in x.) We shall confine our discussion to the case when that number is two.

In other words, let

$$m(m - 1)P_0 x^{m-2} + mP_1 x^{m-1} + P_2 x^m$$

reduce to

$$f(m) \cdot x^r + g(m) \cdot x^{r+s} \qquad (s > 0), \tag{12}$$

where from the manner in which they arise it is evident that at least one of the two, $f(m)$ or $g(m)$, must be of the second degree in m. Let us assume that $f(m)$ is of that degree.

Thus, the substitution $y = x^m$ transforms the left-hand member of

$$y'' + xy' + \left(1 - \frac{2}{x^2}\right) y = 0$$

into

$$(m^2 - m - 2)x^{m-2} + (m + 1)x^m,$$

and $f(m) \equiv m^2 - m - 2$ is of degree two. Again, the substitution $y = x^{m+s}$ will transform the left-hand member of (11) into

$$(m + s)(m + s - 1)P_0 x^{m+s-2} + (m + s)P_1 x^{m+s-1} + P_2 x^{m+s},$$

which is evidently

$$f(m + s) \cdot x^{r+s} + g(m + s) \cdot x^{r+2s}. \tag{13}$$

It is now clear that the substitution

$$y = A_0 x^m + A_1 x^{m+s} + A_2 x^{m+2s} + \cdots + A_k x^{m+ks} + \cdots \tag{14}$$

will transform (11) into

$$
\begin{aligned}
&A_0 f(m) \cdot x^r + A_0 g(m) \cdot x^{r+s} \\
&+ A_1 f(m + s) \cdot x^{r+s} + A_1 g(m + s) \cdot x^{r+2s} \\
&+ A_2 f(m + 2s) \cdot x^{r+2s} + A_2 g(m + 2s) \cdot x^{r+3s} \\
&+ \cdots \cdots \cdots \cdots \cdots \cdots \\
&+ \cdots \cdots \cdots \cdots \cdots \cdots \\
&+ A_k f(m + ks) \cdot x^{r+ks} + A_k g(m + ks) \cdot x^{r+(k+1)s} \\
&+ A_{k+1} f(m + (k + 1)s) \cdot x^{r+(k+1)s} \\
&+ A_{k+1} g(m + (k + 1)s) \cdot x^{r+(k+2)s} + \cdots \equiv 0,
\end{aligned} \tag{15}
$$

and for this to be satisfied—that is, for (14) to be a solution of (11)— it is necessary and sufficient that the coefficients of the distinct powers of x vanish, $i.\ e.$, that

$$
\begin{cases}
f(m) = 0, \\
A_k g(m + ks) + A_{k+1} f(m + (k + 1)s) = 0
\end{cases} \tag{16}
$$
$$(k = 0, 1, 2, 3, \cdots),$$

be satisfied. (We shall call the first of (16) the *indicial equation* of (11).) By hypothesis, $f(m)$ is of degree two; hence it has roots m_1 and m_2, and the succeeding equations of (16) are

$$A_k g(m_i + ks) + A_{k+1} f(m_i + (k + 1)s) = 0 \qquad (i = 1, 2),$$

whence,

$$
A_{k+1} = \frac{-A_k \cdot g(m_i + ks)}{f(m_i + (k + 1)s)} \tag{17}
$$
$$
= \frac{A_{k-1} \cdot g(m_i + (k - 1)s)}{f(m_i + ks)} \cdot \frac{g(m_i + ks)}{f(m_i + (k + 1)s)}
$$
$$
= \frac{-A_{k-2} \cdot g(m_i + (k - 2)s)}{f(m_i + (k - 1)s)} \cdot \frac{g(m_i + (k - 1)s)}{f(m_i + ks)} \cdot \frac{g(m_i + ks)}{f(m_i + (k + 1)s)}
$$
$$
= \cdots = (-1)^{k+1} A_0 \frac{g(m_i) \cdot g(m_i + s) \cdots g(m_i + ks)}{f(m_i + s) \cdot f(m_i + 2s) \cdots f(m_i + (k + 1)s)}.
$$

Thus, (17) takes on the two distinct forms (if m_1 and m_2 are distinct),

$$y = A_0(x^{m_1} + a_1 x^{m_1+s} + a_2 x^{m_1+2s} + a_3 x^{m_1+3s} + \cdots)$$

and

$$y = B_0(x^{m_2} + b_1 x^{m_2+s} + b_2 x^{m_2+2s} + b_3 x^{m_2+3s} + \cdots)$$

according as m_1 or m_2 is used in (17). (The change from A_0 to B_0 in the second series is legitimate, since A_0 is arbitrary.) Hence the general solution of (11) is, by the linearity of (11),

$$y = A_0(x^{m_1} + a_1 x^{m_1+s} + a_2 x^{m_1+2s} + \cdots)$$
$$+ B_0(x^{m_2} + b_1 x^{m_2+s} + b_2 x^{m_2+2s} + \cdots). \quad (18)$$

To illustrate, we return to

$$y'' + xy' + \left(1 - \frac{2}{x^2}\right) y = 0,$$

the equation referred to above.

The substitution $y = x^m$, we found, changed its left-hand member to

$$(m^2 - m - 2)x^{m-2} + (m + 1)x^m.$$

Hence,

$$s = 2 \qquad\qquad \text{[see (12)],}$$

and so we assume as its solution

$$y = A_0 x^m + A_1 x^{m+2} + A_2 x^{m+4} + A_3 x^{m+6} + \cdots + A_k x^{m+2k}$$
$$+ A_{k+1} x^{m+2k+2} + \cdots.$$

This substituted, our equation becomes

$$A_0(m^2 - m - 2)x^{m-2} + [A_0(m + 1) + A_1(m^2 + 3m)]x^m$$
$$+ [A_1(m + 3) + A_2(m^2 + 7m + 10)]x^{m+2} + \cdots$$
$$+ [A_k(m + 2k + 1) + A_{k+1}(m + 2k)(m + 2k + 3)]x^{m+2k} + \cdots \equiv 0$$

(the student may check this against (15) with $f(m) \equiv m^2 - m - 2$, $g(m) \equiv m + 1$, $r = m - 2$, $s = 2$), whence

$$m^2 - m - 2 = 0 \quad \text{(the indicial equation)}$$

and

$$m = 2 \text{ or } m = -1.$$

If $m = 2$, the succeeding equations are

$$\begin{cases} 3A_0 + 2 \cdot 5A_1 = 0, \\ 5A_1 + 4 \cdot 7A_2 = 0, \\ \cdots\cdots\cdots\cdots\cdots\cdots\cdots\cdots \\ (3 + 2k)A_k + (2 + 2k)(5 + 2k)A_{k+1} = 0, \\ \cdots\cdots\cdots\cdots\cdots\cdots\cdots\cdots \end{cases}$$

whence

$$\begin{cases} A_1 = \dfrac{-3A_0}{2 \cdot 5}, \\[2mm] A_2 = \dfrac{-5A_1}{4 \cdot 7} = \dfrac{3 \cdot 5 \cdot A_0}{(2 \cdot 4)(5 \cdot 7)}, \\[2mm] \cdots \cdots \cdots \cdots \cdots \\[1mm] A_{k+1} = -\dfrac{(3 + 2k)A_k}{(2 + 2k)(5 + 2k)}, \\[2mm] \cdots \cdots \cdots \cdots \cdots \end{cases}$$

The last equation enables us to determine any coefficient in the series from its predecessor; therefore,

$$A_3 = \frac{-7A_2}{6 \cdot 9} = \frac{-3 \cdot 5 \cdot 7 A_0}{(2 \cdot 4 \cdot 6)(5 \cdot 7 \cdot 9)}, \text{ etc.}$$

and one solution is

$$y = A_0 \left[x^2 - \frac{3}{2 \cdot 5} x^4 + \frac{3 \cdot 5}{(2 \cdot 4)(5 \cdot 7)} x^6 - \frac{3 \cdot 5 \cdot 7}{(2 \cdot 4 \cdot 6)(5 \cdot 7 \cdot 9)} x^8 \right.$$
$$+ \cdots + (-1)^{n-1} \frac{3 \cdot 5 \cdot 7 \cdots (2n - 1)x^{2n}}{(2 \cdot 4 \cdot 6 \cdots 2n - 2)(5 \cdot 7 \cdot 9 \cdots 2n + 1)}$$
$$\left. + \cdots \right] \equiv A_0 y_1.$$

If $m = -1$, we have

$$A_0 \cdot 0 + A_1(-2) = 0,$$
$$2A_1 + A_2(4) = 0,$$
$$\cdots \cdots \cdots \cdots \cdots \cdots$$
$$2kA_k + (2k - 1)(2k + 2)A_{k+1} = 0,$$
$$\cdots \cdots \cdots \cdots \cdots \cdots$$

which evidently makes all the coefficients from A_1 on equal to zero, and thus yields as a solution

$$y = A_0 x^{-1} \equiv A_0 y_2.$$

The general solution is now obtained as

$$y = Ay_1 + By_2.$$

Note: In regard to the convergence of the two series in the solution (18) of (11), the following may be remarked. The test ratio in each series, *i. e.*, the ratio of a term to its predecessor, is, by (17),

$$r = - \frac{g(m + ks)x^s}{f(m + ks + s)},$$

where the coefficient of x^s is a function of k alone (different for each series if m_1, m_2 are distinct).   Hence:

(a) If $f(m)$ is of degree two (as was assumed in our discussion) and $g(m)$ of less degree,

$$r = \frac{(L + Mk)x^s}{R + Sk + Tk^2}   \quad (L, M, R, S, T \text{ fixed for each series})$$

and this will become and remain numerically less than 1 for any x, however large, if k is taken large enough.   Each series in the solution will then converge for every value of x.

(b) If $g(m)$ is also of degree two,

$$r = \frac{N + Pk + Qk^2}{U + Vk + Wk^2} x^s   \quad (N, P, Q, U, V, W \text{ fixed for each series})$$

and this tends, as k is increased indefinitely, to

$$\frac{Q}{W} x^s$$

as a limit; hence each series is convergent for some definite range of values of x, and divergent for all other values.

(c) If $f(m)$ is of degree one (in which case the indicial equation has one root only, and only one solution in series is obtained), then $g(m)$ is of degree two, and

$$r = \frac{C + Dk + Ek^2}{F + Gk} x^s   \quad (C, D, E, F, G \text{ fixed})$$

and hence, for a large enough k the numerical value of r will exceed 1, however small x is taken; wherefore the one solution obtained diverges for all values of x other than zero.

The difficulty encountered in this case is obviated by the following modification of the process outlined above.   Assume as a solution

$$y = A_0x^m + A_1x^{m-s} + A_2x^{m-2s} + \cdots + A_kx^{m-ks} + \cdots$$
$$[s \text{ as in } (12)]. \quad (19)$$

This substituted in (11), the latter becomes

$$\begin{aligned}
&A_0f(m)x^r + A_0g(m)x^{r+s} \\
&+ A_1f(m - s)x^{r-s} + A_1g(m - s)x^r \\
&+ A_2f(m - 2s)x^{r-2s} + A_2g(m - 2s)x^{r-s} \\
&+ \ldots \ldots \ldots \ldots \ldots \ldots \ldots \ldots \quad (20) \\
&+ A_kf(m - ks)x^{r-ks} + A_kg(m - ks)x^{r-ks+s} \\
&+ A_{k+1}f(m - ks - s)x^{r-ks-s} + A_{k+1}g(m - ks - s)x^{r-ks} \\
&+ \cdots \equiv 0,
\end{aligned}$$

and the set of equalities for determining the coefficients becomes

$$\begin{cases} g(m) = 0 & \text{(this is now the indicial equation),} \\ A_k f(m - ks) + A_{k+1}g(m - ks - s) = 0 \ (k = 0, 1, 2, \cdots \ ), \end{cases} \quad (21)$$

and corresponding to the two roots, m_1, m_2 (assumed distinct), of the indicial equation there arise two solutions in series, analogous to (18). Let the student discuss the convergence of the two series in this case.

To illustrate, consider the equation

$$x^4 y'' + xy' - 2y = 0.$$

Now, $y = x^m$ converts its left-hand member into

$$(m - 2)x^m + (m^2 - m)x^{m+2},$$

and hence, $f(m)$ is of degree one and $g(m)$ of degree two (and $s = 2$).

We assume as a solution

$$y = A_0 x^m + A_1 x^{m-2} + A_2 x^{m-4} + \cdots + A_k x^{m-2k} + A_{k+1}x^{m-2k-2} + \cdots,$$

and this transforms our equation into

$$A_0(m^2 - m)x^{m+2} + [A_0(m - 2) + A_1(m - 2)(m - 3)]x^m + \cdots \\ + [A_k(m - 2k - 2) + A_{k+1}(m - 2k - 2)(m - 2k - 3)]x^{m-2k} \\ + \cdots \equiv 0,$$

whence,

$$m^2 - m = 0 \quad \text{(the indicial equation),}$$

and

$$m = 0, \text{ or } 1.$$

For $m = 0$,

$$A_k(-2k - 2) + A_{k+1}(-2k - 2)(-2k - 3) = 0 \\ (k = 0, 1, 2, \cdots \ ),$$

$$\therefore \qquad A_{k+1} = \frac{A_k}{2k + 3},$$

whence,

$$A_1 = \frac{A_0}{3},$$

$$A_2 = \frac{A_1}{5} = \frac{A_0}{3 \cdot 5},$$

$$A_3 = \frac{A_2}{7} = \frac{A_0}{3 \cdot 5 \cdot 7},$$

$$\cdots \cdots \cdots,$$

and the corresponding solution is

$$y = A_0 \left(1 + \frac{1}{3x^2} + \frac{1}{3 \cdot 5 \cdot x^4} - \frac{1}{3 \cdot 5 \cdot 7 \cdot x^6} + \cdots \right.$$
$$\left. + \frac{1}{3 \cdot 5 \cdot 7 \cdots (2n+1)x^{2n}} + \cdots \right)$$
$$\equiv A_0 y_1.$$

For $m = 1$,

$$A_k(-2k-1) + A_{k+1}(-2k-1)(-2k-2) = 0$$
$$(k = 0, 1, 2, \cdots),$$

$$\therefore \qquad A_{k+1} = \frac{A_k}{2k+2},$$

whence,

$$A_1 = \frac{A_0}{2},$$
$$A_2 = \frac{A_1}{4} = \frac{A_0}{2 \cdot 4},$$
$$A_3 = \frac{A_2}{6} = \frac{A_0}{2 \cdot 4 \cdot 6},$$
$$\cdots \cdots \cdots,$$

and the corresponding solution is

$$y = A_0 \left(x + \frac{1}{2x} + \frac{1}{2 \cdot 4x^3} + \frac{1}{2 \cdot 4 \cdot 6x^5} + \cdots \right.$$
$$\left. + \frac{1}{2 \cdot 4 \cdot 6 \cdots (2n)x^{2n-1}} + \cdots \right)$$
$$\equiv A_0 y_2.$$

The student may verify that y_1 and y_2 are linearly independent (see page 73) and that, therefore, the complete solution of our *linear* equation is

$$y = Ay_1 + By_2.$$

Exercises

1. Integrate in series:

    (a) $y'' - xy' + 2y = 0.$

    (b) $y'' + \left(\frac{1}{x} + x^2 \right) y' - \frac{y}{x^2} = 0.$

    (c) $y'' + \left(x + \frac{2}{x} \right) y' + \left(1 - \frac{2}{x^2} \right) y = 0.$

(handwritten top) to $x^2y'' + x\left(2 + \frac{1}{x}\right)y' - \frac{y}{x^2} = 0$

(handwritten) Compared

(d) $x^3y'' + (2x^2 + 1)y' - \dfrac{y}{x} = 0.$

(handwritten left margin: Done in class →) (e) $x^4y'' + (x - 2x^3)y' + 2y = 0.$ *(handwritten: also solve by Factoring $\alpha = b_1x^n$ $\beta = b_2x^n$)*

(f) $x^2y'' + 3xy' - 3y = 0.$

2. Adapt the theory of the text to a linear equation of the third order, and solve in series:

(a) $xy''' + 3y'' + xy = 0.$

(handwritten: C.K.L →) (b) $x^6y''' + x^2y'' - 2y = 0.$

(c) $x^3y''' + 8x^2y'' - 16y = 0.$

3. Integrate in series:

$$(1 + x^2)y'' + 2xy' = 0.$$

Note that there are two possible solutions, because $f(m)$ and $g(m)$ are each of the second degree. Note also the relation between the two solutions.

4. Integrate in series:

(a) $(1 + x^3)y'' + \left(x^2 - \dfrac{1}{x}\right)y' - xy = 0.$

(b) $(1 + x^2)y'' + \left(2x - \dfrac{2}{x}\right)y' - 2y = 0.$

46. Roots of indicial equation equal. If the two roots of the indicial equation are equal, they evidently lead to only one solution in series, and the need arises for a method to obtain a second solution in order that the differential equation may be integrated completely.

Consider now the fact that the substitution of (14) into (11) transforms the latter into (15), and that, furthermore, all the terms in (15), from the second on, cancel each other in pairs if the coefficients are computed by (17); in other words,

$$P_0y_1'' + P_1y_1' + P_2y_1 \equiv f(m)x^r$$

if y_1 designates the series (14), and the coefficients satisfy (17). The right-hand (and hence the left-hand) member of the last equation vanishes if we set m equal to a, the value of the double root which the indicial equation, $f(m) = 0$, possesses by hypothesis. But the derivative, with respect to m, of the right-hand member will also vanish for $m = a$, by the property of the double root of an equation, and so will, consequently, the derivative, with respect to m, of the left-hand member; in other words,

$$\frac{\partial}{\partial m} (P_0 y_1'' + P_1 y_1' + P_2 y_1) = 0 \qquad \text{(for } m = a),$$

whence,

$$P_0 \frac{\partial}{\partial m} (y_1'') + P_1 \frac{\partial}{\partial m} (y_1') + P_2 \frac{\partial}{\partial m} (y_1) = 0$$

$$\text{(for } m = a; \text{ since } P_i \text{ are independent of } m),$$

and

$$P_0 \left(\frac{\partial}{\partial m} y_1 \right)'' + P_1 \left(\frac{\partial}{\partial m} y_1 \right)' + P_2 \left(\frac{\partial}{\partial m} y_1 \right) = 0 \quad \text{(for } m = a),$$

from which it is seen that $\left(\dfrac{\partial}{\partial m} \cdot y_1 \right)$ is a solution of (11) if m is put equal to a. (Let the student satisfy himself that $\dfrac{\partial}{\partial m} (y_1') = \left(\dfrac{\partial}{\partial m} y_1 \right)'$ and $\dfrac{\partial}{\partial m} (y_1'') = \left(\dfrac{\partial}{\partial m} y_1 \right)''$, by proving it for a typical term of y_1, say cx^{m+h}.)

As an illustration, consider the equation,

$$x^2 y'' - xy' + (x^2 + 1)y = 0.$$

The substitution $y = x^m$ transforms the left-hand member into

$$(m^2 - 2m + 1)x^m + x^{m+2},$$

the indicial equation is $m^2 - 2m + 1 = 0$, with the double root $m = 1$, and the solution obtained is

$$y = A \left(x - \frac{x^3}{2^2} + \frac{x^5}{(2 \cdot 4)^2} - \frac{x^7}{(2 \cdot 4 \cdot 6)^2} + \cdots \right.$$
$$\left. + \frac{(-1)^n x^{2n+1}}{(2 \cdot 4 \cdot 6 \cdots (2n))^2} + \cdots \right) \equiv A y_1.$$

Write now $A y_1$ with the coefficients in terms of m, i. e., with

$$A_{k+1} = - A_k \cdot \frac{1}{(m + 2k + 1)^2},$$

and hence,

$$A_1 = - A_0 \frac{1}{(m + 1)^2},$$

$$A_2 = - A_1 \frac{1}{(m + 3)^2} = \frac{A_0}{[(m + 1)(m + 3)]^2},$$

$$A_3 = - A_2 \frac{1}{(m + 5)^2} = \frac{- A_0}{[(m + 1)(m + 3)(m + 5)]^2}, \text{ etc.,}$$

so that

$$Ay_1 \equiv Ax^m \left(1 - \frac{x^2}{(m+1)^2} + \frac{x^4}{[(m+1)(m+3)]^2} \right.$$
$$\left. - \frac{x^6}{[(m+1)(m+3)(m+5)]^2} + \cdots \right),$$

and

$$\frac{\partial}{\partial m} y_1 \equiv x^m \log x \left(1 - \frac{x^2}{(m+1)^2} + \frac{x^4}{[(m+1)(m+3)]^2} \right.$$
$$\left. - \frac{x^6}{[(m+1)(m+3)(m+5)]^2} + \cdots \right)$$
$$+ x^m \left(\frac{2x^2}{(m+1)^3} - \frac{2x^4(2m+4)}{[(m+1)(m+3)]^3} \right.$$
$$\left. + \frac{2x^6(3m^2+18m+23)}{[(m+1)(m+3)(m+5)]^3} + \cdots \right)$$
$$\equiv y_1 \log x + x^m \left[2x^2 \cdot \frac{1}{(m+1)^3} - 2x^4 \left(\frac{1}{(m+1)^2(m+3)^3} \right. \right.$$
$$\left. + \frac{1}{(m+1)^3(m+3)^2} \right) + 2x^6 \left(\frac{1}{(m+1)^3(m+3)^2(m+5)^2} \right.$$
$$\left. \left. + \frac{1}{(m+1)^2(m+3)^3(m+5)^2} + \frac{1}{(m+1)^2(m+3)^2(m+5)^3} \right) \right.$$
$$\left. + \cdots \right].$$

On putting $m = 1$, we have as a second solution

$$y = y_1 \log x + x \left[2x^2 \cdot \frac{1}{2^3} - 2x^4 \left(\frac{1}{2^2 \cdot 4^3} + \frac{1}{2^3 \cdot 4^2} \right) \right.$$
$$\left. + 2x^6 \left(\frac{1}{2^2 \cdot 4^2 \cdot 6^3} + \frac{1}{2^2 \cdot 4^3 \cdot 6^2} + \frac{1}{2^3 \cdot 4^2 \cdot 6^2} \right) - \cdots \right].$$

This, multiplied by an arbitrary constant B, is still a solution, and the general solution is

$$y = (A + B \log x) \left(x - \frac{x^3}{2^2} + \frac{x^5}{(2 \cdot 4)^2} + \cdots \right.$$
$$\left. + \frac{(-1)^n x^{2n+1}}{(2 \cdot 4 \cdot 6 \cdots 2n)^2} + \cdots \right)$$
$$+ 2Bx \left[x^2 \cdot \frac{1}{2^3} - x^4 \left(\frac{1}{2^3 \cdot 4^2} + \frac{1}{2^2 \cdot 4^3} \right) \right.$$
$$\left. + x^6 \left(\frac{1}{2^3 \cdot 4^2 \cdot 6^2} + \frac{1}{2^2 \cdot 4^3 \cdot 6^2} + \frac{1}{2^2 \cdot 4^2 \cdot 6^3} \right) \right.$$

$$- \cdots + (-1)^{n-1} x^{2n} \left(\frac{1}{2^3 \cdot 4^2 \cdot 6^2 \cdots (2n)^2} + \frac{1}{2^2 \cdot 4^3 \cdot 6^2 \cdots (2n)^2} \right.$$
$$\left. + \cdots + \frac{1}{2^2 \cdot 4^2 \cdot 6^2 \cdots (2n)^3} \right) + \cdots \Bigg].$$

Exercises

1. Integrate in series:

    (a) $x^2 y'' + 5xy' + (4 - 2x^3)y = 0$. ← *done in class*

    (b) $xy'' + y' - y = 0$. ← *C.K.L*

    (c) $x^4 y'' + x^3 y' + y = 0$.

    (d) $(x^2 + x)y'' + (1 - x)y' + y = 0$.

2. Adapt the theory of the text to the case where the indicial equation $g(m) = 0$ has equal roots, and solve:

    (a) $x^3 y'' + (x^2 + x)y' - 2y = 0$.

    (b) $x^3 y'' + (1 - x^2)y' + xy = 0$.

47. A coefficient in the series becoming infinite. Let the roots of the indicial equation, $f(m) = 0$,[*] be m_1 and m_2, where $m_2 = m_1 + is$ (i a positive integer). From Formula (17), *viz.*,

$$A_{k+1} = -A_k \frac{g(m + ks)}{f(m + (k+1)s)} \quad (k = 0, 1, 2, \cdots),$$

it is seen that in setting up the coefficients in the series corresponding to $m = m_1$, the denominator will become $f(m_2)$, *i. e.*, zero, for $k = i - 1$. The corresponding coefficient A_i will then become infinite (unless there be also a vanishing factor in the numerator). To treat this case, note that, by hypothesis,

$$f(m) \equiv (m - m_1)(m - m_2),[\dagger]$$

hence,

$$f(m + (k+1)s) \equiv f(m + is) \equiv (m + is - m_1)(m + is - m_2)$$
$$\equiv (m + is - m_1)(m - m_1),$$

and that it is the second factor in the last product that vanishes when m is set equal to m_1. This suggests setting $A_0 = a(m - m_1)$

---

[*] The case where the indicial equation is $g(m) = 0$ is amenable to the same reasoning, and gives the same conclusions.

[†] More exactly, $f(m) = a(m - m_1)(m - m_2)$, where a is a constant not zero, but the omission of a has no effect on the ensuing discussion.

(a arbitrary, since A_0 is arbitrary), and when this is done the series

$$A_0x^m + A_1x^{m+s} + A_2x^{m+2s} + \cdots + A_ix^{m+is} + \cdots$$

becomes

$$ax^m\left[(m - m_1) + (m - m_1)\frac{A_1}{A_0}x^s + (m - m_1)\frac{A_2}{A_0}x^{2s} + \cdots \right.$$
$$\left. + \frac{(m - m_1)A_i}{A_0}x^{is} + \cdots \right].$$

Since A_i is the first coefficient which becomes infinite for $m = m_1$, the first i terms in the series bracketed become zero, when we set $m = m_1$, while that factor in the denominator of A_i which vanishes for $m = m_1$ has been removed by the factor introduced. A solution in series is then obtained,

$$y = ay_1 \equiv ax^m[c_ix^{is} + c_{i+1}x^{(i+1)s} + \cdots] \text{ (the c's fixed constants).}$$

To illustrate, consider the equation

$$xy'' - y' + y = 0,$$

for which $f(m) \equiv m^2 - 2m$, $g(m) \equiv 1$, $s = 1$, and the roots of the indicial equation are $m_1 = 0$ and $m_2 = 2$. By (17),

$$A_{k+1} = \frac{-A_k}{(m + k + 1)(m + k - 1)} \qquad (k = 0, 1, 2, \cdots),$$

whence,

$$A_1 = \frac{-A_0}{(m + 1)(m - 1)},$$
$$A_2 = \frac{-A_1}{(m + 2)m} = \frac{A_0}{(m + 1)(m - 1)(m + 2)(m)},$$
$$A_3 = -\frac{A_2}{(m + 3)(m + 1)}$$
$$= \frac{-A_0}{(m + 1)(m - 1)(m + 2)(m)(m + 3)(m + 1)}, \text{ etc.,}$$

and for $m = 0$, A_2 is infinite. Replacing A_0 by $a(m - m_1)$, i. e., by am, we write the solution as

$$y = ax^m\left[m + m\left(\frac{-1}{(m + 1)(m - 1)}\right)x + \frac{1}{(m + 1)(m - 1)(m + 2)}x^2 \right.$$
$$\left. - \frac{1}{(m + 1)(m - 1)(m + 2)(m + 3)(m + 1)}x^3 + \cdots \right],$$

and for $m = 0$, we now have

$$y = a\left[-\frac{x^2}{2} + \frac{x^3}{2\cdot 3} - \frac{x^4}{2\cdot 3\cdot 4\cdot 2} + \cdots\right]$$

$$\equiv a\left[-\frac{1}{1\cdot 2}x^2 + \frac{1}{1^2\cdot 2\cdot 3}x^3 - \frac{1}{1^2\cdot 2^2\cdot 3\cdot 4}x^4\right.$$

$$\left. + \frac{1}{1^2\cdot 2^2\cdot 3^2\cdot 4\cdot 5}x^5 - \cdots\right] \equiv ay_1,$$

a solution, in series, of the given equation. Note that by the substitution here made for A_0, the first equation displayed in Section 46 now becomes

$$P_0y_1'' + P_1y_1' + P_2y_1 \equiv a(m - m_1)f(m)x^r$$
$$\equiv a(m - m_1)^2(m - m_2)x^r.$$

It appears that m_1 is a double root of the right-hand member, and by the same argument as employed in Section 46 it is concluded that $\left(\dfrac{\partial y_1}{\partial m}\right)_{m=m_1}$ is also a solution of the differential equation. For the illustration at hand,

$$\frac{\partial y_1}{\partial m} \equiv x^m \log x\left[m - \frac{m}{(m+1)(m-1)}x + \frac{1}{(m+1)(m-1)(m+2)}x^2\right.$$

$$\left. - \frac{1}{(m+1)(m-1)(m+2)(m+3)(m+1)}x^3 + \cdots\right]$$

$$+ x^m\left[1 + \frac{m^2+1}{(m+1)^2(m-1)^2}x - \frac{1}{(m+1)(m-1)(m+2)}\left\{\frac{1}{m+1}\right.\right.$$

$$\left. + \frac{1}{m-1} + \frac{1}{m+2}\right\}x^2 + \frac{1}{(m+1)(m-1)(m+2)(m+3)(m+1)}$$

$$\left.\left\{\frac{1}{m+1} + \frac{1}{m-1} + \frac{1}{m+2} + \frac{1}{m+3} + \frac{1}{m+1}\right\}x^3 + \cdots\right].$$

For $m = m_1 = 0$, this becomes

$$\log x\left[-\frac{1}{1\cdot 2}x^2 + \frac{1}{1^2\cdot 2\cdot 3}x^3 - \frac{1}{1^2\cdot 2^2\cdot 3\cdot 4}x^4 + \cdots\right]$$

$$+ \left[1 + x + \frac{1}{1\cdot 2}\left(\frac{1}{1} + \frac{1}{2} - \frac{1}{1}\right)x^2 - \frac{1}{1^2\cdot 2\cdot 3}\left(\frac{2}{1} + \frac{1}{2} + \frac{1}{3} - \frac{1}{1}\right)x^3\right.$$

$$\left. + \frac{1}{1^2\cdot 2^2\cdot 3\cdot 4}\left(\frac{2}{1} + \frac{2}{2} + \frac{1}{3} + \frac{1}{4} - \frac{1}{1}\right)x^4 - \cdots\right],$$

and the complete solution is

$$y = (a + b \log x)y_1 + by_2$$

(where y_2 is the series in the last bracket) involving, as it does, two arbitrary constants. It remains to see what the solution corresponding to $m = m_2 = 2$ may be. The series of coefficients is given for this solution by

$$A_{k+1} = \frac{-A_k}{(3 + k)(1 + k)} \quad (k = 0, 1, 2, \cdots),$$

whence,

$$A_1 = -\frac{A_0}{3 \cdot 1},$$

$$A_2 = -\frac{A_1}{4 \cdot 2} = \frac{A_0}{(3 \cdot 1)(4 \cdot 2)},$$

$$A_3 = -\frac{A_2}{5 \cdot 3} = \frac{-A_0}{(3 \cdot 1)(4 \cdot 2)(5 \cdot 3)}, \text{ etc.,}$$

and the solution is

$$y = A_0\left[x^2 - \frac{1}{3 \cdot 1}x^3 + \frac{1}{3 \cdot 1 \cdot 4 \cdot 2}x^4 - \frac{1}{3 \cdot 1 \cdot 4 \cdot 2 \cdot 5 \cdot 3}x^5 + \cdots \right]$$

$$\equiv -2A_0\left[-\frac{1}{1 \cdot 2}x^2 + \frac{1}{1^2 \cdot 2 \cdot 3}x^3 - \frac{1}{1^2 \cdot 2^2 \cdot 3 \cdot 4}x^4 \right.$$

$$\left. + \frac{1}{1^2 \cdot 2^2 \cdot 3^2 \cdot 4 \cdot 5}x^5 - \cdots \right]$$

$$\equiv -2A_0y_1.$$

The solution due to $m = 2$ is, therefore, a repetition of one of the solutions (18) due to $m = 0$. This might have been expected, for

$$A_{k+1} = \frac{-A_k}{(m_1 + k + 1)(m_1 + k - 1)},$$

the law governing the coefficients in the series corresponding to $m = m_1$, is identical with

$$A_{k+3} = \frac{-A_{k+2}}{(m_1 + k + 3)(m_1 + k + 1)} = \frac{-A_{k+2}}{(m_2 + k + 1)(m_2 + k - 1)}$$

(since $m_1 + 2 = m_2$), and this last is the law governing the coefficients in the series arising from $m = m_2$. The apparent discrepancy, by two, in the values of k between the two laws is caused by the vanishing of the first two coefficients in the series due to $m = m_1 = 0$. More generally, in any case that comes under the treatment of this section, we have

$$A_{k+1} = -A_k \frac{g(m_1 + ks)}{f(m_1 + (k + 1)s)},$$

and this leads to

$$A_{k+i+1} = -A_{k+i} \frac{g(m_1 + (k + i)s)}{f(m_1 + (k + i + 1)s)}$$

$$= -A_{k+i} \frac{g(m_2 + ks)}{f(m_2 + (k + 1)s)} \quad \text{(by } m_1 + is = m_2\text{).}$$

Thus is exhibited the identity between the series due to $m = m_2$ and that due to $m = m_1$, the discrepancy, by i, in the values of k in the two cases, being caused by the vanishing of the first i coefficients in the second series.

Exercises

1. Solve in series:

    (a) $x^2y'' + xy' + (x^2 - 1)y = 0.$

    (b) $xy'' - 2y' + y = 0.$

    (c) $x^2y'' + xy' + (x - 1)y = 0.$

    (d) $x^2y'' + 2xy' + (x - 2)y = 0.$

2. Extend the theory of this section to the case in which the indicial equation is $g(m) = 0$, and a coefficient of the series becomes infinite.

3. Solve in series: $x^4y'' + (x^3 + x)y' - x^2y = 0.$

48. The particular integral. The student will recall that for the non-homogeneous linear equation

$$P_0y'' + P_1y' + P_2y = Q, \tag{21}$$

the complete solution consists of the sum of the complementary function, *i. e.*, the complete solution of the corresponding homogeneous equation, and of any particular integral of (21). We shall assume that Q is a sum of powers of x, positive or negative, and seek to find a particular integral corresponding to a term ax^l of Q. A particular integral of (21) will then be the sum of the particular integrals corresponding to the several terms of Q. The substitution (14) of Section 45, *viz.*,

$$y = A_0x^m + A_1x^{m+s} + A_2x^{m+2s} + \cdots$$

reduces (21) to

$$A_0f(m)x^r + \sum_{k=0}^{\infty} [A_k g(m + ks) + A_{k+1}f(m + (k + 1)s)]x^{r+(k+1)s} \equiv Q$$

[see (15)], where $f(m)$, $g(m)$, r, and s have the same significance as in Section 45. The last equality is satisfied identically if, and only if,

$$\begin{cases} A_0 f(m)x^r \equiv ax^l & \text{(replacing } Q \text{ by } ax^l), \\ A_{k+1} = -A_k \dfrac{g(m + ks)}{f(m + (k + 1)s)} & (k = 0, 1, 2, \cdots). \end{cases} \tag{22}$$

The first of (22) determines m as m_0 by

$$r = l \quad \text{(since } r \text{ is a linear function of } m), \tag{23}$$

and A_0 by

$$A_0 = \frac{a}{f(m_0)}, \tag{24}$$

while the subsequent equations (22), with m put equal to m_0, determine the successive coefficients in the series. Thus, let the equation to be solved be given as

$$y'' + xy' + \left(1 - \frac{2}{x^2}\right) y = 2x - \frac{1}{x}.$$

The complementary function has been found in the illustration of Section 45 to be

$$y = A\left[x^2 - \frac{3}{2 \cdot 5} x^4 + \frac{3 \cdot 5}{(2 \cdot 4)(5 \cdot 7)} x^6 - \frac{3 \cdot 5 \cdot 7}{(2 \cdot 4 \cdot 6)(5 \cdot 7 \cdot 9)} x^8 \right.$$
$$\left. + \cdots \right] + \frac{B}{x} \equiv Ay_1 + By_2.$$

For the particular integral, note that

$$\begin{aligned} r &= m - 2, \\ f(m) &\equiv (m + 1)(m - 2), \qquad f(m+(k+1)s) = (m+2k+3)(m+2\,\,\\ g(m) &\equiv m + 1, \qquad\qquad g(m+ks) = (m+2k+1)\\ s &= 2. \end{aligned}$$

Hence, corresponding to the term $2x$ on the right-hand side of the equation,

$$m_0 - 2 = 1, \quad \therefore \ m_0 = 3,$$
$$A_0 = \frac{2}{f(3)} = \frac{2}{4} = \frac{1}{2},$$
$$A_{k+1} = -A_k \frac{m + 2k + 1}{(m + 2k)(m + 2k + 3)} = -A_k \frac{4 + 2k}{(3 + 2k)(6 + 2k)}$$
$$= -A_k \frac{2 + k}{(3 + k)(3 + 2k)},$$

whence,

$$A_1 = -A_0 \frac{2}{3 \cdot 3},$$

$$A_2 = -A_1 \frac{3}{4 \cdot 5},$$

$$A_3 = -A_2 \frac{4}{5 \cdot 7}, \text{ etc.,}$$

and the corresponding particular integral is

$$y = \frac{1}{2} x^3 \left[1 - \frac{2}{3 \cdot 3} x^2 + \frac{2 \cdot 3}{(3 \cdot 4)(3 \cdot 5)} x^4 \right. \\ \left. - \frac{2 \cdot 3 \cdot 4}{(3 \cdot 4 \cdot 5)(3 \cdot 5 \cdot 7)} x^6 + \cdots \right] \equiv u.$$

For the term $-\dfrac{1}{x}$ of the right-hand member,

$$m_0 - 2 = -1, \therefore m_0 = 1,$$

$$A_0 = -\frac{1}{f(1)} = \frac{1}{2},$$

$$A_{k+1} = -A_k \frac{2k + 2}{(2k + 1)(2k + 4)} = -A_k \frac{k + 1}{(k + 2)(2k + 1)},$$

whence,

$$A_1 = -A_0 \cdot \frac{1}{2 \cdot 1},$$

$$A_2 = -A_1 \cdot \frac{2}{3 \cdot 3},$$

$$A_3 = -A_2 \cdot \frac{3}{4 \cdot 5}, \text{ etc.,}$$

and the corresponding particular integral is

$$y = \frac{1}{2} x \left[1 - \frac{1}{2 \cdot 1} x^2 + \frac{1 \cdot 2}{(2 \cdot 3)(1 \cdot 3)} x^4 \right. \\ \left. - \frac{1 \cdot 2 \cdot 3}{(2 \cdot 3 \cdot 4)(1 \cdot 3 \cdot 5)} x^6 + \cdots \right] \equiv v.$$

The particular integral in the form of a power series of the given equation is then equal to $u + v$. Its complete solution is, therefore,

$$y = Ay_1 + By_2 + u + v.$$

Note that by (24) this method of finding a particular integral fails if $f(m_0) = 0$.

Exercises

1. Show that if the indicial equation is $g(m) = 0$, (23) and (24) of the text are replaced by

$$r + s = l,$$

$$A_0 = \frac{a}{g(m_0)},$$

where m_0 is the value of m obtained from the preceding equation.

2. Find the particular integral for the following equations:

C·K·L $\longrightarrow$ (a) $xy'' + (x^2 + 2)y' - \dfrac{2y}{x} = 2x^3$.

C·K·L $\longrightarrow$ (b) $xy'' + (4 + x^3)y' + x^2y = 1 - \dfrac{1}{x^2}$.

C·K·L $\longrightarrow$ (c) $x^4y'' + (x^3 + x)y' + y = 2x - \dfrac{1}{x}$.

3. Find the particular integral of the equation

$$xy'' + (x - 2)y' + 2y = 2.$$

Hint: The student will find $f(m) \equiv m(m - 3)$, $g(m) \equiv m + 2$, $m = 1$, $A_0 = \dfrac{2}{1(-2)}$, and A_2 infinite. Set $m = 1 + h$. The following is obtained:

$$A_0 = \frac{2}{f(1 + h)} = \frac{2}{(1 + h)(-2 + h)},$$

$$A_1 = -A_0 \frac{3 + h}{(2 + h)(-1 + h)},$$

$$A_2 = -A_1 \frac{4 + h}{(3 + h)h},$$

$$A_3 = -A_2 \frac{5 + h}{(4 + h)(1 + h)}, \text{ etc.}$$

Write the particular integral as

$$y = u_1 \equiv \frac{2}{(1 + h)(-2 + h)} x^{1+h}$$

$$- \frac{2(3 + h)}{(1 + h)(-2 + h)(2 + h)(-1 + h)} x^{2+h}$$

$$+ \frac{\left[\dfrac{2(3 + h)(4 + h)}{(1 + h)(-2 + h)(2 + h)(-1 + h)(3 + h)} \right]}{h} \cdot x^h$$

$$\cdot \left[x^3 - \frac{5 + h}{(4 + h)(1 + h)} x^4 + \cdots \right]$$

$$\equiv \frac{2}{(1+h)(-2+h)}\, x^{1+h}$$

$$-\frac{2(3+h)}{(1+h)(-2+h)(2+h)(-1+h)}\, x^{2+h}$$

$$+\frac{F(h)}{h}\left(1+h\log x+\frac{h^2}{2!}(\log x)^2+\cdots\right)G(h),$$

where the last but one factor is the Taylor expansion of x^h, as a function of h, and the last factor is likewise considered as a function of h only.   Note now that

$$G(h)\equiv G(0)+hG'(0)+\frac{h^2}{2!}G''(0)+\cdots,$$

and that

$$G(0)\equiv x^3-\frac{5}{4\cdot 1}\, x^4+\frac{5\cdot 6}{4\cdot 1\cdot 5\cdot 2}\, x^6+\cdots$$

is identical with y_1, viz., with that part of the complementary function arising from the root $m=3$ of the indicial equation.   (Let the student verify this fact.)   Hence,

$$u_1\equiv\frac{2}{(1+h)(-2+h)}\, x^{1+h}-\frac{2(3+h)}{(1+h)(-2+h)(2+h)(-1+h)}\, x^{2+h}$$

$$+\frac{F(h)}{h}\cdot\left[1+h\log x+\frac{h^2}{2!}(\log x)^2+\cdots\right]$$

$$\cdot\left[y_1+hG'(0)+\frac{h^2}{2!}G''(0)+\cdots\right]$$

$$\equiv\frac{2}{(1+h)(-2+h)}\, x^{1+h}-\frac{2(3+h)}{(1+h)(-2+h)(2+h)(-1+h)}\, x^{2+h}$$

$$+\frac{F(h)}{h}\cdot y_1+F(h)\cdot\log x\cdot y_1+F(h)\cdot G'(0)+\cdots,$$

where all the terms beyond those written out contain powers of h. Now, $\dfrac{F(h)}{h}\cdot y_1$ is contained in the complementary function and need not be included in the particular integral.   We therefore obtain the particular integral as

$$y=u\equiv\lim_{h\to 0}u_1\equiv\frac{2}{(1)(-2)}\, x-\frac{2\cdot 3}{(1)(-2)(2)(-1)}\, x^2$$

$$+F(0)\cdot\log x\cdot y_1+F(0)\cdot G'(0)$$

$$\equiv -x-\frac{3}{2}\, x^2+2y_1\log x+2G'(0),$$

where $G'(0)$ is the value, for $h = 0$, of

$$\frac{\partial}{\partial h}\left[x^3 - \frac{5 + h}{(4 + h)(1 + h)}\, x^4 + \frac{(5 + h)(6 + h)}{(4 + h)(1 + h)(5 + h)(2 + h)}\, x^5 \right.$$
$$\left. - \cdots \right].$$

4. Find the particular integral of:

C.K.L. ⟶   (a) $x^2 y'' + x^3 y' + (x^2 - 2)y = \dfrac{2}{x^3}.$ ← done in class

     (b) $x^2 y'' + (x^2 + x)y' + (x - 1)y = \dfrac{1}{x^2}.$

5. Show that in the case treated in Exercise 3, y_1 is that part of the complementary function arising from the root a of the indicial equation, such that $a - m_0 = ls$ (m_0 the value of m in the particular integral, and l a positive integer).

49. The Legendre equation. In the remaining sections of this chapter we shall consider certain homogeneous linear differential equations whose solutions are of particular interest in pure and applied mathematics.

First, let us take the Legendre equation*

$$(1 - x^2)y'' - 2xy' + n(n + 1)y = 0. \tag{23}$$

It will be convenient to obtain the solutions of this equation as series in descending powers of x, for which purpose we choose $g(m) = 0$ as the indicial equation, the resulting complete integral being, as the student should satisfy himself,

$$y = Au + Bv,$$

where

$$u \equiv x^n - \frac{n(n - 1)}{2(2n - 1)}\, x^{n-2} + \frac{n(n - 1)(n - 2)(n - 3)}{2 \cdot 4(2n - 1)(2n - 3)}\, x^{n-4}$$
$$- \frac{n(n - 1)(n - 2)(n - 3)(n - 4)(n - 5)}{2 \cdot 4 \cdot 6(2n - 1)(2n - 3)(2n - 5)}\, x^{n-6} + \cdots$$

and

$$v \equiv x^{-n-1} + \frac{(n + 1)(n + 2)}{2(2n + 3)}\, x^{-n-3} + \frac{(n + 1)(n + 2)(n + 3)(n + 4)}{2 \cdot 4(2n + 3)(2n + 5)}\, x^{-n-5}$$
$$+ \frac{(n + 1)(n + 2)(n + 3)(n + 4)(n + 5)(n + 6)}{2 \cdot 4 \cdot 6(2n + 3)(2n + 5)(2n + 7)}\, x^{-n-7}$$
$$+ \cdots.$$

---

* Named after the celebrated French mathematician, Adrian Marie Legendre (1752–1833).

The student may further satisfy himself that each series converges for values of x outside the interval from -1 to 1. Particular interest attaches to the function u, which obviously reduces to a polynomial whenever n is a positive integer or zero. If we denote by $u_m(x)$ the value of $u(x)$ for $n = m$, we have

$$u_0(x) \equiv 1,$$
$$u_1(x) \equiv x,$$
$$u_2(x) \equiv x^2 - \frac{1}{3}, \text{ etc.}$$

Instead of the set of functions $u_m(x)$, we shall consider the set $P_m(x)$ defined by

$$P_m(x) \equiv \frac{(2m)!}{2^m (m!)^2} u_m(x) \qquad (m = 0, 1, 2, \cdots) \quad (24)$$

so that

$$P_0(x) \equiv u_0(x) \equiv 1,$$
$$P_1(x) \equiv u_1(x) \equiv x,$$
$$P_2(x) \equiv \frac{1 \cdot 3}{2!} u_2(x) \equiv \frac{3}{2} x^2 - \frac{1}{2},$$
$$P_3(x) \equiv \frac{1 \cdot 3 \cdot 5}{3!} u_3(x) \equiv \frac{5}{2} x^3 - \frac{3}{2} x,$$
$$P_4(x) \equiv \frac{1 \cdot 3 \cdot 5 \cdot 7}{4!} u_4(x) \equiv \frac{5 \cdot 7}{2 \cdot 4} x^4 - 2 \frac{3 \cdot 5}{2 \cdot 4} x^2 + \frac{1 \cdot 3}{2 \cdot 4},$$
$$P_5(x) \equiv \frac{1 \cdot 3 \cdot 5 \cdot 7 \cdot 9}{5!} u_5(x) \equiv \frac{7 \cdot 9}{2 \cdot 4} x^5 - 2 \frac{5 \cdot 7}{2 \cdot 4} x^3 + \frac{3 \cdot 5}{2 \cdot 4} x,$$
$$P_6(x) \equiv \frac{1 \cdot 3 \cdot 5 \cdot 7 \cdot 9 \cdot 11}{6!} u_6(x) \equiv \frac{7 \cdot 9 \cdot 11}{2 \cdot 4 \cdot 6} x^6 - 3 \frac{5 \cdot 7 \cdot 9}{2 \cdot 4 \cdot 6} x^4$$
$$+ 3 \frac{3 \cdot 5 \cdot 7}{2 \cdot 4 \cdot 6} x^2 - \frac{1 \cdot 3 \cdot 5}{2 \cdot 4 \cdot 6}, \text{ etc.}$$

These functions (24) are called *Legendre polynomials* (also *Legendre coefficients;* also *zonal harmonics*). Evidently, they are solutions of the Legendre equation in which n has been set equal to m. They have the further property

$$P_m(1) = 1 \ (m = 0, 1, 2, \cdots). \qquad (25)$$

The student will do well to verify (25) for various integral values of m. He will be asked to prove it in one of the exercises below.

From the list displayed above, we get

$$1 \equiv P_0(x),$$
$$x \equiv P_1(x),$$

$$x^2 \equiv \left[P_2(x) + \frac{1}{2} \right] \cdot \frac{2}{3} \equiv \frac{2}{3} P_2(x) + \frac{1}{3} P_0(x),$$

$$x^3 \equiv \left[P_3(x) + \frac{3}{2} x \right] \cdot \frac{2}{5} \equiv \frac{2}{5} P_3(x) + \frac{3}{5} P_1(x), \text{ etc.,}$$

which makes it evident that for any positive integer k

$$x^k \equiv a_0 P_k(x) + a_1 P_{k-1}(x) + \cdots + a_k P_0(x),$$

the coefficients a_i being unique and not all zero ($i = 0, 1, 2, \cdots , k$). Let us now rewrite (23) in the equivalent form

$$\frac{d}{dx} [(1 - x^2) y'] + n(n + 1)y = 0 \qquad (26)$$

and obtain from it an important theorem on Legendre polynomials. If $P_r(x)$ and $P_s(x)$ are two such polynomials, we have

$$\frac{d}{dx} [(1 - x^2) P_r'] + r(r + 1) P_r \equiv 0,$$

$$\frac{d}{dx} [(1 - x^2) P_s'] + s(s + 1) P_s \equiv 0.$$

Multiplying the upper equation by P_s, the lower by P_r, and subtracting, we get

$$P_s \frac{d}{dx} [(1 - x^2) P_r'] - P_r \frac{d}{dx} [(1 - x^2) P_s'] + (r - s)(r + s + 1)$$
$$P_r P_s \equiv 0.$$

Integrating this equation between -1 and 1, we have

$$\int_{-1}^{+1} P_s \frac{d}{dx} [(1 - x^2) P_r'] dx - \int_{-1}^{+1} P_r \frac{d}{dx} [(1 - x^2) P_s'] dx$$
$$+ (r - s)(r + s + 1) \int_{-1}^{+1} P_r P_s \, dx = 0.$$

Integrating each of the first two by parts, we find

$$\left[(P_s P_r' - P_r P_s')(1 - x^2) \right]_{-1}^{+1} + (r - s)(r + s + 1) \int_{-1}^{+1} P_r P_s \, dx = 0,$$

whence

$$(r - s)(r + s + 1) \int_{-1}^{+1} P_r P_s \, dx = 0,$$

or

$$\int_{-1}^{+1} P_r P_s \, dx = 0 \qquad\qquad (r \neq s), \quad (27)$$

the theorem we wished to prove.   A set of functions $f_n(x)$ ($n = 0$, 1, 2, $\cdots$), continuous in the interval from $x = a$ to $x = b$ and having the property

$$\int_a^b f_r(x) f_s(x) \, dx = 0 \qquad\qquad (r \neq s)$$

is said to be a set of *orthogonal* functions (orthogonal in that interval).   By (27), the Legendre polynomials are such a set in the interval $x = -1$ to $x = 1$.

We now prove the following:

THEOREM. $P_m(x)$ *is the coefficient of* h^m *in the expansion of* $(1 - 2xh + h^2)^{-\frac{1}{2}}$ *as a power series in* h, *i. e.,*

$$(1 - 2xh + h^2)^{-\frac{1}{2}} = P_0(x) + hP_1(x) + h^2 P_2(x) + \cdots$$
$$+ h^m P_m(x) + \cdots, \quad (28)$$

for all values of h *and* x *for which both members are defined.*

Proof

$$(1 - u)^{-\frac{1}{2}} \equiv 1 + \frac{1}{2} u + \frac{1 \cdot 3}{2 \cdot 4} u^2 + \frac{1 \cdot 3 \cdot 5}{2 \cdot 4 \cdot 6} u^3 + \cdots$$
$$+ \frac{1 \cdot 3 \cdots (2m - 1)}{2 \cdot 4 \cdots (2m)} u^m + \cdots,$$

whence

$$(1 - 2xh + h^2)^{-\frac{1}{2}} \equiv 1 + \frac{1}{2} (2xh - h^2) + \frac{1 \cdot 3}{2 \cdot 4} (2xh - h^2)^2 + \cdots$$
$$+ \frac{1 \cdot 3 \cdots (2m - 1)}{2 \cdot 4 \cdots (2m)} (2xh - h^2)^m + \cdots$$
$$\equiv 1 + hx + h^2 \left(\frac{3}{2} x^2 - \frac{1}{2} \right)$$
$$+ h^3 \left(\frac{5}{2} x^3 - \frac{3}{2} x \right) + \cdots.$$

For the lower powers of h, the truth of the theorem is apparent at once.   For any m whatever, it is seen that h^m will arise:

(a) In the first term of the expansion of $(2xh - h^2)^m$, and with the coefficient

$$\frac{1 \cdot 3 \cdots (2m - 1)}{2 \cdot 4 \cdots (2m)} \cdot 2^m \cdot x^m \equiv \frac{1 \cdot 3 \cdots (2m - 1)}{m!} x^m;$$

(b) In the second term of the expansion of $(2xh - h^2)^{m-1}$, and with the coefficient

$$\frac{1 \cdot 3 \cdots (2m - 3)}{2 \cdot 4 \cdots (2m - 2)} \cdot (m - 1) \cdot 2^{m-2} \cdot x^{m-2}$$

$$\equiv - \frac{1 \cdot 3 \cdots (2m - 3)}{2(m - 2)!} x^{m-2};$$

(c) In the third term of the expansion of $(2xh - h^2)^{m-2}$, and with the coefficient

$$\frac{1 \cdot 3 \cdots (2m - 5)}{2 \cdot 4 \cdots (2m - 4)} \cdot \frac{(m - 2)(m - 3)}{2} \cdot 2^{m-4} \cdot x^{m-4}$$

$$\equiv \frac{1 \cdot 3 \cdots (2m - 5)}{2 \cdot 4(m - 4)!} x^{m-4}, \text{ etc.}$$

The sum of these coefficients is

$$\frac{1 \cdot 3 \cdot 5 \cdots (2m - 1)}{m!} \left[x^m - \frac{m(m - 1)}{2(2m - 1)} x^{m-2} \right.$$
$$\left. + \frac{m(m - 1)(m - 2)(m - 3)}{2 \cdot 4(2m - 1)(2m - 3)} x^{m-4} - \cdots \right] \equiv P_m(x) \quad \text{[by (24)]},$$

which proves the theorem.

We apply the theorem now to the evaluation of an important definite integral. By (28),

$$\frac{1}{1 - 2xh + h^2} \equiv P_0^2(x) + h^2 P_1^2(x) + h^4 P_2^2(x) + \cdots + h^{2m} P_m^2(x)$$

$$+ \cdots + 2 \sum_{\substack{r, s = 0 \\ r \neq s}}^{\infty} h^r h^s P_r(x) P_s(x).$$

Hence,

$$\int_{-1}^{1} \frac{1}{1 - 2xh + h^2} \, dx \equiv \int_{-1}^{1} P_0^2(x) \, dx + h^2 \int_{-1}^{1} P_1^2(x) \, dx + \cdots$$

$$+ h^{2m} \int_{-1}^{1} P_m^2(x) \, dx + \cdots + 2 \sum_{\substack{r, s = 0 \\ r \neq s}}^{\infty} h^{r+s} \int_{-1}^{1} P_r(x) P_s(x) \, dx,$$

and the integrals under the last summation sign are all zero, by (27). Carrying out the integration, we find, on the left side of the equation,

$$-\frac{1}{2h}\log(1-2xh+h^2)\Big]_{-1}^{1} \equiv -\frac{1}{2h}\log\frac{(1-h)^2}{(1+h)^2}$$

$$\equiv \frac{1}{h}[\log(1+h)-\log(1-h)]$$

$$\equiv 2\left(1+\frac{h^2}{3}+\frac{h^4}{5}+\frac{h^6}{7}+\cdots+\frac{h^{2m}}{2m+1}+\cdots\right),$$

whence, equating the coefficients of like powers of h on both sides of the equation, we find that

$$\int_{-1}^{1} P_m^2(x)\, dx = \frac{2}{2m+1} \quad (m = 0, 1, 2, \cdots). \quad (29)$$

Exercises

1. Prove that any polynomial $Q(x)$ of degree l can be expressed as

$$Q(x) \equiv b_0 P_l(x) + b_1 P_{l-1}(x) + \cdots + b_l P_0(x),$$

the constants b_i being unique and not all zero $(i = 0, 1, 2, \cdots, l)$.

2. Prove that if $Q(x)$ is a polynomial of degree $l < r$,

$$\int_{-1}^{1} P_r(x)Q(x)\, dx = 0.$$

3. Prove that:

    (a) $P_{2m}(-x) \equiv P_{2m}(x)$.

    (b) $P_{2m+1}(-x) \equiv -P_{2m+1}(x)$.

    (c) $P_{2m}(0) = (-1)^m \dfrac{1 \cdot 3 \cdot 5 \cdots (2m-1)}{2 \cdot 4 \cdot 6 \cdots (2m)}$.

    (d) $P_{2m+1}(0) = 0$.

4. Prove that $P_m(1) = 1$ $(m = 0, 1, 2, \cdots)$. *Hint:* Put $x = 1$ in (28).

5. Prove that $y = \dfrac{d^n}{dx^n}(x^2-1)^n$ is a solution of the Legendre equation. *Hint:* Set $z = (x^2-1)^n$. Differentiate and obtain $(x^2-1)z' = 2nxz$. Take the $(n+1)^{st}$ derivative of each member of this equation, and obtain

$$(x^2-1)\frac{d^{n+2}z}{dx^{n+2}} + 2x(n+1)\frac{d^{n+1}z}{dx^{n+1}} + (n+1)n\frac{d^nz}{dx^n}$$

$$= 2nx\frac{d^{n+1}z}{dx^{n+1}} + 2n(n+1)\frac{d^nz}{dx^n}$$

The result will follow promptly.

C.K.L. ⟶ **6.** Explain why $\dfrac{d^n}{dx^n}(x^2 - 1)^n$ (see Exercise 5) must be a constant multiple of $P_n(x)$. Verify for sundry values of n that $P_n(x) \equiv \dfrac{1}{n!2^n}\dfrac{d^n}{dx^n}(x^2 - 1)^n$.

C.K.L. ⟶ **7.** Show that if $f(x)$ can be expanded, in the interval from -1 to 1, into

$$f(x) \equiv a_0 P_0(x) + a_1 P_1(x) + a_2 P_2(x) + \cdots$$

then, assuming that the series obtained by multiplying the above right-hand member by $P_m(x)$ may be integrated term by term,

$$a_m = \frac{2m + 1}{2}\int_{-1}^{1} f(x)P_m(x)\,dx \quad (m = 0, 1, 2, \cdots).$$

c.K.L ⟶ **8.** Verify the result of Exercise 7 for

$$f(x) \equiv x^2 + 1.$$

C.K.L ⟶ **9.** Show that if $f(x)$ can be expanded as in Exercise 7, the expansion is unique. *Hint:* Assume $f(x) \equiv b_0 P_0(x) + b_1 P_1(x) + \cdots$ and show that $a_m - b_m = 0$ $(m = 0, 1, 2, \cdots)$.

C.K.L. ⟶ **10.** Prove that

$$(n + 1)P_{n+1}(x) - (2n + 1)xP_n(x) + nP_{n-1}(x) \equiv 0$$
$$(n = 0, 1, 2, \cdots).$$

Hint: Put

$$s \equiv (1 - 2xh + h^2)^{-1/2} \equiv P_0(x) + hP_1(x) + h^2 P_2(x) + \cdots$$

and obtain

$$\frac{\partial s}{\partial h}\cdot(1 - 2hx + h^2) \equiv s\cdot(x - h).$$

Use (28) and equate coefficients of h^n on both sides of the resulting equation.

c.K.L ⟶ **11.** Prove that

$$xP_n'(x) - P_{n-1}'(x) \equiv nP_n(x).$$

Hint: Obtain $(x - h)\dfrac{\partial s}{\partial x} \equiv h\dfrac{\partial s}{\partial h}$ (s as in Exercise 10). Expand by (28), and equate coefficients of h.

50. The Bessel equation.   The equation

$$x^2 y'' + xy' + (x^2 - n^2)y = 0 \qquad (29)$$

is called the Bessel equation.*   We leave it to the student to obtain its solutions in series as

$$y = u \equiv x^n \left[1 - \frac{x^2}{4 \cdot 1(1+n)} + \frac{x^4}{4^2 \cdot 2!(1+n)(2+n)} \right.$$
$$- \frac{x^6}{4^3 \cdot 3!(1+n)(2+n)(3+n)} + \cdots$$
$$\left. + (-1)^k \frac{x^{2k}}{4^k \cdot k!(1+n)(2+n)\cdots(k+n)} + \cdots \right]$$

$$y = v \equiv x^{-n} \left[1 - \frac{x^2}{4 \cdot 1(1-n)} + \frac{x^4}{4^2 \cdot 2!(1-n)(2-n)} \right.$$
$$- \frac{x^6}{4^3 \cdot 3!(1-n)(2-n)(3-n)} + \cdots$$
$$\left. + (-1)^k \frac{x^{2k}}{4^k \cdot k!(1-n)(2-n)\cdots(k-n)} + \cdots \right],$$

and hence its complete solution as

$$y = Au + Bv, \qquad (30)$$

provided u and v are linearly independent and are both defined, which is the case when n is not zero or an integer.   For $n = 0$, u and v are identical, and recourse must be had to the method of Section 46 of this chapter to obtain a second solution.   When n is a positive integer, u is defined but v is not, since from a certain term on, the coefficients of v become infinite; when n is a negative integer, the coefficients of u become infinite, while v is defined.   In either case, it is necessary to resort to the method of Section 47 to obtain a second independent solution.

If, as in Section 49, we denote by $u_m(x)$ the value of $u(x)$ corresponding to $n = m$, the Bessel Functions of the first kind are defined by

$$\begin{cases} J_m(x) \equiv \dfrac{u_m(x)}{2^m \cdot m!} & (m \text{ a positive integer}), \\ J_0(x) \equiv u_0(x), \end{cases} \qquad (31)$$

---

* After Friedrich Wilhelm Bessel (1784–1846), an astronomer who earned a place of prominence in mathematics by the study of an important class of functions which bear his name.

in other words,

$$J_m(x) \equiv \frac{x^m}{2^m \cdot m!} \left[1 - \frac{x^2}{4 \cdot 1(1+m)} + \frac{x^4}{4^2 \cdot 2!(1+m)(2+m)} \right. $$

$$\left. - \frac{x^6}{4^3 \cdot 3!(1+m)(2+m)(3+m)} + \cdots \right]$$

$$\equiv \sum_{k=0}^{\infty} (-1)^k \frac{x^{2k+m}}{2^{2k+m} \cdot k!(k+m)!},$$

where $m = 0, 1, 2, \cdots$ and $0! = 1$. Note now that

$$x^m J_m(x) \equiv \sum_{k=0}^{\infty} (-1)^k \frac{x^{2k+2m}}{2^{2k+m} \cdot k!(k+m)!},$$

and hence,

$$\frac{d}{dx}[x^m J_m(x)] = \sum_{k=0}^{\infty} (-1)^k \cdot \frac{(2k+2m)x^{2k+2m-1}}{2^{2k+m} \cdot k!(k+m)!}$$

$$\equiv \sum_{k=0}^{\infty} (-1)^k \cdot x^m \frac{x^{2k+m-1}}{2^{2k+m-1} \cdot k!(k+m-1)!}.$$

In other words

$$\frac{d}{dx}[x^m J_m(x)] \equiv x^m \cdot J_{m-1}(x). \tag{32}$$

Likewise, the student may derive

$$\frac{d}{dx}[x^{-m} J_m(x)] \equiv -x^{-m} \cdot J_{m+1}(x). \tag{33}$$

The last two formulas may be rewritten as

$$x^m \frac{d}{dx}[J_m(x)] + mx^{m-1} J_m(x) \equiv x^m \cdot J_{m-1}(x),$$

$$x^{-m} \frac{d}{dx}[J_m(x)] - mx^{-m-1} J_m(x) \equiv -x^{-m} J_{m+1}(x),$$

whence,

$$J_{m-1}(x) - J_{m+1}(x) \equiv 2 \frac{d}{dx}[J_m(x)] \tag{34}$$

and

$$J_{m-1}(x) + J_{m+1}(x) \equiv \frac{2m}{x} J_m(x). \tag{35}$$

We now define Bessel's Functions of the first kind for negative integral values of m by imposing the condition that (35) hold for every integral m. We thus obtain

(setting $m = 0$)

$$J_{-1}(x) + J_1(x) \equiv 0, \ \therefore \ J_{-1}(x) \equiv -J_1(x);$$

(setting $m = 1$)

$$J_0(x) + J_2(x) \equiv \frac{2}{x} J_1(x)$$

(setting $m = -1$)

$$J_{-2}(x) + J_0(x) \equiv -\frac{2}{x} J_{-1}(x)$$

$$\therefore \ J_{-2}(x) \equiv J_2(x);$$

(setting $m = 2$)

$$J_1(x) + J_3(x) \equiv \frac{4}{x} J_2(x)$$

(setting $m = -2$)

$$J_{-3}(x) + J_{-1}(x) \equiv -\frac{4}{x} J_{-2}(x)$$

$$\therefore \ J_{-3}(x) \equiv -J_3(x).$$

Continuing in this vein, we obtain

$$J_{-m}(x) \equiv (-1)^m \cdot J_m(x) \quad (m = 1, 2, 3, \cdots).$$

It is easy to verify that (32), (33), and (34) will also hold for negative integral values of m. Thus, for $m = -p$ (p a positive integer), we have

$$\frac{d}{dx}[x^{-p} \cdot J_{-p}(x)] \equiv \frac{d}{dx}[x^{-p} \cdot (-1)^p \cdot J_p(x)] \equiv (-1)^p \cdot -x^{-p} \cdot J_{p+1}(x)$$

$$\equiv (-1)^{p+1} \cdot x^{-p} \cdot J_{p+1}(x) \equiv x^{-p} \cdot J_{-p-1}(x),$$

which verifies (32). When m is fractional, the symbol $m!$ is meaningless, and the Bessel Function of order m of the first kind is defined as

$$J_m(x) \equiv \frac{u_m(x)}{2^m \cdot \Gamma(m+1)}.^*$$ (36)

Again, $u_m(x)$ and $v_m(x)$ are now both defined, they are independent, and $J_{-m}(x)$ is defined directly by

---

* The Gamma Function of m is defined as $\Gamma(m) \equiv \displaystyle\int_0^\infty x^{m-1}e^{-x}dx$. For integral values of m, it is proved $\Gamma(m+1) \equiv m!$. See Wilson, p. 378.

$$J_{-m}(x) \equiv \frac{v_m(x)}{2^{-m}\Gamma(-m+1)}. \tag{37}$$

Formulas (32) to (35) can be verified to hold also for the Bessel Functions of fractional order.

We close this section by proving the following:

THEOREM. *In the expansion of* $e^{\frac{x}{2}\left(h-\frac{1}{h}\right)}$ *in integral powers of* h,

of the form $\displaystyle\sum_{m=-\infty}^{\infty} C_m \cdot h^m, \; C_m \equiv J_m(x),$ *i. e.,*

$$e^{\frac{x}{2}\left(h-\frac{1}{h}\right)} \equiv J_0(x) + h \cdot J_1(x) + h^2 J_2(x) + h^3 J_3(x) + \cdots$$
$$+ h^{-1}J_{-1}(x) + h^{-2}J_{-2}(x) + h^{-3}J_{-3}(x) + \cdots. \tag{38}$$

Proof

$$e^{\frac{x}{2}\left(h-\frac{1}{h}\right)} \equiv e^{xh/2} \cdot e^{-x/2h} \equiv \left(1 + \frac{xh}{2} + \frac{x^2h^2}{4\cdot 2!} + \frac{x^3h^3}{8\cdot 3!} + \cdots\right)\left(1\right.$$
$$\left. - \frac{x}{2h} + \frac{x^2}{4h^2\cdot 2!} - \frac{x^3}{8h^3\cdot 3!} + \cdots\right).$$

Hence, the coefficient of h^m in the product is

$$\frac{x^m}{2^m\cdot m!} - \frac{x^{m+1}}{2^{m+1}(m+1)!}\cdot\frac{x}{2} + \frac{x^{m+2}}{2^{m+2}(m+2)!}\cdot\frac{x^2}{4\cdot 2!}$$
$$- \frac{x^{m+3}}{2^{m+3}(m+3)!}\cdot\frac{x^3}{8\cdot 3!} + \cdots$$
$$\equiv \frac{x^m}{2^m\cdot m!}\left[1 - \frac{x^2}{4(1+m)} + \frac{x^4}{4^2\cdot 2!(1+m)(2+m)}\right.$$
$$\left. - \frac{x^6}{4^3\cdot 3!(1+m)(2+m)(3+m)} + \cdots\right]$$
$$\equiv \frac{u_m(x)}{2^m\cdot m!} \equiv J_m(x).$$

Likewise, h^{-m} enters in the product with the coefficient

$$(-1)^m\left[\frac{x^m}{2^m\cdot m!} - \frac{x^{m+1}}{2^{m+1}(m+1)!}\cdot\frac{x}{2}\right.$$
$$\left. + \frac{x^{m+2}}{2^{m+2}(m+2)!}\cdot\frac{x^2}{4\cdot 2!} - \cdots\right] \equiv (-1)^m\cdot J_m(x) \equiv J_{-m}(x).$$

Exercises

C.K.L.

1. Apply the method of Section 46 of this chapter to obtain a second solution of the Bessel equation [independent of $J_0(x)$] for the case when $n = 0$.   Obtain it in the form:

$$K_0(x) \equiv J_0(x) \cdot \log x + \frac{x^2}{2^2} - \frac{x^4}{2^2 \cdot 4^2}\left(1 + \frac{1}{2}\right)$$

$$+ \frac{x^6}{2^2 \cdot 4^2 \cdot 6^2}\left(1 + \frac{1}{2} + \frac{1}{3}\right) - \cdots$$

$$+ (-1)^{k-1} \cdot \frac{x^{2k}}{2^2 \cdot 4^2 \cdots (2k)^2}\left(1 + \frac{1}{2} + \cdots + \frac{1}{k}\right) + \cdots.$$

2. Apply the method of Section 47 of this chapter to obtain a second solution of the Bessel equation [independent of $u_n(x)$] for the case when n is a positive integer.   Show that the quotient of that solution by $(2^n \cdot n!)$ is

$$K_n(x) \equiv J_n(x) \cdot \log x - \left[2^{n-1}(n-1)! \, x^{-n} + \frac{2^{n-3}(n-2)!}{1!} x^{-n+2} \right.$$

$$\left. + \frac{2^{n-5}(n-3)!}{2!} x^{-n+4} + \cdots + \frac{1}{2^{n-1}(n-1)!} x^{n-2} \right]$$

$$+ \sum_{k=0}^{\infty} \frac{(-1)^{k-1} \cdot x^{n+2k}}{2^{n+2k} \cdot k!(n+k)!} \left(\frac{1}{2} + \frac{1}{4} + \frac{1}{6} + \cdots + \frac{1}{2k} + \frac{1}{2} \right.$$

$$\left. + \frac{1}{4} + \frac{1}{6} + \cdots + \frac{1}{2n+2k} \right)$$

The terms $\frac{1}{2} + \cdots + \frac{1}{2k}$ are to be omitted for $k = 0$.

$K_0(x)$ and $K_n(x)(n = 1, 2, 3, \cdots)$ are called the Bessel Functions of the second kind.

3. Show that $K_n(x)$ satisfies formulas (32) to (35) of this section, and thence argue, as in the text, that

$$K_{-n}(x) \equiv (-1)^n K_n(x) \quad (n = 1, 2, 3, \cdots).$$

4. Show that:

C.K.L.
(a) $y = x^{-n} J_n(x)$ is a solution of the equation
$$xy'' + (1 + 2n)y' + xy = 0.$$
C.K.L.
(b) $y = x^n J_n(x)$ is a solution of the equation
$$xy'' + (1 - 2n)y' + xy = 0.$$

C.K.L. $\to$ (c) $y = x^{-n/2}J_n(2\sqrt{x})$ is a solution of the equation
$$xy'' + (1 + n)y' + y = 0.$$

C.K.L. $\to$ (d) $y = J_n(e^x)$ is a solution of the equation
$$y'' + (e^{2x} - n^2)y = 0.$$

C.K.L. $\to$ (e) $y = J_0(ax)$ is a solution of the equation
$$xy'' + y' + a^2xy = 0.$$

C.K.L. $\to$ (f) $y = \sqrt{x} \cdot J_n(ax)$ is a solution of the equation
$$4x^2y'' + (4a^2x^2 - 4n^2 + 1)y = 0.$$

5. Prove:

C.K.L. $\longrightarrow$ (a) $\dfrac{d}{dx} J_0(x) \equiv -J_1(x).$

C.K.L $\to$ (b) $\dfrac{d}{dx} [x^n J_n(hx)] \equiv hx^n J_{n-1}(hx).$

C.K.L. $\longrightarrow$ (c) $\dfrac{d^2}{dx^2} [J_n(x)] \equiv \dfrac{1}{4} [J_{n-2}(x) - 2J_n(x) + J_{n+2}(x)].$

C.K.L $\to$ **6.** Prove:

$$(b^2 - a^2) \int_0^x x \cdot J_n(ax) \cdot J_n(bx)\, dx$$
$$\equiv x[aJ_n(bx) \cdot J_n'(ax) - bJ_n(ax) \cdot J_n'(bx)].$$

Hint: Set $u = \sqrt{x} \cdot J_n(ax)$, $v = \sqrt{x} \cdot J_n(bx)$. By Exercise 4(f),
$$4x^2u'' + (4a^2x^2 - 4n^2 + 1)u = 0,$$
$$4x^2v'' + (4b^2x^2 - 4n^2 + 1)v = 0.$$

Multiply these by v and $-u$, respectively, add, and then integrate.

C.K.L $\to$ **7.** If $a_1, a_2, a_3, \cdots$ are the positive roots of $J_n(x) = 0$ (it can be shown that the number of such roots is infinite), show that the functions
$$\sqrt{x} \cdot J_n(a_1x), \quad \sqrt{x} \cdot J_n(a_2x), \quad \sqrt{x} \cdot J_n(a_3x), \cdots$$
are orthogonal in the interval from $x = 0$ to $x = 1$, *i. e.*, that
$$\int_0^1 \sqrt{x} \cdot J_n(a_rx) \cdot \sqrt{x} \cdot J_n(a_sx)\, dx = 0 \qquad (r \neq s).$$

Hint: Use the formula in Exercise 6.

C.K.L. $\to$ **8.** If a_i are as in Exercise 7 ($i = 1, 2, 3, \cdots$), prove that
$$\int_0^1 x \cdot [J_n(a_rx)]^2\, dx = \frac{1}{2} [J_n'(a_r)]^2.$$

Hint: Differentiate the formula of Exercise 6 partially with respect to b, then set $b = a$.

C.K.L.

9. (a) Derive a formula alternative to the one in Exercise 6, *viz.*,

(see Page 178 eq 33)

$$(b^2 - a^2) \int_0^x x \cdot J_n(ax) \cdot J_n(bx) \, dx$$
$$\equiv x[bJ_n(ax)J_{n+1}(bx) - aJ_n(bx)J_{n+1}(ax)].$$

C.K.L.

(b) From this establish a formula alternative to the one in Exercise 8, *viz.*,

$$\int_0^1 x \cdot [J_n(a_r x)]^2 \, dx = -\frac{1}{2} J_n'(a_r) \cdot J_{n+1}(a_r) = \frac{1}{2} [J_{n+1}(a_r)]^2.$$

C.K.L.

10. Show that if $f(x)$ can be developed into a series (see Pipes)

$$f(x) \equiv c_1 J_n(a_1 x) + c_2 J_n(a_2 x) + \cdots + c_r J_n(a_r x) + \cdots$$

(where a_i have the same meaning as in Exercise 7), and if the series multiplied by $x \cdot J_n(a_k x)$ may be integrated term by term, then

$$c_k = \frac{2 \int_0^1 x f(x) \cdot J_n(a_k x) \, dx}{[J_{n+1}(a_k)]^2}.$$

11. Prove that

$$J_{1/2}(x) \equiv \sqrt{\frac{2}{\pi x}} \cdot \sin x.$$

Hint: Use (36).   Make use of the fact that

$$\Gamma(n + 1) \equiv n\Gamma(n) \text{ and } \Gamma\left(\frac{1}{2}\right) = \sqrt{\pi}.$$

12. Prove that

$$J_{-1/2}(x) \equiv \sqrt{\frac{2}{\pi x}} \cdot \cos x.$$

Hint: Use (37).

13. By repeated use of (35), prove:

$$J_{n-1}(x) \equiv \frac{2}{x} [nJ_n(x) - (n + 2)J_{n+2}(x) + (n + 4)J_{n+4}(x)$$
$$- (n + 6)J_{n+6}(x) + \cdots].$$

Note that

$$\lim_{n \to \infty} J_n(x) = 0.$$

14. By means of (38) prove:

$$\text{(a)} \quad J_n(x + y) \equiv \sum_{k=-\infty}^{\infty} J_k(x) \cdot J_{n-k}(y),$$

where n is an integer.

$$\text{(b)} \quad J_0(x) + 2J_2(x) + 2J_4(x) + 2J_6(x) + \cdots \equiv 1.$$
$$\text{(c)} \quad J_1(x) + 3J_3(x) + 5J_5(x) + 7J_7(x) + \cdots \equiv \frac{x}{2}.$$

51. The Gauss equation. The equation

$$(x^2 - x)y'' + [(\alpha + \beta + 1)x - \gamma]y' + \alpha\beta y = 0 \qquad (39)$$

is called the Gauss equation, after Karl Friedrich Gauss (1777–1855), an outstanding name in the history of mathematics.

We leave it to the student to verify that $f(m)$ and $g(m)$ of (12), computed for (39), are both of the second degree, and to obtain the complete solution of the Gauss equation in each of the forms

$$y = Au + Bv$$

and

$$y = Cu_1 + Dv_1,$$

where

$$u \equiv 1 + \frac{\alpha \cdot \beta}{1!\gamma} x + \frac{\alpha(\alpha + 1) \cdot \beta(\beta + 1)}{2!\gamma(\gamma + 1)} x^2$$
$$+ \frac{\alpha(\alpha + 1)(\alpha + 2) \cdot \beta(\beta + 1)(\beta + 2)}{3!\gamma(\gamma + 1)(\gamma + 2)} x^3 + \cdots,$$

$$v \equiv x^{1-\gamma}\left[1 + \frac{(1 + \alpha - \gamma) \cdot (1 + \beta - \gamma)}{1!(2 - \gamma)} x \right.$$
$$+ \frac{(1 + \alpha - \gamma)(2 + \alpha - \gamma) \cdot (1 + \beta - \gamma)(2 + \beta - \gamma)}{2!(2 - \gamma)(3 - \gamma)} x^2$$
$$+ \frac{(1+\alpha-\gamma)(2+\alpha-\gamma)(3+\alpha-\gamma) \cdot (1+\beta-\gamma)(2+\beta-\gamma)(3+\beta-\gamma)}{3!(2 - \gamma)(3 - \gamma)(4 - \gamma)} x^3$$
$$\left. + \cdots \right],$$

$$u_1 \equiv x^{-\alpha} \left[1 + \frac{\alpha \cdot (1 + \alpha - \gamma)}{1!(1 + \alpha - \beta)} \cdot \frac{1}{x} \right.$$

$$+ \frac{\alpha(\alpha + 1) \cdot (1 + \alpha - \gamma)(2 + \alpha - \gamma)}{2!(1 + \alpha - \beta)(2 + \alpha - \beta)} \cdot \frac{1}{x^2}$$

$$+ \frac{\alpha(\alpha + 1)(\alpha + 2) \cdot (1 + \alpha - \gamma)(2 + \alpha - \gamma)(3 + \alpha - \gamma)}{3!(1 + \alpha - \beta)(2 + \alpha - \beta)(3 + \alpha - \beta)} \cdot \frac{1}{x^3}$$

$$\left. + \cdots \right],$$

$$v_1 \equiv x^{-\beta} \left[1 + \frac{\beta \cdot (1 + \beta - \gamma)}{1!(1 + \beta - \alpha)} \cdot \frac{1}{x} \right.$$

$$+ \frac{\beta(\beta + 1) \cdot (1 + \beta - \gamma)(2 + \beta - \gamma)}{2!(1 + \beta - \alpha)(2 + \beta - \alpha)} \cdot \frac{1}{x^2}$$

$$+ \frac{\beta(\beta + 1)(\beta + 2) \cdot (1 + \beta - \gamma)(2 + \beta - \gamma)(3 + \beta - \gamma)}{3!(1 + \beta - \alpha)(2 + \beta - \alpha)(3 + \beta - \alpha)} \cdot \frac{1}{x_3}$$

$$\left. + \cdots \right].$$

We now define as the hypergeometric series a series of the form

$$1 + \frac{\alpha \cdot \beta}{1! \, \gamma} z + \frac{\alpha(\alpha + 1) \cdot \beta(\beta + 1)}{2!\gamma(\gamma + 1)} z^2$$

$$+ \frac{\alpha(\alpha + 1)(\alpha + 2) \cdot \beta(\beta + 1)(\beta + 2)}{3!\gamma(\gamma + 1)(\gamma + 2)} z^3$$

$$+ \cdots \quad (40)$$

and denote it, as is customary, by $F(\alpha, \beta, \gamma, z)$. It is seen that the four series which arise as solutions of the Gauss equation are each of this type (the equation itself is frequently called the hypergeometric equation, on that account), and can be designated as

$$u \equiv F(\alpha, \beta, \gamma, x),$$
$$v \equiv x^{1-\gamma} \cdot F(1 + \alpha - \gamma, 1 + \beta - \gamma, 2 - \gamma, x),$$
$$u_1 \equiv x^{-\alpha} \cdot F\left(\alpha, 1 + \alpha - \gamma, 1 + \alpha - \beta, \frac{1}{x}\right),$$
$$v_1 \equiv x^{-\beta} \cdot F\left(\beta, 1 + \beta - \gamma, 1 + \beta - \alpha, \frac{1}{x}\right).$$

A variety of special cases arises, depending on the values of α, β, γ. Thus, when $\gamma = 1$, u and v are identical, and to obtain a second solution independent of u, it is necessary to resort to the method of Section 46 of this chapter. However, u_1 and v_1 are not in that case identical, except when $\alpha = \beta$, and the complete solution of (39) is available in the second form written above, *viz.*, $y = Cu_1 + Dv_1$. Again, if γ is a negative integer (or zero), the coefficients in u presently become infinite, and a second solution, independent of v, must be sought by the method of Section 47 of this chapter. This situation, however, is modified if either α or β is a negative integer of lesser numerical value than γ, so that u reduces to a polynomial. In any event, again in this case, the second form of the complete solution may be available.

Other possibilities for the values of α, β, γ which lead to the exceptional cases that are wont to arise in integration by series, will readily occur to the student.

The hypergeometric series (40) converges for $|z| < 1$, and diverges for $|z| > 1$, whatever the values of α, β, γ.* For $z = 1$, it converges when, and only when, $\alpha + \beta < \gamma$. For $z = -1$, it converges when, and only when, $\alpha + \beta < \gamma + 1$. (For proof of these statements, the student may turn to Section 29 in Pierpont's *Functions of a Complex Variable.*)

It is of interest to note the great variety of functions that can be expressed as hypergeometric series. Thus

(a) $\log (1 + x) \equiv x - \dfrac{x^2}{2} + \dfrac{x^3}{3} - \dfrac{x^4}{4} + \dfrac{x^5}{5} - \cdots$

$$\equiv x \left[1 - \frac{1}{2}x + \frac{1}{3}x^2 - \frac{1}{4}x^3 + \frac{1}{5}x^4 - \cdots \right]$$

$$\equiv x \left[1 - \frac{1 \cdot 1}{1! \, 2} x + \frac{1 \cdot 2 \cdot 1 \cdot 2}{2! \, 2 \cdot 3} x^2 \right.$$

$$\left. - \frac{1 \cdot 2 \cdot 3 \cdot 1 \cdot 2 \cdot 3}{3! \, 2 \cdot 3 \cdot 4} x^3 + \cdots \right]$$

$$\equiv x \cdot F(1, 1, 2, -x).$$

The function converges for $|x| < 1$, and diverges for $|x| > 1$. For $-x = 1 (\therefore x = -1)$ it diverges, since $\alpha + \beta \not< \gamma$. For $-x = -1$ $(\therefore x = 1)$ it converges, since $\alpha + \beta < \gamma + 1$, .

(b) $(1 + x)^n \equiv 1 + nx + \dfrac{n(n - 1)}{2!} x^2 + \dfrac{n(n - 1)(n - 2)}{3!} x^3$

$$+ \cdots$$

$$\equiv 1 + \frac{(-n)(-x)}{1!} + \frac{(-n)(-n + 1)}{2!} (-x)^2$$

$$+ \frac{(-n)(-n + 1)(-n + 2)}{3!} (-x)^3 + \cdots$$

$$\equiv F(-n, \beta, \beta, -x),$$

---

* Except, of course, when the number of terms is finite, in which case the series converges for all finite values of z.

where β is any constant.   The function converges for $|x| < 1$, and
diverges for $|x| > 1$.   For $-x = 1(\therefore x = -1)$ it converges when,
and only when, $-n + \beta < \beta (\therefore n > 0)$.   For $-x = -1 (\therefore x = 1)$
it converges when, and only when, $-n + \beta < \beta + 1 (\therefore n > -1)$,

(c) $$\cos x \equiv 1 - \frac{x^2}{2!} + \frac{x^4}{4!} - \frac{x^6}{6!} + \cdots$$

$$\equiv 1 + \frac{\alpha \cdot \beta}{1! \, \frac{1}{2}} \left(-\frac{x^2}{4\alpha\beta} \right) + \lim_{\substack{\alpha \to \infty \\ \beta \to \infty}} \frac{\alpha(\alpha + 1) \cdot \beta(\beta + 1)}{2! \, \frac{1}{2} \cdot \frac{3}{2}} \left(-\frac{x^2}{4\alpha\beta} \right)^2$$

$$+ \lim_{\substack{\alpha \to \infty \\ \beta \to \infty}} \frac{\alpha(\alpha + 1)(\alpha + 2) \cdot \beta(\beta + 1)(\beta + 2)}{3! \, \frac{1}{2} \cdot \frac{3}{2} \cdot \frac{5}{2}} \left(-\frac{x^2}{4\alpha\beta} \right)^3 + \cdots$$

$$= \lim_{\substack{\alpha \to \infty \\ \beta \to \infty}} F\left(\alpha, \beta, \tfrac{1}{2}, -\frac{x^2}{4\alpha\beta} \right).$$

Exercises

1. Express as hypergeometric series:

(a) $(1 + x)^n + (1 - x)^n$.
(b) $(1 + x)^n - (1 - x)^n$.
(c) $\log \dfrac{1 + x}{1 - x}$.
(d) $\dfrac{1}{1 + x}$.   Examine for convergence.
(e) $\dfrac{1}{1 - x}$.   Examine for convergence.
(f) $\sin x$.
(g) e^x.

2. Solve the following equations:

(a) $(x^2 - x)y'' + (4x - 3)y' + 2y = 0$.
(b) $(x^2 - x)y'' + (2x - 1)y' - 2y = 0$.

3. Examine the following series for convergence:

(a) $F\left(2, 3, 1, \dfrac{5 - x}{3} \right)$.

(b) $F\left(1, -1, \tfrac{1}{2}, \dfrac{x - 2}{2} \right)$.

$\int \log x \, dx =$ $u = \log x$; $du = \frac{1}{x} dx$
$dv = dx$
$x \log x - \int \frac{x \, dx}{x} = x \log x - x$

4. Prove:

(a) $(\beta - \alpha) \cdot F(\alpha, \beta, \gamma, x) + \alpha \cdot F(\alpha + 1, \beta, \gamma, x) - \beta \cdot F(\alpha, \beta + 1, \gamma, x) \equiv 0.$

(b) $(\gamma - \alpha - \beta) \cdot F(\alpha, \beta, \gamma, x) + \alpha(1 - x) \cdot F(\alpha + 1, \beta, \gamma, x) + (\beta - \gamma) \cdot F(\alpha, \beta - 1, \gamma, x) \equiv 0.$

5. Write down the Gauss equation of which

$$y = F(\alpha, \beta, \gamma, -x)$$

is a solution.

6. By making use of the expression as a hypergeometric series for $\log (1 + x)$, write down the Gauss equation of which

$$y = \frac{\log (1 + x)}{x}$$

is a solution.

7. Express $\dfrac{d^m}{dx^m} F(\alpha, \beta, \gamma, x)$ as a hypergeometric series.

8. Reduce the equation

$$(Ax^2 + Bx + C)y'' + (Dx + E)y' + Fy = 0$$

to a Gauss equation. *Hint:* Set $x = lz + m$ in the given equation. l and m will be determined by $\begin{cases} Am^2 + Bm + C = 0 \\ -Al = 2Am + B \end{cases}$, to the effect of yielding a Gauss equation in z.

52. Miscellaneous exercises on Chapter VI.

1. Integrate in series:

(a) $x^2y'' + x^2y' - 2y = 0.$
(b) $(1 - x^2)y'' + 2xy' + y = 0.$
(c) $x^2y'' - xy' + (x^2 + 1)y = 0.$
(d) $(1 + x^2)y'' + xy' - 9y = 0.$
(e) $xy'' - 3y' + x^2y = 0.$
(f) $x^4y'' + (x - 2x^3)y' + y = 4x + 5.$

(g) $x^2y'' + (x^3 + x)y' = \dfrac{1}{x} + 9y.$

2. Prove:

(a) $(1 - x^2)P_n'(x) \equiv nP_{n-1}(x) - nxP_n(x).$
(b) $(1 - x^2)P_n'(x) \equiv (n + 1)[xP_n(x) - P_{n+1}(x)].$
(c) $P_{n+1}'(x) - P_{n-1}'(x) \equiv (2n + 1)P_n(x).$

Similar to your eq.

3. Show that:

(a) $y = x^{n/2} \cdot J_n(2\sqrt{x})$ is a solution of the equation $xy'' + (1 - n)y' + y = 0$.

(b) $y = K_0(2\sqrt{x})$ is a solution of the equation $xy'' + y' + y = 0$.

(c) $x[J_n(x) + J_{n+2}(x)] \equiv 2(n + 1)J_{n+1}(x)$.

4. Show that:

(a) $J_{3/2}(x) \equiv \sqrt{\dfrac{2}{\pi x}} \left(\dfrac{\sin x}{x} - \cos x \right)$.

Hint: Use (35), with $m = \tfrac{1}{2}$; also Exercises 11 and 12 of Section 50.

(b) $J_{-3/2}(x) \equiv \sqrt{\dfrac{2}{\pi x}} \left(-\dfrac{\cos x}{x} - \sin x \right)$.

(c) $J_{5/2}(x) \equiv \sqrt{\dfrac{2}{\pi x}} \left[\sin x \left(\dfrac{3}{x^2} - 1 \right) - \dfrac{3 \cos x}{x} \right]$.

5. By formula (34) and Exercise 13 of Section 50 prove:

$$\frac{d}{dx} J_n(x) \equiv \frac{2}{x} \left[\frac{n}{2} J_n(x) - (n + 2)J_{n+2}(x) + (n + 4)J_{n+4}(x) \right.$$
$$\left. - (n + 6)J_{n+6}(x) + \cdots \right].$$

6. By formula (38), prove:

(a) $\cos (x \sin \varphi) \equiv J_0(x) + 2J_2(x) \cdot \cos 2\varphi + 2J_4(x) \cdot \cos 4\varphi + 2J_6(x) \cdot \cos 6\varphi + \cdots$.

(b) $\sin (x \sin \varphi) \equiv 2J_1(x) \cdot \sin \varphi + 2J_3(x) \cdot \sin 3\varphi + 2J_5(x) \cdot \sin 5\varphi + \cdots$.

Hint: In (38), set $h = e^{i\varphi} \left(\therefore \dfrac{1}{h} = e^{-i\varphi} \right)$. Make use of the formula $[e^{i\varphi}]^m \equiv e^{mi\varphi} \equiv \cos m\varphi + i \sin m\varphi$. After substituting, equate the real and imaginary parts on each side of (38).

7. From the formula in Exercise 6(a), obtain

(a) $J_0(x) \equiv \dfrac{1}{\pi} \displaystyle\int_0^{\pi} \cos (x \sin \varphi) \, d\varphi$.

Obtain also an alternative formula

$$\text{(b)} \quad J_0(x) \equiv \frac{1}{\pi} \int_0^\pi \cos\,(x \cos \varphi)\, d\varphi.$$

8. Express as hypergeometric series:

(a) $\sin^{-1} x$.   (b) $\tan^{-1} x$.   (c) $\cosh x$.

9. Prove:

$$(\gamma - \alpha - 1) \cdot F(\alpha, \beta, \gamma, x) + \alpha \cdot F(\alpha + 1, \beta, \gamma, x) + (1 - \gamma) \cdot$$
$$F(\alpha, \beta, \gamma - 1, x) \equiv 0.$$

10. By making use of the expression as a hypergeometric series for $(1 + x)^n$, write down a Gauss equation of which $y = (1 + x)^n$ is a solution.

11. On the basis of Exercise 8, prove:

$$\theta \equiv \sin\,\theta \cdot F(\tfrac{1}{2}, \tfrac{1}{2}, \tfrac{3}{2}, \sin^2 \theta)$$
$$\equiv \tan\,\theta \cdot F(\tfrac{1}{2}, 1, \tfrac{3}{2}, -\tan^2 \theta).$$

CHAPTER VII

Ordinary Differential Equations in More Than Two Variables

53. Total differential equations; introductory remarks. In books on calculus* it is proved that the differential of a function $u = f(x, y, z, \cdots)$ is given by the formula

$$du = f_x \, dx + f_y \, dy + f_z \, dz + \cdots,$$

provided, of course, that the partial derivatives $f_x, f_y, f_z, \cdots$ exist and are continuous.

If we take the differential of each side of the equation

$$x^2 y - e^x + \cos z = 7, \tag{1}$$

we obtain

$$(2xy - e^x) \, dx + x^2 \, dy - \sin z \, dz = 0. \tag{2}$$

An equation such as (2)† is called a *total differential equation*, and an equality, like (1), which identically satisfies it, is called a *solution*. Obviously, the relation (1) would still satisfy (2) if the constant 7 in the right-hand member were changed to any other; so the equation

$$x^2 y - e^x + \cos z = c,$$

where c is an arbitrary constant, is a solution, and will be called the *general* solution.

Before going into the question of the solvability of total differential equations, let us look at the example

$$x^2 y - e^{x^3 z} = c.$$

It is at once noticeable that the factor x may be removed from the corresponding differential equation

$$(2xy - 3x^2 z e^{x^3 z}) \, dx + x^2 \, dy - x^3 e^{x^3 z} \, dz = 0,$$

---

* Wilson's *Advanced Calculus*, page 93.

† More generally, a total differential equation is one of the form $P(x, y, z, t, \cdots) \, dx + Q(x, y, z, t, \cdots) \, dy + R(x, y, z, t, \cdots) \, dz + S(x, y, z, t, \cdots) \, dt + \cdots = 0$.

producing the equation

$$(2y - 3xze^{x^3z}) \, dx + x \, dy - x^2 e^{x^3z} \, dz = 0.$$

If one were confronted with this equation to solve, he would find it expedient first to multiply by the *integrating factor* x, thus rendering the equation *exact*.

54. Condition for exactness. Let us study the differential equation

$$P \, dx + Q \, dy + R \, dz = 0, \tag{3}$$

where P, Q, and R are continuous functions of x, y, and z, having continuous first partial derivatives.   We shall first suppose equation (3) to be exact, that is, that there exists a function $\varphi(x, y, z)$ which is continuous and has continuous first and second partial derivatives such that

$$\varphi_x \equiv P, \; \varphi_y \equiv Q, \; \varphi_z \equiv R. \tag{4}$$

In this case we find, by further differentiation, that

$$\varphi_{xy} \equiv P_y \equiv Q_x, \; \varphi_{xz} \equiv P_z \equiv R_x, \; \varphi_{yz} \equiv Q_z \equiv R_y,$$

from which we draw the necessary condition

$$P_y \equiv Q_x, \; R_x \equiv P_z, \; Q_z \equiv R_y. \tag{5}$$

Let us now discard the assumption that such a function φ exists, and assume instead that the relations (5) hold.   With this hypothesis we seek to prove the existence of a function φ for which the relations (4) are true.   To prove this we follow the style of Section 8, Chapter II, and set up the function

$$\varphi(x, y, z) \equiv \int_a^x P(x, y, z) \, dx + \int_b^y Q(a, y, z) \, dy + \int R(a, b, z) \, dz,$$

where each integral is to be evaluated with all variables in its integrand, other than the variable of integration, held constant, and a and b are any constants for which the integrals exist.   Forming the partial derivatives, φ_x, φ_y, and φ_z, we obtain

$$\varphi_x \equiv P(x, y, z),$$
$$\varphi_y \equiv \frac{\partial}{\partial y} \int_a^x P(x, y, z) dx + Q(a, y, z)$$
$$\equiv \int_a^x P_y(x, y, z) dx + Q(a, y, z)$$

$$\equiv \int_a^x Q_x(x,\, y,\, z)dx + Q(a,\, y,\, z)$$

$$\equiv Q(x,\, y,\, z) \Big|_{x=a}^{x=x} + Q(a,\, y,\, z)$$

$$\equiv Q(x,\, y,\, z),$$

$$\varphi_z \equiv \frac{\partial}{\partial z}\left[\int_a^x P(x,\, y,\, z)dx + \int_b^y Q(a,\, y,\, z)dy\right] + R(a,\, b,\, z)$$

$$\equiv \int_a^x P_z(x,\, y,\, z)dx + \int_b^y Q_z(a,\, y,\, z)dy + R(a,\, b,\, z)$$

$$\equiv \int_a^x R_x(x,\, y,\, z)dx + \int_b^y R_y(a,\, y,\, z)dy + R(a,\, b,\, z)$$

$$\equiv R(x,\, y,\, z) \Big|_{x=a}^{x=x} + R(a,\, y,\, z) \Big|_{y=b}^{y=y} + R(a,\, b,\, z)$$

$$\equiv R(x,\, y,\, z).$$

Thus we see that this function φ has the desired properties, and that the conditions (5) are sufficient for the exactness of the given equation (3). These conditions for exactness can easily be remembered if one notes that they consist of the three conditions for the exactness of the three differential equations $P\, dx + Q\, dy = 0$, $P\, dx + R\, dz = 0$, and $Q\, dy + R\, dz = 0$ obtained from (3) by supposing, first, $z = c$, then $y = c$, then $x = c$.

55. Conditions for integrability. If the differential equation (3) is not exact, it may be possible to make it so by use of an integrating factor $\mu(x,\, y,\, z)$, which gives the equation

$$\mu P\, dx + \mu Q\, dy + \mu R\, dz = 0.$$

For this equation to be exact, it is necessary and sufficient that the relations (5) hold, with μP, μQ, μR replacing P, Q, and R, respectively. In this form the relations (5) become

$$\begin{aligned}
\mu P_y + P\mu_y &\equiv \mu Q_x + Q\mu_x, \\
\mu R_x + R\mu_x &\equiv \mu P_z + P\mu_z, \\
\mu Q_z + Q\mu_z &\equiv \mu R_y + R\mu_y.
\end{aligned} \tag{6}$$

Now this system of partial differential equations (6) may or may not have a solution $\mu(x,\, y,\, z)$. If it has no solution, then the given total differential equation (3) has no solution. Furthermore, if (3) has no solution, we should like to have a test by which we could determine the fact, and so avoid a vain attempt to set up the solution. Relation (6) may be considered to furnish such a test, inasmuch as (4) has a solution if, and only if, the system (6) has a solution.   To solve the system (6) for μ might be very difficult in some cases.   However, it happens that if we multiply the first of these equations by R, the second by Q, and the third by P, add the three results, and divide by μ, we obtain

$$P(Q_z - R_y) + Q(R_x - P_z) + R(P_y - Q_x) \equiv 0.$$

This relation does not contain μ, and so may be used as a test upon the functions P, Q, and R appearing in any equation of the form (3).   It may be shown to be sufficient for the existence of an integrating factor μ of (3), and is called the *condition of integrability* of that equation.   This condition is easily remembered by noting that PQR, QRP, and RPQ, appearing, respectively, in the first, second, and third terms, are all in the cyclic* order PQR, while the small letters run $zyxzyx$.

56. Total differential equations which are integrable.   If a total differential equation is found to be exact, it may be integrated at once as in the example

$$(2x + y + z)dx + (2y + x + z)dy + (x + y + 2z)dz = 0,$$

which has the general solution

$$x^2 + y^2 + z^2 + xy + yz + zx = c.$$

If an equation is integrable but not exact, it may be possible to find an integrating factor by inspection.   For example, the equation

$$x\,dx + y\,dy - \sqrt{1 - x^2 - y^2}\,dz = 0$$

is integrable but not exact.   We note that the variable z is not present in P, Q, or R, and hence division by $\sqrt{1 - x^2 - y^2}$ isolates the variable z.   The resulting equation,

$$\frac{x\,dx + y\,dy}{\sqrt{1 - x^2 - y^2}} - dz = 0,$$

is exact and has the general solution

$$\sqrt{1 - x^2 - y^2} + z = c.$$

If the student is unable to discover an integrating factor by inspection, he may proceed as in the example

$$\left(2 - \frac{2y}{x} + \frac{z^3}{x}\right) dx - 2dy + 3z^2\,dz = 0. \tag{7}$$

---

* By *cyclic order* is meant the order in which one may read off the letters if they are arranged around a circle, with the first letter succeeding the last one.

Assume, for the present, that x is a constant and, hence, that $dx = 0$.   The resulting equation

$$-2dy + 3z^2\, dz = 0 \tag{8}$$

has the solution

$$-2y + z^3 = f(x). \tag{9}$$

Here, since we are holding x constant, we replace the constant of integration by an arbitrary function of x.   If the quantity x had appeared in (8), we would have solved it, regarding x as a constant. We shall now evaluate the function $f(x)$ in (9) in such a way that (9) will be a solution of the given equation (7), the quantity x being allowed to vary.   If we take the differential of both sides of (9), we obtain

$$-2dy + 3z^2\, dz = f'(x)\, dx.$$

Now note that the term

$$\left(2 + \frac{-2y + z^3}{x}\right) dx$$

in (7) may be written

$$\left(2 + \frac{f(x)}{x}\right) dx$$

in view of (9), and so equation (7) takes the form

$$\left(2 + \frac{f}{x} + f'\right) dx = 0,$$

which can be written

$$\left(2 + \frac{f}{x}\right) dx + df = 0,$$

and solved by the use of the integrating factor x.   The solution

$$f = \frac{c - x^2}{x}$$

may be substituted in (9) to yield the result

$$-2y + z^3 = \frac{c - x^2}{x}$$

as the complete solution of (7).

Exercises

1. Test the following equations for exactness.   Find an integrating factor by inspection if the equation is not exact.   Solve all equations.

(a) $(2xy - 1)dx + (x^2 + \cos z)dy - (y \sin z + 2z)dz = 0.$

(b) $[x(x^2 + y^2) - y]dx + [y(x^2 + y^2) + x]dy +$
$$(x^2 + y^2)dz = 0.$$

(c) $z(2xz + 1)dx + 2yz^2\, dy + (z - x)dz = 0.$

(d) $(y + a)^2\, dx + z\, dy - (y + a)dz = 0.$

(e) $(x - 1)dx - \sqrt{4 - z^2 - (x - 1)^2}\, dy + z\, dz = 0.$

(f) $\left(\dfrac{e^{xy}}{z} + \dfrac{e^{xz}}{y}\right)\dfrac{dx}{x} + \left(\dfrac{e^{xy}}{z} + \dfrac{e^{yz}}{x}\right)\dfrac{dy}{y} + \left(\dfrac{e^{xz}}{y} + \dfrac{e^{yz}}{x}\right)\dfrac{dz}{z} = 0.$

(g) $(\sinh y + z \cosh x)dx + (\sinh z + x \cosh y)dy +$
$(\sinh x + y \cosh z)dz = 0.$

2. Test the following equations for integrability, and solve those which are integrable:

(a) $(x + z)dx + zx^2\, dy + (yx^2 - x)dz = 0.$

(b) $(x + y + z + 1)dx + dy + dz = 0.$

(c) $x\, dy - y\, dx + z\, dz = 0.$

(d) $(y - xz)dx - (z - \sin^{-1} x) \sqrt{1 - x^2}\, dy + (1 - x^2$
$- y \sqrt{1 - x^2})\, dz = 0.$

(e) $(y^3 - xy^2)dx + x^2y\, dy + 2z\, dz = 0.$

(f) $dx + (x \tan y + z \sec y - \tan y)\, dy + \sin y\, dz = 0.$

3. If P, Q, and R are homogeneous functions of x, y, and z, of the same degree, show that the substitution $x = uz$, $y = vz$ in the equation $P\, dx + Q\, dy + R\, dz = 0$ will separate the variable z from the variables u and v. For the definition of homogeneous functions, see Section 10, Chapter II.

4. Solve the following homogeneous total differential equations, using a substitution of the type of Exercise 3:

(a) $(2yz + 3xy + 4x^2)dx + (xz + x^2)dy + xy\, dz = 0.$

(b) $(y^3 + 2xyz)dx + (4xy^2 + 2x^2z)dy + x^2y\, dz = 0.$

(c) $y^2z^2\, dx + (2xyz^2 \log x - 2xyz^2 \log z - 3xy^2z)dy -$
$(xzy^2 - xy^3)dz = 0.$

(d) $y\, dx - (x + z)dy + y\, dz = 0.$

5. Show that if the equation $P\, dx + Q\, dy + R\, dz = 0$ is exact and homogeneous, of degree not -1, its solution is $xP + yQ + zR = c$. *Hint:* See footnote to Exercise 10, page 30.

6. Solve the following exercises, using the proposition of Exercise 5:

(a) $\dfrac{dx + dz}{y^2} - \dfrac{2(x + z)}{y^3}\, dy = 0.$

(b) $\dfrac{4dx}{x^5} + \dfrac{dy}{z^5} - \dfrac{5y\,dz}{z^6} = 0.$

(c) $(4x^3 + y^2z)dx + 2xyz\,dy + (y^2x + z^3)dz = 0.$

7. Prove that if the variables x, y, and z in the integrable differential equation $P\,dx + Q\,dy + R\,dz = 0$ are replaced by the substitution $x = X(r, s, t)$, $y = Y(r, s, t)$, $z = Z(r, s, t)$, where X, Y, and Z are continuous functions of r, s, and t, having continuous first and second partial derivatives, then the resulting equation is integrable.

8. Find conditions necessary for the exactness of the equation $P\,dx + Q\,dy + R\,dz + S\,dt = 0$, and prove that those conditions are sufficient. *Hint:* To find the necessary conditions, suppose x, y, z, and t to be constant in pairs, and write down the conditions that the equations in two variables thus obtained be exact. To prove the conditions sufficient, suppose that they hold, and set up a function $\varphi(x, y, z, t)$, as in the text, page 192.

9. Test the following equations for exactness, and solve those which are exact:

(a) $(t + y)dx + (x + z)dy + (y + t)dz + (z + x)dt = 0.$

(b) $y\,dx + z\,dy + t\,dz + x\,dt = 0.$

(c) $3x^2y^2\,dx + (2x^3y + 2z)dy + (2y + t)dz + z\,dt = 0.$

10. The following equations are not exact, but integrable. Find the general solution.

(a) $(2xy + 2x^2z - 2xt + z)dx + dy + x\,dz - dt = 0.$

(b) $t^2\,dx + 2xyt^2\,dy + xt^2\,dz + x\,dt + xt^2\,du + 2xt^2v\,dv$
$$= 0.$$

11. Prove that if the equation $P\,dx + Q\,dy + R\,dz + S\,dt = 0$ is exact and homogeneous, and of degree not -1, then the solution is

$$xP + yQ + zR + tS = c.$$

Hint: See hint of Exercise 5, above.

12. Use the proposition of Exercise 11 to write down the solution of

$(4x^3 + 3x^2y + 2xyz + yzt)dx + (x^3 + x^2z + xzt)dy$
$$+ (x^2y + xyt)dz + xyz\,dt = 0.$$

13. By following a method similar to that of Section 55 of this chapter, show that if the equation

$$P\,dx + Q\,dy + R\,dz + S\,dt = 0$$

is integrable, the relations

$$P(Q_z - R_y) + Q(R_x - P_z) + R(P_y - Q_x) \equiv 0,$$
$$P(Q_t - S_y) + Q(S_x - P_t) + S(P_y - Q_x) \equiv 0,$$
$$P(R_t - S_z) + R(S_x - P_t) + S(P_z - R_x) \equiv 0,$$
$$Q(R_t - S_z) + R(S_y - Q_t) + S(Q_z - R_y) \equiv 0,$$

hold. Show also that if any three of these relations hold, then the fourth one holds.

57. Geometric significance. For the sake of clarity, geometric nomenclature will be employed occasionally in the discussions which are to follow. If the set of variables (x, y, z) are taken as the rectangular coördinates of a point in space, then a relation among them, such as $x^2y - e^x + \cos z = 3$, represents a surface. Two equations, considered as simultaneous, represent a curve which is the curve of intersection of the two surfaces represented by the two equations, considered separately. The differentials dx, dy, and dz determine a line through the point (x, y, z) and the point $(x + dx, y + dy, z + dz)$ having the direction ratios $dx:dy:dz$. If we think of x, y, and z as fixed coördinates of a point, and dx, dy, and dz as variables in a differential equation

$$P\,dx + Q\,dy + R\,dz = 0, \tag{3}$$

we may assign the quantities dy and dz arbitrarily, and solve* for dx. This freedom makes it possible to satisfy (3), with x, y, and z fixed, by an infinite number of directions $dx:dy:dz$. If we consider P, Q, and R as direction ratios, we see that (3) is satisfied by any direction $dx:dy:dz$ which is perpendicular to the direction $P:Q:R$. Hence, these directions $dx:dy:dz$, satisfying (3) with x, y, and z fixed, while infinite in number, are all in a plane.†

58. Pairs of total differential equations. Let us consider simultaneously two equations

$$P_1\,dx + Q_1\,dy + R_1\,dz = 0, \tag{10}$$
$$P_2\,dx + Q_2\,dy + R_2\,dz = 0.$$

---

* Assuming $P \neq 0$.

† This plane is unique for every point (x, y, z), excepting those points for which $P = Q = R = 0$. At such points the direction $P:Q:R$ is indeterminate, and equation (3) is satisfied by every direction $dx:dy:dz$.

Geometrically, (10_1) is satisfied at each point (x, y, z) by the direction $dx:dy:dz$ of any line in a plane π_1, while (10_2) is satisfied at each point by the direction $dx:dy:dz$ of any line in another* plane π_2. Then both of the equations (10) are satisfied by at least one direction, *viz.*, that of any line common to the planes π_1 and π_2. In other words, we expect equations (10) to determine a direction $dx:dy:dz$ unique for every point $P(x, y, z)$ of space, excepting at those points for which

$$P_1:Q_1:R_1 = P_2:Q_2:R_2.$$

If we eliminate dz between (10_1) and (10_2), we obtain

$$(R_1P_2 - R_2P_1)dx = (Q_1R_2 - Q_2R_1)dy,$$

or

$$\frac{dx}{Q_1R_2 - Q_2R_1} = \frac{dy}{R_1P_2 - R_2P_1}.$$

If we eliminate dx, we obtain

$$\frac{dy}{R_1P_2 - R_2P_1} = \frac{dz}{P_1Q_2 - P_2Q_1}.$$

These two equations may be written in the form

$$\frac{dx}{P} = \frac{dy}{Q} = \frac{dz}{R}, \tag{11}$$

where $P \equiv \lambda(Q_1R_2 - Q_2R_1)$, $Q \equiv \lambda(R_1P_2 - R_2P_1)$, $R \equiv \lambda(P_1Q_2 - P_2Q_1)$, $\lambda \not\equiv 0$. Equations (11) are said to be the *symmetric* form of equations (10), and show that the direction $dx:dy:dz$ which the equations define for the point (x, y, z), if unique, is that given by the ratios $P:Q:R$.

59. Solutions of a pair of total differential equations in three variables. We have seen that a pair of total differential equations of the form (10) define a direction through each point (x, y, z). Another method of representing a direction through each point of space is to give the equations of two one-parameter families of surfaces such that through each point (x, y, z) passes one surface of each family. The two, being distinct surfaces,† determine a curve

---

* This plane π_2 will coincide with π_1 only in case $P_1:Q_1:R_1 = P_2:Q_2:R_2$, at (x, y, z).

† If the surfaces of the family $u(x, y, z) = C$ coincide with the surfaces of the family $v(x, y, z) = c$, then u is a function of v, and the functions u and v are dependent. A discussion of dependence of functions appears in Section 61.

through the point, the tangent to which provides a direction. We are thus led intuitively to expect the solution of the pair of equations (10) to be a pair of relations

$$f(x, y, z, c_1) = 0, \, g(x, y, z, c_2) = 0. \tag{12}$$

In the event that each of the equations (10) is separately integrable, we have (12) immediately by taking the solution of (10_1) as (12_1) and the solution of (10_2) as (12_2). For example, the equations

$$\begin{cases} y^2 \, dx + z \, dy - y \, dz = 0, \\ (2y - 3z)dx + (z - 2x)dy + (3x - y)dz = 0, \end{cases} \tag{13}$$

are each integrable. The complete solution of (13_1) is

$$(x + c_1)y - z = 0, \tag{14_1}$$

while the complete solution of (13_2) is

$$2x - z + c_2(2y - 3z) = 0. \tag{14_2}$$

These two equations (14), considered simultaneously, form the solution to (13) considered simultaneously, since every curve on a surface of (14_1) has a direction satisfying (13_1), and every curve on a surface of (14_2) has a direction satisfying (13_2). Every curve of intersection (14), being on both types of surfaces, has a direction satisfying both equations (13).

If only one of equations (10), say (10_1), is integrable, let its solution be (12_1). We may employ (10_1), (10_2), and (12_1) to eliminate one variable and its differential, obtaining a differential equation in the other two variables. Its solution may be called (12_2). For example, consider

$$\begin{cases} (2x + z + y)dx + (1 - z)dy + (7 - y)dz = 0, \\ (z + y)dx + dy + dz = 0. \end{cases} \tag{15}$$

The first equation is not integrable, but the second one is, and has as solution

$$e^x y + e^x z = c_1. \tag{16}$$

If we eliminate dz between the two equations (15) by subtracting $(7 - y)$ times the second one from the first, we obtain

$$(2x - 6y - 6z + y^2 + yz)dx + (y - 6 - z)dy = 0. \tag{17}$$

From (16) we have the result that

$$z = c_1 e^{-x} - y,$$

which we may substitute in (17) to obtain

$$(2x - 6c_1 e^{-x} + c_1 y e^{-x})dx + (2y - 6 - c_1 e^{-x})dy = 0.$$

This equation is exact and has as solution

$$x^2 + 6c_1 e^{-x} - c_1 y e^{-x} + y^2 - 6y = c_2. \tag{18}$$

We may then consider (16) and (18) simultaneously as the solution of (15). If we substitute the value $(y + z)e^x$ of c_1 from (16) into (18), the latter reduces to

$$x^2 - yz + 6z = c_2, \tag{19}$$

which is not only simpler, but is free of c_1. Equations (16) and (18), or (16) and (19), furnish the desired solution of (15).

By ratio and proportion we may pass from (11) to the relation

$$\frac{dx}{P} = \frac{dy}{Q} = \frac{dz}{R} = \frac{l\,dx + m\,dy + n\,dz}{lP + mQ + nR},$$

where l, m, and n are any quantities whatever. It may be possible that the denominator $lP + mQ + nR$ is identically zero. Then the numerator must vanish, and if the resulting equation

$$l\,dx + m\,dy + n\,dz = 0$$

is integrable, we can find a solution. For example, if in the equations

$$\frac{dx}{x^2 + z^2 - 2yz} = \frac{dy}{2yz - 2xy} = \frac{dz}{2xy - x^2 - z^2} \tag{20}$$

we use the multipliers 1, 1, 1, we have the result

$$\frac{dx}{x^2 + z^2 - 2yz} = \frac{dy}{2yz - 2xy} = \frac{dz}{2xy - x^2 - z^2} = \frac{dx + dy + dz}{0}$$

or

$$dx + dy + dz = 0.$$

This equation is exact and has the solution

$$x + y + z = c_1. \tag{21}$$

Substitution of this into (20) gives

$$\frac{dx}{2x^2 + 4xy + 3y^2 - 2c_1x - 4c_1y + c_1^2} = \frac{dy}{2c_1y - 4xy - 2y^2},$$

or

$$(2c_1y - 4xy - 2y^2)dx - (2x^2 + 4xy + 3y^2 - 2c_1x - 4c_1y + c_1^2)dy = 0.$$

This equation is exact and has as solution

$$2c_1xy - 2x^2y - 2xy^2 - y^3 + 2c_1y^2 - c_1^2y = c_2.$$

If we substitute $c_1 = x + y + z$ into this, upon simplification we have

$$x^2y + yz^2 = c_2. \tag{22}$$

We may note that (22) could be obtained directly by taking the multipliers $l = 2xy$, $m = x^2 + z^2$, $n = 2yz$, which makes the members of (20) equal to

$$\frac{2xy\, dx + (x^2 + z^2)dy + 2yz\, dz}{2xy(x^2+z^2) - 4xy^2z + 2x^2yz + 2yz^3 - 2xy(x^2+z^2) + 4xy^2z - 2x^2yz - 2yz^3}$$

of which the denominator is identically zero, and gives

$$2xy\, dx + (x^2 + z^2)dy + 2yz\, dz = 0,$$

which is exact and has (22) as its solution.

Exercises

1. Solve the following pairs of integrable equations:

(a) $\begin{cases} y\, dx + (x + 2yz)dy + y^2\, dz = 0, \\ 3x^2yz\, dx + x^3z\, dy - x^3y\, dz = 0. \end{cases}$

 (b) $\dfrac{2x^3\, dx}{yz} = \dfrac{y\, dy}{x^2z} = \dfrac{dz}{y}.$

(c) $\begin{cases} z\, dx + (xz - y^2 - 2y)dy + x\, dz = 0, \\ yz^2\, dx - z(xz + y^2)dy + y^3\, dz = 0. \end{cases}$

(d) $\dfrac{dx}{-2x^3y^3z} = \dfrac{dy}{z} = \dfrac{dz}{2y^3}.$

(e) $\begin{cases} x\, dx + y\, dy + z\, dz = 0, \\ (y + z)dx + (z + x)dy + (x + y)dz = 0. \end{cases}$

(f) $\dfrac{dx}{y^2} = \dfrac{dy}{x^2} = \dfrac{dz}{x^2y^2e^z}.$

2. Solve the following pairs of equations, in each of which one equation is integrable:

(a) $\dfrac{dx}{y} = \dfrac{dy}{x} = \dfrac{dz}{z}.$

(b) $\begin{cases} (2xy + z^2)dx + (2yz + x^2)dy + (2xz + y^2)dz = 0, \\ (2xy - z^2)dx + (2yz + x^2)dy - (2xz - y^2)dz = 0. \end{cases}$

(c) $\dfrac{dx}{x^2z^2 - 4y^2z^2 - 1} = \dfrac{dy}{xyz^2} = \dfrac{dz}{-2xz^3}.$

(d) $-\dfrac{dx}{y} = \dfrac{dy}{x} = \dfrac{dz}{\sqrt{1 - z^2}}.$

(e) $\dfrac{du}{uz} = -\dfrac{dv}{vz} = \dfrac{dz}{2u}.$

(f) $\begin{cases} 2(z - 2x)dx = (z - 3x)dz, \\ (z - x)dy = (xz - x^2 + yz - xy + 3x - z)(dz - dx). \end{cases}$

(g) $\dfrac{x - y}{dx} = \dfrac{x + y - 10}{dy} = \dfrac{0}{dz}.$

(h) $\dfrac{dx}{3x(y - 2x)} = \dfrac{dy}{3y(2y - x)} = \dfrac{dz}{z(x - y)}.$

3. Solve the following pairs of equations by use of multipliers l, m, and n, as on page 201:

(a) $\dfrac{dx}{6(y - z)} = \dfrac{2dy}{3(z - x)} = \dfrac{3dz}{2(x - y)}.$

(b) $\dfrac{dx}{9y - 3z} = \dfrac{dy}{4x + 6y} = \dfrac{dz}{12x + 6z}.$

(c) $\dfrac{dx}{x(3y - 4z)} = \dfrac{dy}{y(4z - 2x)} = \dfrac{dz}{z(2x - 3y)}.$

(d) $\dfrac{dx}{3yz} = -\dfrac{dy}{3xz} = \dfrac{dz}{xy}.$

(e) $\dfrac{dx}{x(4y^2 - z^2)} = \dfrac{-dy}{y(z^2 + 9x^2)} = \dfrac{dz}{z(9x^2 + 4y^2)}.$

(f) $\dfrac{dx}{x(y^3 - z^3)} = \dfrac{dy}{y(z^3 - x^3)} = \dfrac{dz}{z(x^3 - y^3)}.$

4. Show that a system of equations of the form

$$\dfrac{dx}{P} = \dfrac{dy}{Q} = \dfrac{dz}{R} \tag{11}$$

can be reduced to a linear equation of order 2 in two variables.

Hint: Solve (11) for $\dfrac{dy}{dx}$ and $\dfrac{dz}{dx}$ to obtain

$$\frac{dy}{dx} = \frac{Q}{P} \tag{23}$$

and

$$\frac{dz}{dx} = \frac{R}{P}. \tag{24}$$

Differentiate (23) with respect to x, replacing $\dfrac{dz}{dx}$ by $\dfrac{R}{P}$ from (24) whenever it appears, to obtain

$$\frac{d^2y}{dx^2} = \frac{PQ_y - QP_y}{P^2} \cdot \frac{dy}{dx} + \frac{RPQ_z - QRP_z + P^2Q_x - PQP_x}{P^3}. \tag{25}$$

Now eliminate z between (23) and (25) if it appears in the former. If it is not in (23), it will not be in (25).

5. Solve the following systems of equations by first reducing each system to a linear equation, as in Exercise 4:

$$\text{(a)} \quad \frac{dx}{1} = \frac{dy}{4y - z} = \frac{dz}{3y - x}.$$

Hint: The method of Exercise 4 gives the linear equation

$$\frac{d^2y}{dx^2} - 4\frac{dy}{dx} + 3y = x,$$

of which

$$y = c_1 e^x + c_2 e^{3x} + \frac{x}{3} + \frac{4}{9} \tag{26}$$

is the general solution. If from the given equation we draw the equation

$$\frac{dy}{dx} = 4y - z,$$

which is free of dz, we may solve for z to obtain

$$z = 4y - \frac{dy}{dx},$$

$$z = 4\left(c_1 e^x + c_2 e^{3x} + \frac{x}{3} + \frac{4}{9}\right) - \left(c_1 e^x + 3c_2 e^{3x} + \frac{1}{3}\right),$$

$$z = 3c_1 e^x + c_2 e^{3x} + \frac{4x}{3} + \frac{13}{9}. \tag{27}$$

The relations (26) and (27) furnish the general solution. They may be solved for c_1 and c_2 to obtain

$$\begin{cases} e^{-x}(z - y - x - 1) = 2c_1, \\ e^{-3x}(27y - 9z + 3x + 1) = 18c_2, \end{cases}$$

or

$$\begin{cases} z - y - x - 1 = c_1 e^x, \\ 27y - 9z + 3x + 1 = c_2 e^{3x}, \end{cases}$$

where $2c_1$ has been called c_1 and $18c_2$ has been called c_2.

(b) $\dfrac{dy}{dx} = 6y - 2z, \dfrac{dz}{dx} = 2y + 2z.$

(c) $\begin{cases} (15y + 9z)dx + 3dy + dz = 0, \\ (12y + 3z)dx + 6dy - dz = 0. \end{cases}$

(d) $\dfrac{dx}{1} = \dfrac{dy}{-5y + z + e^x} = \dfrac{dz}{2y - 6z + 2e^{2x}}.$

(e) $\dfrac{dx}{1} = \dfrac{dy}{y + 4z + \sin x} = \dfrac{dz}{y + 4z + \cos x}.$

(f) $\dfrac{dx}{1} = \dfrac{dy}{3y + z + 12e^{2x}} = \dfrac{dz}{-y + z + 6xe^{2x}}.$

(g) $\dfrac{dx}{1} = \dfrac{dy}{ay + bz + f(x)} = \dfrac{dz}{cy + gz + \varphi(x)}.$

6. Solve the system of equations

$$\frac{dy}{dx} + X_0 \cdot (a_1 y + b_1 z) = X_1,$$

$$\frac{dz}{dx} + X_0 \cdot (a_2 y + b_2 z) = X_2,$$

where X_0, X_1, and X_2 are functions of x. By multiplying the second equation by m and adding it to the first, we obtain

$$\frac{dy}{dx} + m\frac{dz}{dx} + X_0[(a_1 + ma_2)y + (b_1 + mb_2)z] = X_1 + mX_2.$$

It is noticeable that the first two terms can be written as $\dfrac{d}{dx}(y + mz)$. If we select m so that $[(a_1 + ma_2)y + (b_1 + mb_2)z]$ is a constant multiple of $(y + mz)$, the equation becomes linear in the two variables $y + mz$, and x. This requires that $\dfrac{a_1 + ma_2}{b_1 + mb_2} = \dfrac{1}{m}$, or that m be a solution of the quadratic equation

$$a_2 m^2 + (a_1 - b_2)m - b_1 = 0.$$

7. Solve by the method of Exercise 6:

(a) $\begin{cases} \dfrac{dy}{dx} + x^2(4y + 2z) = e^{x^3}, \\[2mm] \dfrac{dz}{dx} + x^2(y + 5z) = 3x^2e^{x^3}. \end{cases}$

(b) $\begin{cases} \dfrac{dy}{dx} + \dfrac{3}{x}\,(2y - z) = x^2 - \dfrac{3}{x}, \\[2mm] \dfrac{dz}{dx} + \dfrac{1}{x}\,(y + 2z) = x^2 - \dfrac{1}{x}. \end{cases}$

(c) $\begin{cases} \dfrac{dy}{dx} - 2(y - 3z) = \sinh x, \\[2mm] \dfrac{dz}{dx} + y + z = \cosh x. \end{cases}$

(d) $\begin{cases} \dfrac{dy}{dx} + \tan x \cdot 8z = \sec x, \\[2mm] \dfrac{dz}{dx} + \tan x \cdot (y + z) = \sec^2 x. \end{cases}$

8. If $f(x, y, z) = c_1$ and $g(x, y, z) = c_2$ furnish a solution of the pair of differential equations $\dfrac{dx}{P} = \dfrac{dy}{Q} = \dfrac{dz}{R}$, show that $f(x, y, z) + \lambda g(x, y, z) = c_1$ and $f(x, y, z) + kg(x, y, z) = c_2$ are a solution, where λ and k are different constants. Explain geometrically.

9. Test each equation in the system below for integrability. Find the solution of each equation, and draw your conclusions about the number of relations in four variables which can satisfy three ordinary differential equations simultaneously.

$$\begin{cases} (y + w)dx + (w + x)dy + 2z\,dz + (x + y)dw = 0, \\ y(z - w)dx - x(x - w)dy + y^2\,dz - y^2\,dw = 0, \\ (5x^3 + 4x^2y + 3xz^2 + 2w^3)dx + x^3\,dy + 2x^2z\,dz + 3xw^2\,dw = 0. \end{cases}$$

60. Non-integrable equations. We have seen that a differential equation

$$P\,dx + Q\,dy + R\,dz = 0 \tag{3}$$

may be non-integrable, while a pair of equations such as

$$\begin{aligned} P_1\,dx + Q_1\,dy + R_1\,dz = 0, \\ P_2\,dx + Q_2\,dy + R_2\,dz = 0, \end{aligned} \tag{10}$$

is always integrable as a pair. This suggests the expedient of annexing, to a non-integrable equation of the form (3), an arbitrary equation such as

$$P' \, dx + Q' \, dy + R' \, dz = 0 \tag{28}$$

and solving (3) and (28) simultaneously as a pair. For convenience, one may choose (28) as an equation which is integrable and whose solution is known to satisfy any desired condition. Geometrically, this means that while we can find no surface such that every direction on the surface satisfies (3) at each point, we may find curves on an arbitrary surface, such that the direction of each curve satisfies (3).

Exercises

In each of the following, find the equations of the curves which lie on the surface defined by relation (b) and which satisfy the differential equation (a):

1. (a) $2y \, dx - 3x \, dy + z \, dz = 0$,
 (b) $x^2 + y^2 + z^2 = c$.

2. (a) $aby \, dx + abx \, dy - c(ax + by + cz)dz = 0$,
 (b) $ax + by + cz = d$.

3. (a) $x(a \cos^2 y + b \sin^2 y)dx + x^2(b^2 - a^2) \sin y \cos y \, dy + (1 - x^2)^{1/2}dz = 0$,
 (b) $x^2 + z^2 = 1$.

4. (a) $x \, dy - y \, dx + z \, dz = 0$,
 (b) $x = c$.

5. (a) $(y^3 - xy^2)dx + x^2y \, dy + 2z \, dz = 0$,
 (b) $2z^2 = x^2y^2$.

6. (a) $dx = z \, dy + dz$,
 (b) $z = f(y)$.

61. Dependence and functional determinants. Let us consider n functions

$$u'(x_1, \cdots, x_n), u''(x_1, \cdots, x_n), \cdots, u^{(n)}(x_1, \cdots, x_n)$$

of the same n independent variables $x_1, \cdots, x_n$, which have continuous first partial derivatives $u_{x_i}^{(j)}$. If there exists a function $\varphi(u', u'', \cdots, u^{(n)})$ of the n arguments $u', \cdots, u^{(n)}$ having first partial derivatives $\varphi_{u^{(j)}} (j = 1, \cdots, n)$ such that the relation

$$\varphi(u', u'', \cdots, u^{(n)}) \equiv 0 \tag{29}$$

is satisfied, the functions $u^{(j)}$ are said to be *dependent*. If no such function exists, the functions $u^{(j)}$ are called *independent*.

To find a criterion for the dependence of a set of functions, let us assume that (29) holds, with φ and the $u^{(j)}$ subject to the restrictions cited above. Taking the first partial derivative of each side of (29) with respect to each variable x_i, we obtain thus the n relations

$$\begin{cases} \varphi_{u'}\, u'_{x_1} + \varphi_{u''}\, u''_{x_1} + \cdots + \varphi_{u^{(n)}}\, u^{(n)}_{x_1} \equiv 0, \\ \varphi_{u'}\, u'_{x_2} + \varphi_{u''}\, u''_{x_2} + \cdots + \varphi_{u^{(n)}}\, u^{(n)}_{x_2} \equiv 0, \\ \;\cdot\;\cdot\;\cdot\;\cdot\;\cdot\;\cdot\;\cdot\;\cdot\;\cdot\;\cdot\;\cdot\;\cdot\;\cdot\;\cdot\;\cdot\;\cdot\;\cdot\;\cdot \\ \;\cdot\;\cdot\;\cdot\;\cdot\;\cdot\;\cdot\;\cdot\;\cdot\;\cdot\;\cdot\;\cdot\;\cdot\;\cdot\;\cdot\;\cdot\;\cdot\;\cdot\;\cdot \\ \varphi_{u'}\, u'_{x_n} + \varphi_{u''}\, u''_{x_n} + \cdots + \varphi_{u^{(n)}} \cdot u^{(n)}_{x_n} \equiv 0. \end{cases}$$

In order that these n linear equations in the n derivatives $\varphi_{u^{(j)}}$ hold simultaneously, with $\varphi_u{}^{(j)}$ not all zero, it is necessary and sufficient that the determinant of the coefficients vanish identically, *i. e.*,

$$\begin{vmatrix} u'_{x_1} & u''_{x_1} & \cdots & u^{(n)}_{x_1} \\ u'_{x_2} & u''_{x_2} & \cdots & u^{(n)}_{x_2} \\ \cdot & \cdot & \cdots & \cdot \\ \cdot & \cdot & \cdots & \cdot \\ u'_{x_n} & u''_{x_n} & \cdots & u^{(n)}_{x_n} \end{vmatrix} \equiv 0.$$

This determinant is met with very frequently in mathematics, and is known as the *functional determinant* of the functions involved. It is also called their *Jacobian*, in honor of the German mathematician Jacobi (1804–1851), who made important contributions to many branches of pure and applied mathematics.

From the results above, we draw

THEOREM I. *If* $u^{(j)}$($j = 1, \cdots, n$) *are* n *dependent functions of* n *independent variables* x_i($i = 1, \cdots, n$) *having continuous first partial derivatives* $u^{(j)}_{x_i}$, *the Jacobian of the* u's *vanishes identically.*

It can be shown,* conversely, that, if the Jacobian of the u's vanishes identically, the functions are dependent.

In an entirely similar manner we define n functions

$$u', u'', \cdots, u^{(n)}$$

in more than n variables x_i($i = 1, \cdots, n + t$), having continuous first partial derivatives $u^{(j)}_{x_i}$, to be *dependent* if there exists a function φ of n arguments, having first partial derivatives with

---

* Wilson's *Advanced Calculus*, page 129 ff.

respect to those arguments, such that (29) holds. Under these circumstances we may form the system

$$\begin{cases} \varphi_{u'} \, u'_{x_1} + \cdots + \varphi_{u^{(n)}} \, u^{(n)}_{x_1} \equiv 0, \\ \cdots \cdots \cdots \cdots \cdots \cdots \cdots \\ \varphi_{u'} \, u'_{x_m} + \cdots + \varphi_{u^{(n)}} \, u^{(n)}_{x_m} \equiv 0 \qquad (m = n + t), \end{cases}$$

of m equations in n functions $\varphi_{u^{(j)}}$. Since $m > n$, we can find solutions* with $\varphi_{u^{(j)}}$ not all zero if, and only if, the matrix of coefficients

$$\begin{pmatrix} u'_{x_1} & \cdots & u^{(n)}_{x_1}, \\ \cdots & \cdots & \cdots \\ u'_{x_m} & \cdots & u^{(n)}_{x_m}, \end{pmatrix} \tag{30}$$

has a rank† less than n, and this is therefore a necessary condition for the dependence of the functions $u^{(j)}$. We shall employ this result without the formality of stating it in a theorem.

The converse of the above proposition is also true, as can be established by adjoining to the matrix (30) $m - n$ new columns

$$\begin{array}{ccc} u^{(n+1)}_{x_1} & \cdots & u^{(m)}_{x_1} \\ \cdots & \cdots & \cdots \\ u^{(n+1)}_{x_m} & \cdots & u^{(m)}_{x_m}, \end{array}$$

where $u^{(n+1)}, \cdots, u^{(m)}$ are arbitrary functions, and then applying the converse of Theorem 1.

62. Determinate systems involving several variables. Let us consider n simultaneous equations

$$u^{(j)} = c_j \qquad (j = 1, \cdots, n), \quad (31)$$

where the $u^{(j)}$ are n independent functions of the variables $z, x_1, \cdots, x_n$, as the *solution* of the system of ordinary differential equations

$$\begin{cases} u'_z \, dz + u'_{x_1} \, dx_1 + \cdots + u'_{x_n} \, dx_n = 0, \\ u''_z \, dz + u''_{x_1} \, dx_1 + \cdots + u''_{x_n} \, dx_n = 0, \\ \cdots \cdots \cdots \cdots \cdots \cdots \cdots \cdots \\ \cdots \cdots \cdots \cdots \cdots \cdots \cdots \cdots \\ u^{(n)}_z \, dz + u^{(n)}_{x_1} \, dx_1 + \cdots + u^{(n)}_{x_n} \, dx_n = 0. \end{cases} \tag{32}$$

---

* Bocher's *Higher Algebra*, page 47, Theorem 3.

† If at least one r-rowed determinant of a matrix is not zero (identically), while every determinant of order higher than r is zero (identically), the matrix is said to have the *rank* r.

We can solve this system for the ratios of the differentials, and obtain

$$\frac{dz}{X_0} = \frac{dx_1}{X_1} = \frac{dx_2}{X_2} = \cdots = \frac{dx_n}{X_n},$$ (33)

where

$$X_0 \equiv |u_{x_1}^{(j)}\ u_{x_2}^{(j)}\ u_{x_3}^{(j)} \cdots u_{x_n}^{(j)}|,$$
$$X_1 \equiv -\ |u_z^{(j)}\ u_{x_2}^{(j)}\ u_{x_3}^{(j)} \cdots u_{x_n}^{(j)}|,$$
$$X_2 \equiv |u_z^{(j)}\ u_{x_1}^{(j)}\ u_{x_3}^{(j)} \cdots u_{x_n}^{(j)}|,$$ (34)
$$\cdots \cdots \cdots \cdots \cdots \cdots \cdots \cdots$$
$$X_n \equiv (-1)^n\ |u_z^{(j)}\ u_{x_1}^{(j)}\ u_{x_2}^{(j)} \cdots u_{x_{n-1}}^{(j)}|,$$

the symbols on the right representing determinants, of which the jth row is displayed. The functions $X_i (i = 0, \cdots, n)$ cannot all be zero, since in that case the n-rowed matrix whose j^{th} row is

$$(u_z^{(j)}\ u_{x_1}^{(j)}\ u_{x_2}^{(j)}\ u_{x_3}^{(j)} \cdots u_{x_n}^{(j)})$$ (35)

would have a rank less than n, and the functions $u^{(j)}$ would be dependent, which is contrary to the hypothesis. In the event that $X_i \equiv 0$ for $i = i_0, i_1, \cdots, i_p$ and $X_i \not\equiv 0$ for $i = i_{p+1}, \cdots, i_n$ we shall understand (33) to mean

$$dx_{i_e} = 0 \qquad\qquad (e = 0, \cdots, p),$$
$$\frac{dx_{i_{p+1}}}{X_{i_{p+1}}} = \frac{dx_{i_{p+2}}}{X_{i_{p+2}}} = \cdots = \frac{dx_{i_n}}{X_{i_n}},$$

where z is denoted by x_0.

The n simultaneous equations (31) define a system of *curves* in space of $n + 1$ *dimensions*. The ratios $dz:dx_1:dx_2: \cdots :dx_n$ are uniquely determined for every *point* $(z, x_1, \cdots, x_n)$ for which the X_i do not all vanish, and are said to define a *direction*. The curves defined by (31) are called the *characteristics* of the system (32). A single characteristic is, thus, the locus of points which satisfy all of the equations (31) with a set of particular values assigned to the n arbitrary constants c_j. The coördinates of any fixed point $(\zeta, \xi_1, \xi_2, \cdots, \xi_n)$ satisfy all equations (31) with $c_j = u^{(j)}(\zeta, \xi_1, \cdots, \xi_n)$, and hence there is one, and only one, characteristic through each point.

If, now, we set up n independent functions $v^{(j)}(j = 1, \cdots, n)$ of the u's of (31) and form the n equations

$$v^{(j)} = d_j \qquad\qquad (j = 1, \cdots, n) \quad (36)$$

and form from (36) the system

$$\frac{dz}{Y_0} = \frac{dx_1}{Y_1} = \frac{dx_2}{Y_2} = \cdots = \frac{dx_n}{Y_n} \quad (37)$$

Corresponding to (33), we have

$$Y_0 \equiv |v_{x_1}^{(j)} \, v_{x_2}^{(j)} \, \cdots \, v_{x_n}^{(j)}|,$$
$$Y_1 \equiv - |v_z^{(j)} \, v_{x_2}^{(j)} \, \cdots \, v_{x_n}^{(j)}|,$$
$$\cdots \cdots \cdots \cdots$$
$$Y_n \equiv (-1)^n |v_z^{(j)} \, v_{x_1}^{(j)} \, \cdots \, v_{x_{n-1}}^{(j)}|.$$

Now, since

$$v_{x_i}^{(j)} = v_{u'}^{(j)} \, u'_{x_i} + v_{u''}^{(j)} \, u''_{x_i} + \cdots + v_{u^{(n)}}^{(j)} \, u_{x_i}^{(n)},$$

the element in the jth row and i^{th} column of the determinant

$$|v_{x_1}^{(j)} \, v_{x_2}^{(j)} \, \cdots \, v_{x_n}^{(j)}|$$

defining Y_0, is the sum of the products of the corresponding elements from the jth row of

$$\Delta \equiv |v_{u'}^{(j)} \, v_{u''}^{(j)} \, \cdots \, v_{u^{(n)}}^{(j)}|$$

and the ith column of

$$X_0 \equiv |u_{x_1}^{(j)} \, u_{x_2}^{(j)} \, \cdots \, u_{x_n}^{(j)}|.$$

Thus, by the rule for the product of determinants,

$$Y_0 \equiv \Delta X_0.$$

Similarly,

$$Y_i \equiv \Delta X_i \qquad\qquad (i = 1, \, \cdots, \, n),$$

and since the functions $v^{(j)}$ are independent, their Jacobian Δ is not zero, and we may reduce (37) to (33) by multiplying its members by Δ.

Let us now note that all points on the characteristic passing through $(\zeta, \xi_1 \cdots, \xi_n)$ satisfy all equations

$$u^{(j)} = u^{(j)}(\zeta, \xi_1, \, \cdots, \, \xi_n) = C_j \quad (j = 1, \, \cdots, \, n).$$

They therefore satisfy all equations

$$v^{(j)} = v^{(j)}(C_1, C_2, \, \cdots, \, C_n) \quad (j = 1, \, \cdots, \, n),$$

and hence the characteristics can be defined by the simultaneous equations (36).

In the light of the above discussions, we may conclude that any function ϕ of a set of one or more functions $u^{(j)}$, where $u^{(j)} = C_j$ is a solution of (33) for every j, may be used to form the relation

$$\phi(u', u'', \, \cdots, \, u^{(n)}) = 0, \tag{38}$$

which will, in turn, be a solution of (33). Lagrange called the relation (38) the general solution of (33) if the $u^{(j)}$ were independent.

We have seen that (38) always provides a solution. Now, if

$$w(z, x_1, \cdots, x_n) = 0$$

is a solution, then the equation

$$w_z \, dz + w_{x_1} \, dx_1 + \cdots + w_{x_n} \, dx_n = 0$$

is satisfied by the values of the differentials dz, dx_i, which satisfy (32). Then, since not all these are zero, the determinant of the coefficients

$$\begin{vmatrix} w_z & w_{x_1} & \cdots & w_{x_n} \\ u'_z & u'_{x_1} & \cdots & u'_{x_n} \\ \cdot & \cdot \\ \cdot & \cdot & \cdot & \cdot & \cdot & \cdot & \cdot \\ u_z^{(n)} & u_{x_1}^{(n)} & \cdots & u_{x_n}^{(n)} \end{vmatrix}$$

vanishes. But this is the Jacobian of the $n + 1$ functions w, $u^{(i)}$, which are therefore dependent. Hence, w is a function of the $u^{(i)}$, and the solution $w = 0$ is included in the general solution of (38).

Now every point on the characteristic through the point $(\zeta, \xi_1, \cdots, \xi_n)$ satisfies the equations

$$u^{(i)} = u^{(i)}(\zeta, \xi_1, \cdots, \xi_n) = C_j \quad (j = 1, \cdots, n)$$

and hence satisfies

$$\phi(u', \cdots, u^{(n)}) = \phi(C_1, \cdots, C_n),$$

so that any solution of (33) is seen to be a locus of characteristics. It can be shown, conversely, that every locus of characteristics of (33) is a solution.

63. Jacobi's multipliers. An interesting generalization of the notion of an integrating factor is afforded by Jacobi's multipliers. Notice that if the equation

$$X \, dy - Y \, dx = 0 \tag{39}$$

is exact, then

$$X_x \equiv -Y_y$$

Notice that (39) may be written

$$\frac{dx}{X} = \frac{dy}{Y},$$

and that the test for exactness of (39) may be written

$$X_x + Y_y \equiv 0. \tag{40}$$

If this condition holds, there exists a function u such that

$$u_x \equiv Y \text{ and } u_y \equiv -X,$$

and the equation may be written

$$\frac{dy}{u_x} = \frac{dx}{-u_y}.$$

Note, now, that Y is obtained by striking out the first column from the matrix

$$(u_y \; u_x),$$

and that X is obtained by striking out the second column of the same matrix and changing the sign. In an entirely analogous manner the X_0 of (33) is the determinant obtained by striking the first column from the matrix (35), X_1 is obtained by striking out the second column and changing the sign of the determinant remaining, and so on. If a set of n independent functions $u^{(j)}$ exists, by means of which the X's of a given system of the form (33) can be obtained, the system is said to have the property of *generalized exactness*. In seeking a test for this generalized exactness, let us study an example.

Take as the functions

$$u' \equiv x + y + z,$$
$$u'' \equiv x^2 y.$$

Then the system analogous to (33) determined by

$$u' = c_1,$$
$$u'' = c_2,$$

is

$$\frac{dz}{X_0} = \frac{dx_1}{X_1} = \frac{dx_2}{X_2},$$

where

$$X_0 \equiv x^2 - 2xy,$$
$$X_1 \equiv -x^2,$$
$$X_2 \equiv 2xy.$$

Let us form, as a possible generalization of (40), the condition

$$\frac{\partial X_0}{\partial z} + \frac{\partial X_1}{\partial x_1} + \frac{\partial X_2}{\partial x_2} = 0$$

We note that it is satisfied identically in this case. To generalize this we shall establish

THEOREM II.   *If a set of functions* $u^{(j)}(j = 1, \cdots, n)$ *exists such that* X_i $(i = 0, \cdots, n)$ *are defined as in* (34), *then*

$$\frac{\partial X_0}{\partial z} + \frac{\partial X_1}{\partial x_1} + \cdots + \frac{\partial X_n}{\partial x_n} \equiv 0. \tag{41}$$

The X_i in (41) can be thought of as replaced by their values given by (34), and if we denote z by x_0, we can say that the partial derivative $u_{x_i x_l}^{(j)}$ comes only from the jth rows of the determinants, forming the X's and the columns containing $u_{x_i}^{(j)}$ or $u_{x_l}^{(j)}$.   To obtain the terms in $u_{x_0 x_1}^{(j)}$, write

$$\frac{\partial X_0}{\partial x_0} \equiv \frac{\partial}{\partial x_0} \left| u_{x_1}^{(j)}\ u_{x_2}^{(j)} \cdots u_{x_n}^{(j)} \right|,$$

$$\frac{\partial X_1}{\partial x_1} \equiv - \frac{\partial}{\partial x_1} \left| u_{x_0}^{(j)}\ u_{x_2}^{(j)} \cdots u_{x_n}^{(j)} \right|,$$

and expand according to the elements in the jth row, to obtain

$$(-1)^{j-1} \frac{\partial X_0}{\partial x_0} \equiv \frac{\partial}{\partial x_0} \left[u_{x_1}^{(j)} \left| u_{x_2}^{(l)} \cdots u_{x_n}^{(l)} \right| + \cdots \right], \qquad (l \ne j)$$

$$(-1)^{j-1} \frac{\partial X_1}{\partial x_1} \equiv - \frac{\partial}{\partial x_1} \left[u_{x_0}^{(j)} \left| u_{x_2}^{(l)} \cdots u_{x_n}^{(l)} \right| + \cdots \right], \qquad (l \ne j)$$

then the term

$$u_{x_0 x_1}^{(j)}$$

drops out of the sum (41).   Similarly for every term $u_{x_i x_k}^{(j)}$, with $i \ne k$.   Since X_i contains no derivative $u_{x_i}^{(j)}$, no terms of the type $u_{x_i x_i}^{(j)}$ enter into (41).   Hence Theorem II.

The theorem just proved is true conversely in the form of

THEOREM III.   *If* X_i $(i = 0, \cdots, n)$ *are* n + 1 *functions of* z, $x_1, \cdots, x_n$ *such that*

$$\frac{\partial X_0}{\partial z} + \frac{\partial X_1}{\partial x_1} + \frac{\partial X_2}{\partial x_2} + \cdots + \frac{\partial X_n}{\partial x_n} \equiv 0, \tag{41}$$

there exist functions u', u'', $\cdots$, $u^{(n)}$ *of the variables* z, $x_1, \cdots, x_n$ *such that the* X_i *are given by* (34).

To prove this we shall assume* that

$$v^{(j)}(z, x_1, \cdots, x_n) \qquad (j = 1, \cdots, n)$$

are n independent functions such that

$$v^{(j)} = c_j$$

---

*To show that such solutions exist is beyond the scope of this book.

furnish the solution to the system

$$\frac{dz}{X_0} = \frac{dx_1}{X_1} = \cdots = \frac{dx_n}{X_n}. \tag{42}$$

Then, as we have seen before,

$$Y_0 \equiv |v_{x_1}^{(j)}\ v_{x_2}^{(j)}\ \cdots\ v_{x_n}^{(j)}| \qquad\quad \equiv \Delta X_0,$$
$$Y_1 \equiv -\ |v_z^{(j)}\ v_{x_2}^{(j)}\ \cdots\ v_{x_n}^{(j)}| \qquad\quad \equiv \Delta X_1,$$

$$\cdots \cdots \cdots \cdots \cdots \cdots \cdots$$

$$Y_n \equiv (-1)^n |v_z^{(j)}\ v_{x_1}^{(j)}\ \cdots\ v_{x_{n-1}}^{(j)}| \equiv \Delta X_n,$$
$$\Delta \not\equiv 0.$$

Let us employ the notation

$$X(y) \equiv X_0 y_z + X_1 y_{x_1} + \cdots + X_n y_{x_n}.$$

Then,

$$\Delta \cdot X(y) \equiv \Delta X_0 y_z + \Delta X_1 y_{x_1} + \cdots + \Delta X_n y_{x_n}$$
$$\equiv Y_0 y_z + Y_1 y_{x_1} + \cdots + Y_n y_{x_n},$$

or

$$\Delta \cdot X(y) \equiv \begin{vmatrix} y_z & y_{x_1} & \cdots & y_{x_n} \\ v_z' & v_{x_1}' & \cdots & v_{x_n}' \\ \cdots & \cdots & \cdots & \cdots \\ v_z^{(n)} & v_{x_1}^{(n)} & \cdots & v_{x_n}^{(n)} \end{vmatrix}. \tag{43}$$

Now, from Theorem II we see that

$$\frac{\partial}{\partial z}(Y_0) + \frac{\partial}{\partial x_1}(Y_1) + \frac{\partial}{\partial x_2}(Y_2) + \cdots + \frac{\partial}{\partial x_n}(Y_n) \equiv 0,$$

and, since

$$Y_i \equiv \Delta X_i \qquad\qquad (i = 0, 1, \cdots, n),$$

$$X_0 \frac{\partial \Delta}{\partial z} + X_1 \frac{\partial \Delta}{\partial x_1} + \cdots + X_n \frac{\partial \Delta}{\partial x_n}$$
$$+ \Delta \left(\frac{\partial X_0}{\partial z} + \frac{\partial X_1}{\partial x_1} + \cdots + \frac{\partial X_n}{\partial x_n} \right) \equiv 0$$

or

$$X(\Delta) \equiv 0,$$

because the principal hypothesis of this theorem states that the coefficient of Δ in this equation vanishes identically. Let us now employ the multipliers $\Delta_z, \Delta_{x_1}, \cdots, \Delta_{x_n}$ upon the system (42) to obtain

$$\frac{dz}{X_0} = \frac{dx_1}{X_1} = \cdots = \frac{dx_n}{X_n} = \frac{\Delta_z\,dz + \Delta_{x_1}\,dx_1 + \cdots + \Delta_{x_n}\,dx_n}{X_0 \Delta_z + X_1 \Delta_{x_1} + \cdots + X_n \Delta_{x_n}}.$$

The last denominator is $X(\Delta)$, and has been shown to be zero; therefore the numerator is zero and

$$\Delta = 0$$

is a solution of the system (42). Then, by Section 62, Δ is a function of the $v^{(j)}$, say

$$\Delta \equiv \phi(v', v'', \cdots, v^{(n)}).$$

Now let us define a function $V^{(n)}$ by the quadrature

$$V^{(n)} \equiv \int \frac{dv^{(n)}}{\phi(v', \cdots, v^{(n)})},$$

evaluated with $v', v'', \cdots, v^{(n-1)}$ held constant, or

$$\frac{1}{\Delta} \equiv \frac{1}{\phi(v', v'', \cdots, v^{(n)})} \equiv \frac{\partial V^{(n)}}{\partial v^{(n)}} \equiv \begin{vmatrix} 1 & 0 & 0 & \cdots & 0 & 0 \\ 0 & 1 & 0 & \cdots & 0 & 0 \\ 0 & 0 & 1 & \cdots & 0 & 0 \\ \cdot & \cdot & \cdot & \cdots & \cdot & \cdot \\ 0 & 0 & 0 & \cdots & 1 & 0 \\ V_y^{(n)} & V_{v'}^{(n)} & V_{v''}^{(n)} & \cdots & V_{v^{(n-1)}}^{(n)} & V_{v^{(n)}}^{(n)} \end{vmatrix}. \tag{44}$$

Upon multiplying (43) by (44), we have

$$X(y) \equiv \begin{vmatrix} 1 & 0 & 0 & \cdots & 0 & 0 \\ 0 & 1 & 0 & \cdots & 0 & 0 \\ 0 & 0 & 1 & \cdots & 0 & 0 \\ \cdot & \cdot & \cdot & \cdots & \cdot & \cdot \\ 0 & 0 & 0 & \cdots & 1 & 0 \\ V_y^{(n)} & V_{v'}^{(n)} & V_{v''}^{(n)} & \cdots & V_{v^{(n-1)}}^{(n)} & V_{v^{(n)}}^{(n)} \end{vmatrix} \cdot \begin{vmatrix} y_z & y_{x_1} & y_{x_2} & \cdots & y_{x_n} \\ v_z' & v_{x_1}' & v_{x_2}' & \cdots & v_{x_n}' \\ v_z'' & v_{x_1}'' & v_{x_2}'' & \cdots & v_{x_n}'' \\ \cdot & \cdot & \cdot & \cdots & \cdot \\ v_z^{(n)} & v_{x_1}^{(n)} & v_{x_2}^{(n)} & \cdots & v_{x_n}^{(n)} \end{vmatrix}$$

$$\equiv \begin{vmatrix} y_z & y_{x_1} & \cdots & y_{x_n} \\ v_z' & v_{x_1}' & \cdots & v_{x_n}' \\ v_z'' & v_{x_1}'' & \cdots & v_{x_n}'' \\ \cdot & \cdot & \cdots & \cdot \\ v_z^{(n-1)} & v_{x_1}^{(n-1)} & \cdots & v_{x_n}^{(n-1)} \\ V_z^{(n)} & V_{x_1}^{(n)} & \cdots & V_{x_n}^{(n)} \end{vmatrix}$$

$$\equiv X_0 y_z + X_1 y_{x_1} + \cdots + X_n y_{x_n},$$

where the X_i are of the form (34), with $u^{(j)}$ replaced by $v^{(j)}$ ($j = 1, \cdots, n-1$) and $u^{(n)}$ replaced by $V^{(n)}$. Hence Theorem III.

If the X_i in a system such as (42) do not have the property of generalized exactness, but the functions MX_i do have that property, then M is said to be a *multiplier* for the system.

64. Indeterminate systems. We have seen that a system of equations of the form

$$\begin{cases} u_{10}\,dz + u_{11}\,dx_1 + \cdots + u_{1n}\,dx_n = 0, \\ u_{20}\,dz + u_{21}\,dx_1 + \cdots + u_{2n}\,dx_n = 0, \\ \cdot\ \cdot\ \cdot\ \cdot\ \cdot\ \cdot\ \cdot\ \cdot\ \cdot\ \cdot\ \cdot\ \cdot\ \cdot\ \cdot\ \cdot\ \cdot \\ \cdot\ \cdot\ \cdot\ \cdot\ \cdot\ \cdot\ \cdot\ \cdot\ \cdot\ \cdot\ \cdot\ \cdot\ \cdot\ \cdot\ \cdot\ \cdot \\ u_{n0}\,dz + u_{n1}\,dx_1 + \cdots + u_{nn}\,dx_n = 0, \end{cases}$$

determines a unique direction

$$dz : dx_1 : dx_2 : \cdots : dx_n$$

through each point $(z,\ x_1,\ x_2,\ \cdots,\ x_n)$ if the matrix whose j^{th} row is

$$(u_{j0}\ u_{j1}\ \cdots\ u_{jn})$$

has the rank n for the point; and that the system (32) has a complete solution in the form of a system of n relations

$$v^{(j)}(z,\ x_1,\ x_2,\ \cdots,\ x_n) = c_j \quad (j = 1,\ \cdots,\ n).$$

We have also seen that a single equation of the form

$$P\,dx + Q\,dy + R\,dz = 0$$

does not always have a solution, and never determines a unique direction

$$dx : dy : dz.$$

In the same way a system

$$\begin{cases} u_{10}\,dz + u_{11}\,dx_1 + \cdots + u_{1n}\,dx_n = 0, \\ u_{20}\,dz + u_{21}\,dx_1 + \cdots + u_{2n}\,dx_n = 0, \\ \cdot\ \cdot\ \cdot\ \cdot\ \cdot\ \cdot\ \cdot\ \cdot\ \cdot\ \cdot\ \cdot\ \cdot\ \cdot\ \cdot\ \cdot\ \cdot \quad (0 < m < n), \\ \cdot\ \cdot\ \cdot\ \cdot\ \cdot\ \cdot\ \cdot\ \cdot\ \cdot\ \cdot\ \cdot\ \cdot\ \cdot\ \cdot\ \cdot\ \cdot \\ u_{m0}\,dz + u_{m1}\,dx_1 + \cdots + u_{mn}\,dx_n = 0, \end{cases} \quad (45)$$

does not determine a unique direction through each point. In fact, if the rank of matrix

$$\begin{pmatrix} u_{10} & u_{11} & \cdots & u_{1n} \\ u_{20} & u_{21} & \cdots & u_{2n} \\ \cdot & \cdot & \cdots & \cdot \\ \cdot & \cdot & \cdots & \cdot \\ u_{m0} & u_{m1} & \cdots & u_{mn} \end{pmatrix} \quad (46)$$

is r at a given point $(z, x_1, \cdots, x_n)$, then $n + 1 - r$ of the quantities $dz, dx_1, \cdots, dx_n$ may be assigned arbitrarily,* and the remaining r may be expressed linearly in terms of them.   If the matrix (46) has the rank r, the system (45) may be satisfied, in some cases, identically by a system of r relations of the form

$$v^{(j)}(z, x_1, \cdots, x_n) = c_j \qquad (j = 1, \cdots, r),$$

but this will not always be true.   We shall call the system *integrable* in the former case, and *non-integrable* in the latter case.   If the matrix (46) has the rank r, and the system (45) is *nonintegrable*, the system may be augmented by $n - r$ arbitrary equations such that the matrix of the augmented system will have rank n.   The augmented system will be integrable.

65. Exercises.

1. Test the following sets of functions for dependence:

(a) $u' \equiv z + x_1 + x_2 + x_3,\ u'' \equiv z^2 + x_1^2 + x_2^2 + x_3^2,$ $u''' \equiv z(x_1 + x_2 + x_3).$

(b) $u' \equiv zx_1x_2x_3x_4,\ u'' \equiv zx_1,\ u''' \equiv zx_2\ u^{iv} \equiv zx_3x_4.$

(c) $u' \equiv zx_1,\ u'' \equiv zx_1 + x_2,\ u''' \equiv z(x_1 + x_2).$

(d) $u' \equiv ze^{x_1},\ u'' \equiv ze^{x_2},\ u''' \equiv z^2e^{x_1+x_2}.$

(e) $u' \equiv z + x_1 + x_2 + x_3 + x_4,\ u'' \equiv z^2 + x_1^2 + x_2^2 + x_3^2 + x_4^2,\ u''' \equiv z(x_1 + x_2 + x_3 + x_4) + x_1(x_2 + x_3 + x_4) + x_2(x_3 + x_4) + x_3x_4.$

2. For each of the five exercises above, form the system of ordinary differential equations having as solutions the functions displayed in that exercise.   Where possible, put the system in the form

$$\frac{dz}{X_0} = \frac{dx_1}{X_1} = \cdots = \frac{dx_n}{X_n}.$$

3. Test the system

$$\frac{dz}{0} = \frac{dx_1}{-z^2} = \frac{dx_2}{z^2} = \frac{dx_3}{z^2} = \frac{dx_4}{-z^2}$$

for generalized exactness.   If it is exact, find the four functions u', u'', u''', u^{iv} such that

$$X_0 \equiv 0,\ X_1 \equiv -z^2,\ X_2 \equiv z^2,\ X_3 \equiv z^2,\ X_4 \equiv -z^2.$$

---

* Dickson's *First Course* in the Theory of Equations, page 119.

4. Solve the system

$$\frac{dz}{-z} = \frac{dx_1}{2x_1} = \frac{dx_2}{-x_2}, = \frac{dx_3}{0}.$$

5. Solve the system

$$\frac{dx_1}{x_1} = \frac{dx_2}{x_3 + x_4} = \frac{dx_3}{x_2 + x_4} = \frac{dx_4}{x_2 + x_3}.$$

6. Solve the system

$$\frac{dx_1}{x_2 + x_3 + x_4 + x_5} = \frac{dx_2}{x_1 + x_3 + x_4 + x_5} = \frac{dx_3}{x_1 + x_2 + x_4 + x_5}$$
$$= \frac{dx_4}{x_1 + x_2 + x_3 + x_5} = \frac{dx_5}{x_1 + x_2 + x_3 + x_4}.$$

7. Solve the system

$$\frac{dz}{az} = \frac{dx_1}{x_1} = \frac{dx_2}{x_2} = \frac{dx_3}{x_3}.$$

8. Solve the system

$$\frac{dx_1}{x_1} = \frac{dx_2}{x_2} = \frac{dx_3}{x_3} = \frac{x_3\, dx_4}{ax_4x_3 + x_1x_2}.$$

9. Find a multiplier for the system

$$\frac{dx}{x(y - z)} = \frac{dy}{y(z - x)} = \frac{dz}{z(x - y)}.$$

10. Find a multiplier for the system

$$\frac{dx}{-x} = \frac{dy}{y} = \frac{dz}{(x - y)\left(2 + \dfrac{z}{x + y}\right)}.$$

11. Prove that if M and N are two multipliers of the system

$$\frac{dx}{X_0} = \frac{dx_1}{X_1} = \cdots = \frac{dx_n}{X_n},$$

where N is not identically equal to M times a constant, then $\dfrac{M}{N} = C$ is a solution of the system.

12. Show that the condition

$$XY(Z_t - T_z) + YZ(T_x - X_t) + ZT(X_y - Y_x) + TX(Y_z - Z_y)$$
$$\equiv 0$$

is necessary for the integrability of the equation

$$X\,dx + Y\,dy + Z\,dz + T\,dt = 0.$$

13. Solve the system

$$\begin{cases} yzw\,dx + xzw\,dy + xyw\,dz + xyz\,dw = 0, \\ (2xy + w^2)dx + (2yz + x^2)dy + (2zw + y^2)dz + (2wx + z^2)dw \\ \qquad\qquad = 0, \\ 2xy\,dx + (2yz + x^2 - z)dy + (2zw + y^2 - y)dz + z^2\,dw = 0. \end{cases}$$

14. Solve the system

$$\begin{cases} (yw + zw)dx + w\,dy + w\,dz + (y + z)dw = 0, \\ (1 - yw - zw)dx + (z - w)dy + y\,dz - y\,dw = 0, \\ 2yz\,dx + xz\,dy + xy\,dz = 0. \end{cases}$$

CHAPTER VIII

Partial Differential Equations of the First Order

66. Illustrations and definitions. Let us consider z to be a function of two independent variables x and y, defined by the relation

$$x^2 y + az + by = 0. \tag{1}$$

If we differentiate partially with respect to x and y, we obtain the relations

$$\begin{cases} 2xy + a\, z_x = 0, \\ x^2 + a\, z_y + b = 0. \end{cases} \tag{2}$$

We may eliminate a and b from equations (1) and (2) by multiplying (1) by z_x, (2_1) by $yz_y - z$, and (2_2) by $-yz_x$, adding the three resulting equations, and dividing out $2xy$, to obtain a partial differential equation

$$y\, z_y - z = 0, \tag{3}$$

of which (1) is a solution for any constant values of a and b.

If, now, we separate the variables in equation (3), writing the equation in the form

$$\frac{z_y}{z} - \frac{1}{y} = 0,$$

and integrate partially with respect to y, we obtain

$$\log z - \log y = \phi(x),$$

where $\phi(x)$ is an arbitrary function of x. This can be put in the form

$$\frac{z}{y} = e^{\phi(x)},$$

or

$$z = y\, f(x), \tag{4}$$

where $f(x) \equiv e^{\phi(x)}$. Equation (4) is a *solution* of the partial differential equation (3), as we shall see by direct differentiation, and

221

it is what we shall later define as the *general* solution. By differentiating with respect to y, we obtain the equation

$$z_y = f(x),$$

between which and (4), $f(x)$ may be eliminated to give (3). The original equation (1) is a special case of (4), as we can see by solving (1) for z to obtain

$$z = y\left(-\frac{x^2}{a} - \frac{b}{a}\right).$$

We notice that (4) can be written in the form

$$\frac{z}{y} = f(x),$$

where f is an arbitrary function of one argument, and that this equation in turn is equivalent to

$$\phi\left(\frac{z}{y}, x\right) = 0,$$

where ϕ is an arbitrary function of two arguments, since the last equation can be solved for its first argument $\frac{z}{y}$ in terms of its second argument x.

As a generalization of (4) we may take the relation

$$\phi(u, v) = 0, \tag{5}$$

where u and v are known independent functions of x, y, and z, while ϕ denotes an arbitrary function of two arguments. For every choice of the function ϕ, for which $\phi_z \not\equiv 0$, equation (5) defines* a function $z = f(x, y)$, and we may form the partial derivatives z_x and z_y directly from (5), obtaining

$$\begin{cases} \phi_u(u_x + u_z z_x) + \phi_v(v_x + v_z z_x) = 0, \\ \phi_u(u_y + u_z z_y) + \phi_v(v_y + v_z z_y) = 0, \end{cases}$$

from which the quantities ϕ_u and ϕ_v may easily be eliminated to give

$$(v_x + v_z z_x)(u_y + u_z z_y) = (v_y + v_z z_y)(u_x + u_z z_x),$$

or, when coefficients of z_x and z_y are collected,

$$z_x(u_y v_z - u_z v_y) + z_y(u_z v_x - u_x v_z) - (u_x v_y - u_y v_x) = 0.$$

---

* Wilson's *Advanced Calculus*, page 123.

The functions u and v and their derivatives being known functions, we write the above equation in the form

$$P\,Z_x + Q\,Z_y = R, \tag{6}$$

known as a *linear* partial differential equation, where

$$P \equiv \lambda(u_y v_z - u_z v_y),$$
$$Q \equiv \lambda(u_z v_x - u_x v_z),$$
$$R \equiv \lambda(u_x v_y - u_y v_x),$$
$$\lambda \not\equiv 0.$$

By substitution we can verify that $u = c$ satisfies (6), as does $v = c$.   A relation $u = 0$, where u is a known function of x, y, and z having $u_z \not\equiv 0$, which satisfies (6) identically, is called a *particular solution* of (6).   An arbitrary functional relationship between u and v, such as (5), is called the *general solution* of (6) if $u = 0$ and $v = 0$ are particular solutions, while u and v are independent functions.   A relation such as

$$f(x, y, z, a, b) = 0,$$

which has two arbitrary constants and has $f_z \not\equiv 0$ and which satisfies (6) for all values of those constants, is called a *complete solution* of (6).

67. Lagrange's equations.   In Section 66 we employed two independent functions u and v of three variables x, y, and z, to build up equation

$$P\,Z_x + Q\,Z_y = R, \tag{6}$$

whose general solution is

$$\phi(u, v) = 0. \tag{5}$$

Let us now employ the same functions u and v to build up a system of ordinary differential equations whose solution is

$$\begin{cases} u = c_1, \\ v = c_2. \end{cases}$$

Taking the differentials, we obtain

$$\begin{cases} u_x\,dx + u_y\,dy + u_z\,dz = 0, \\ v_x\,dx + v_y\,dy + v_z\,dz = 0. \end{cases}$$

This system can be put into the symmetric form

$$\frac{dx}{u_y v_z - u_z v_y} = \frac{dy}{u_z v_x - u_x v_z} = \frac{dz}{u_x v_y - u_y v_x},$$

or, if we multiply through by $\frac{1}{\lambda}$, into the form

$$\frac{dx}{P} = \frac{dy}{Q} = \frac{dz}{R}, \tag{7}$$

where P, Q, and R are the same functions as in (6). We shall refer to (7) as the *Lagrange system* corresponding to (6).

Since u and v are independent functions, not all of P, Q, and R are zero, as otherwise the matrix

$$\begin{pmatrix} u_x & u_y & u_z \\ v_x & v_y & v_z \end{pmatrix}$$

would have rank less than 2. If some of P, Q, and R are zero, we understand the system to mean that the corresponding numerators are zero, as we did in the preceding chapter.

Since we know how to solve a system like (7), it at once occurs that, if we are given an equation of the form (6) to be solved, we may set up the corresponding system (7), may find two solutions, $u = c_1$, $v = c_2$, such that u and v are independent functions, and with these functions u and v we may set up the general solution (5). It is obvious that any two such functions u and v satisfying (7) will determine P, Q, and R uniquely except for a factor, that they will therefore determine (6) uniquely except for a factor, and that, hence, they will furnish the general solution of the form (5).

Illustration

To find the general solution of the linear partial differential equation

$$x z_x + y z_y = z, \tag{8}$$

note that it is of the form (6), with $P \equiv x$, $Q \equiv y$, and $R \equiv z$, and that the corresponding Lagrange system is

$$\frac{dx}{x} = \frac{dy}{y} = \frac{dz}{z}. \tag{9}$$

An obvious solution of (9) is

$$\frac{z}{x} = a, \frac{z}{y} = b,$$

from which we form the general solution

$$\phi\left(\frac{z}{x}, \frac{z}{y}\right) = 0 \tag{10}$$

of the form (5).   We may verify directly that (10) will satisfy (8) by differentiating to obtain

$$\begin{cases} \phi_u\left(-\dfrac{z}{x^2} + \dfrac{z_x}{x}\right) + \phi_v\left(\dfrac{z_x}{y}\right) = 0, \\[2mm] \phi_u\left(\dfrac{z_y}{x}\right) + \phi_v\left(-\dfrac{z}{y^2} + \dfrac{z_y}{y}\right) = 0. \end{cases}$$

From these, eliminate the ratio $\phi_u : \phi_v$, and obtain

$$\frac{z_x z_y}{xy} = \frac{z_x z_y}{xy} - \frac{z z_x}{xy^2} - \frac{z z_y}{x^2 y} + \frac{z^2}{x^2 y^2},$$

or, upon simplifying,

$$x\, z_x + y\, z_y = z.$$

Any other two independent functions u and v, such that $u = a$, $v = b$ furnishes the solution of (9), could have been used just as well in (10).

Exercises

1. Find the general solution of each of the following:

   (a) $l\, z_x + m\, z_y = n.$
   (b) $x\, z_x + z\, z_y = y.$
   (c) $x\, z_x = y.$
   (d) $y\, z_x + x\, z_y = 5.$
   (e) $(ax + by + cz)z_x + (by + cz)z_y = ax.$
   (f) $(2z - 3y)z_x + (3x - z)z_y = y - 2x.$
   (g) $(xy + y^2 - xz - z^2)z_x + (yz + z^2 - yx - x^2)z_y = (zx + x^2 - zy - y^2).$
   (h) $2yz\, z_x + 2xz\, z_y = -xy.$
   (i) $\operatorname{ctn} x\, z_x + \operatorname{ctn} y\, z_y = \operatorname{ctn} z.$
   (j) $y^2 z\, z_x + z^2 x\, z_y = -xy^2.$
   (k) $3xy\, z_x + z^2 z_y = -yz.$
   (l) $(2xy^4 - xz^4)z_x + (yz^4 - 2x^4 y)z_y = x^4 z - y^4 z.$
   (m) $x\, z_x + y\, z_y + z = 0.$
   (n) $x(\operatorname{ctn} z)z_x - y(\operatorname{ctn} z)z_y + 1 = 0.$

2. Find the most general solution of the equation $zz_x - (x + z)z_y = x$ which passes through the point $(1, 2, 3)$.

3. Find the most general solution of $2z_x - y\, z_y + z = 0$ which passes through the point $(0, 1, 1)$

4. Find the most general solution of $2z_x - y\, z_y + z = 0$ which contains the curve $\begin{cases} x = \log y, \\ y = z \log y. \end{cases}$ *Hint:* If $\begin{cases} u = c_1 \\ v = c_2 \end{cases}$ is the general solution, eliminate x_0, y_0, and z_0 among $u(x, y, z) = u(x_0, y_0, z_0)$, $v(x, y, z) = v(x_0, y_0, z_0)$, $x_0 = \log y_0$, and $y_0 = z_0 \log y_0$.

5. Find the integral surface of

$$(2xy^2 + xz)z_x - (yz + 3x^3y)z_y = 3x^3z - 2y^2z$$

which passes through the parabola $\begin{cases} y^2 = z, \\ x = 2. \end{cases}$

6. Find the integral surface of $4y\, zz_x - z_y + 2y = 0$ which passes through the hyperbola $\begin{cases} x + z = 5, \\ y^2 - z^2 = 9. \end{cases}$

7. Find the integral surfaces of $z_x - y\, z_y + z = 0$ which pass through the curve $\begin{cases} 2(y + z) \cosh x = z^2 + y^2 + 1, \\ 2(y + z) \sinh x = z^2 + y^2 - 1. \end{cases}$

8. Form a linear partial differential equation whose solution is $\phi(z^2 + x^2 + y^2, xy\, z) = 0$.

9. Form a linear partial differential equation whose solution is $\phi(x^2e^z, ye^z) = 0$.

10. Solve completely $z_x - z_y = 0$.

11. Solve completely $x^2z\, z_x + ye^z\, z_y = 0$.

12. Find the linear partial differential equation of all cylinders not parallel to the z-axis. Write its general solution. *Hint:* Let its elements cut the yz-plane in a curve whose equations are $\begin{cases} x = 0, \\ f(y, z) = 0, \end{cases}$ and let the elements remain parallel to the line $\begin{cases} y = ax, \\ z = bx. \end{cases}$ If $(0, \alpha, \beta)$ are the coördinates of the point where an element cuts the yz-plane, then the equations of the element are $\begin{cases} y = ax + \alpha, \\ z = bx + \beta, \end{cases}$ and (α, β) satisfies the equation $f(\alpha, \beta) = 0$.

13. Find the linear partial differential equation of all cones with vertex at the origin. *Hint:* Let its trace in the plane $x = 1$ be represented by $\begin{cases} x = 1, \\ f(y, z) = 0. \end{cases}$ Write its general solution.

14. Find the linear partial differential equation of all cones with vertex at a given point (a, b, c).   Write its general solution.

15. Find the linear partial differential equation of all surfaces of revolution whose axes pass through the origin in a given direction $(\alpha:\beta:\gamma)$, not $(0:0:1)$.   *Hint:* Let the axis have equations $\dfrac{x}{\alpha} = \dfrac{y}{\beta} = \dfrac{z}{\gamma}$. Then the plane $\alpha x + \beta y + \gamma z = \delta$, whose distance from $(0, 0, 0)$ is determined by δ, is perpendicular to the axis and meets a sphere with center at the origin in circles whose centers are on the axis.

16. Find the partial differential equation of the surfaces of revolution whose axes go through a given point (a, b, c) in a given direction not parallel to the z-axis.

17. Find the linear partial differential equation of a conoid whose generating line connects a point on the z-axis to a point on the curve $\begin{cases} x = c, \\ f(y, z) = 0, \end{cases}$ and remains parallel to the xy-plane.   Write its general solution.

18. Show that the ordinary differential equation $M\,dx + N\,dy = 0$ treated in Chapter II has an infinite number of integrating factors.   *Hint:* If μ is an integrating factor of $M\,dx + N\,dy = 0$, then $\dfrac{\partial}{\partial y}(\mu M) = \dfrac{\partial}{\partial x}(\mu N)$, or μ satisfies the partial differential equation $N\mu_x - M\mu_y = \mu(M_y - N_x)$.

19. Find an equation giving all integrating factors of the equation $x\,dy - y\,dx = 0$.   (See page 24.)

68. Functions of several variables. The results of the preceding sections may be readily extended to the case of a function z of n variables $x_1, \cdots, x_n$.   Such a function z may be defined by an equation of the form

$$u(x_1, x_2, \cdots, x_n, z) = 0,$$

where $u_z \neq 0$.   If $u', u'', \cdots, u^{(n)}$ are n such functions which are independent, a relation among them such as

$$\phi(u', u'', \cdots, u^{(n)}) = 0 \tag{11}$$

will ordinarily define z as a function of the x's.   From (11), we set up by differentiation the system of equations

$$\phi_{u'}(u'_{x_1} + u'_z z_{x_1}) + \phi_{u''}(u''_{x_1} + u''_z z_{x_1}) + \cdots$$
$$+ \phi_{u^{(n)}}(u^{(n)}_{x_1} + u^{(n)}_z z_{x_1}) = 0,$$
$$\phi_{u'}(u'_{x_2} + u'_z z_{x_2}) + \phi_{u''}(u''_{x_2} + u''_z z_{x_2}) + \cdots$$
$$+ \phi_{u^{(n)}}(u^{(n)}_{x_2} + u^{(n)}_z z_{x_2}) = 0,$$

$$\phi_{u'}(u'_{x_n} + u'_z z_{x_n}) + \phi_{u''}(u''_{x_n} + u''_z z_{x_n}) + \cdots$$
$$+ \phi_{u^{(n)}}(u^{(n)}_{x_n} + u^{(n)}_z z_{x_n}) = 0.$$

This system of n linear equations in n variables $\phi_u{}^{(j)}$ can have solutions, not all zero, if, and only if, the determinant of its coefficients vanishes. Hence, we have

$$|u'_{x_1} + u'_z z_{x_1} \ \ u'_{x_2} + u'_z z_{x_2} \ \ u'_{x_3} + u'_z z_{x_3} \cdots u'_{x_n} + u'_z z_{x_n}| = 0,$$

where for brevity we have written only the first column of the determinant, *viz.*, the coefficients of $\phi_{u'}$. The above determinant may be expressed as a sum of determinants, in which case we have the equation

$$0 = |u'_{x_1} u'_{x_2} \cdots u'_{x_n}| + z_{x_1} |u'_z u'_{x_2} u'_{x_3} \cdots u'_{x_n}|$$
$$+ z_{x_2} |u'_{x_1} u'_z u'_{x_3} \cdots u'_{x_n}| + \cdots$$
$$+ z_{x_1} z_{x_2} |u'_z u'_z u'_{x_3} u'_{x_4} \cdots u'_{x_n}| + \cdots$$
$$+ z_{x_1} z_{x_2} z_{x_3} |u'_z u'_z u'_z u'_{x_4} \cdots u'_{x_n}| + \cdots,$$

where the determinants whose coefficients are of degree higher than one in the z_{x_i} are all zero, because two columns are alike. This may be written as

$$X_1 z_{x_1} + X_2 z_{x_2} + \cdots + X_n z_{x_n} = X_0, \tag{12}$$

where

$$X_1 \equiv - |u'_z u'_{x_2} u'_{x_3} \cdots u'_{x_n}|,$$
$$X_2 \equiv |u'_z u'_{x_1} u'_{x_3} \cdots u'_{x_n}|,$$
$$X_3 \equiv - |u'_z u'_{x_1} u'_{x_2} u'_{x_4} \cdots u'_{x_n}|,$$

$$X_n \equiv (-1)^n |u'_z u'_{x_1} u'_{x_2} \cdots u'_{x_{n-1}}|,$$
$$X_0 \equiv |u'_{x_1} u'_{x_2} u'_{x_3} \cdots u'_{x_n}|.$$

This special form of the X_i suggests minors of a determinant, and we see by inspection that (12) is actually expressible in the form

$$\begin{vmatrix} -1 & z_{x_1} & z_{x_2} & z_{x_3} & \cdots & z_{x_n} \\ u'_z & u'_{x_1} & u'_{x_2} & u'_{x_3} & \cdots & u'_{x_n} \\ u''_z & u''_{x_1} & u''_{x_2} & u''_{x_3} & \cdots & u''_{x_n} \\ \cdot & \cdot & \cdot & \cdot & & \cdot \\ u^{(n)}_z & u^{(n)}_{x_1} & u^{(n)}_{x_2} & u^{(n)}_{x_3} & \cdots & u^{(n)}_{x_n} \end{vmatrix} = 0. \tag{13}$$

We may now show that for any j, $u^{(j)} = c$ is a solution, which we shall call a *particular solution*, of (12). By differentiation we have

$$u_{x_i}^{(j)} + u_z^{(j)} z_{x_i} = 0 \qquad (i = 1, \cdots, n),$$

hence, remembering that $u_z^{(j)}$ is not zero,

$$z_{x_i} = - \frac{u_{x_i}^{(j)}}{u_z^{(j)}} \qquad (i = 1, \cdots, n),$$

which we may substitute into (13) to obtain

$$\begin{vmatrix} -1 - \dfrac{u_{x_1}^{(j)}}{u_z^{(j)}} & -\dfrac{u_{x_2}^{(j)}}{u_z^{(j)}} & \cdots & -\dfrac{u_{x_n}^{(j)}}{u_z^{(j)}} \\ u_z' & u_{x_1}' & u_{x_2}' & \cdots & u_{x_n}' \\ u_z'' & u_{x_1}'' & u_{x_2}'' & \cdots & u_{x_n}' \\ \cdot & \cdot & \cdot & & \cdot \\ \cdot & \cdot & \cdot & & \cdot \\ u_z^{(n)} & u_{x_1}^{(n)} & u_{x_2}^{(n)} & \cdots & u_{x_n}^{(n)} \end{vmatrix} = 0.$$

Multiplication of the elements of the first row by $u_z^{(j)}$ gives a determinant whose elements in the first row are the negatives of those in the $(j + 1)^{\text{st}}$ row; hence the determinant vanishes for every value of j. We define (11), where ϕ is an arbitrary function, to be the general solution of (12) if $u^{(j)} = c$ ($j = 1, \cdots, n$) are n particular solutions such that the n functions u are independent.

69. Lagrange's equations; case of $n + 1$ variables. If we begin with the same functions $u^{(j)}$ which were used in (11), and build up a system of ordinary differential equations as in Chapter VII, we obtain

$$\frac{dz}{X_0} = \frac{dx_1}{X_1} = \cdots = \frac{dx_n}{X_n}, \tag{14}$$

where the X_i are the same as in (12). This system is called *Lagrange's system*, and its solution gives us the solution of the equation (12). As we have seen in Chapter VII, if $v', v'', \cdots, v^{(n)}$ are n independent functions such that

$$v^{(j)} = c_j \qquad (j = 1, \cdots, n)$$

satisfy (14), then any solution of (14) may be written in the form

$$\phi(v', v'', \cdots, v^{(n)}) = 0, \tag{15}$$

and any such relation is a solution. However, a relation of the form (15) is a solution of the partial differential equation (12) only if $\phi_z \not\equiv 0$, since otherwise ϕ is independent of z.

$$\frac{dy}{dt} = x + y + t$$

$$\frac{dx}{y-z} = \frac{dy}{x+y+t} = \frac{dt}{1} = \frac{dz}{x+z+t}$$

1. Find the general solution of

$$(y - z)z_x + (x + y + t)z_y + z_t = x + z + t.$$

2. Find the general solution of

$$m^2n^2(x_2 - x_3)z_{x_1} + n^2l^2(x_3 - x_1)z_{x_2} + l^2m^2(x_1 - x_2)z_{x_3} = 0.$$

3. Find the general solution of

$$(x_2 + x_3 + x_4 + z)z_{x_1} + (x_1 + x_3 + x_4 + z)z_{x_2}$$
$$+ (x_1 + x_2 + x_4 + z)z_{x_3} + (x_1 + x_2 + x_3 + z)z_{x_4}$$
$$= x_1 + x_2 + x_3 + x_4.$$

4. Find the general solution of

$$x_2x_3z\, z_{x_1} + x_1x_3z\, z_{x_2} + x_1x_2z\, z_{x_3} = x_1x_2x_3.$$

5. Find the general solution of

$$x_3\, z_{x_1} + x_2\, z_{x_2} + x_1\, z_{x_3} = 0.$$

70. Equations not of the first degree; Charpit's method. Let us consider now any first order partial differential equation of one dependent variable z and two independent variables x and y. For convenience we shall employ the notation $z_x \equiv p$, $z_y \equiv q$. The equation may be written in the form

$$F(x, y, z, p, q) = 0, \tag{16}$$

and we seek a function $\phi(x, y)$ such that

$$z = \phi(x, y)$$

satisfies (16) identically. That is, we seek a function such that the equations

$$z = \phi(x, y), \ p = \phi_x(x, y), \ q = \phi_y(x, y)$$

satisfy (16) identically.

If the function $\phi(x, y)$ which we seek were defined implicitly by a relation as

$$\psi(x, y, z) = 0,$$

we would have expressions for p and q defined in terms of x, y, and z as

$$p = g(x, y, z), \ q = h(x, y, z),$$

which satisfy (16).   For example, we might choose $g(x, y, z)$ arbitrarily and, after substituting $p = g(x, y, z)$ into (16), solve for q to obtain $q = h(x, y, z)$.   Unless the choice of g was very fortunate, the functions g and h thus obtained would not be such as to render the equation

$$dz = p\,dx + q\,dy \tag{17}$$

integrable.   However, if a choice of g and h could be made so that (17) was integrable, then a solution of (17) would define z as a function of x and y which would satisfy the given equation (16).

Two equations involving p and q, as

$$F(x, y, z, p, q) = 0 \tag{16}$$

and

$$f(x, y, z, p, q) = 0, \tag{18}$$

may be solved for p and q each as a function of x, y, and z, provided the determinant*

$$\begin{vmatrix} F_p & F_q \\ f_p & f_q \end{vmatrix} \equiv \Delta$$

does not vanish identically; and we seek to find a relation of the form (18) such that the functions p and q,

$$p = g(x, y, z),$$
$$q = h(x, y, z),$$

defined by (16) and (18), will render (17) integrable.   To find such a relation (18), let us differentiate (16) and (18) partially with respect to x to obtain

$$F_x + F_p p_x + F_q q_x = 0, \tag{19}$$
$$f_x + f_p p_x + f_q q_x = 0. \tag{20}$$

Similarly, differentiating (16) and (18) partially with respect to y, and then z, we have

$$F_y + F_p p_y + F_q q_y = 0, \tag{21}$$
$$f_y + f_p p_y + f_q q_y = 0, \tag{22}$$
$$F_z + F_p p_z + F_q q_z = 0, \tag{23}$$
$$f_z + f_p p_z + f_q q_z = 0. \tag{24}$$

Between (19) and (20) we may eliminate p_x to obtain

$$\Delta q_x = F_x f_p - F_p f_x. \tag{25}$$

---

* Wilson's *Advanced Calculus*, page 124.

Similarly, eliminating p_z from (23) and (24), q_y from (21) and (22), and q_z from (23) and (24), we obtain

$$\Delta q_z = F_z f_p - F_p f_z, \tag{26}$$
$$\Delta p_y = -F_y f_q + F_q f_y, \tag{27}$$
$$\Delta p_z = -F_z f_q + F_q f_z. \tag{28}$$

Now, the condition that (17) be integrable reduces to

$$pq_z - qp_z - p_y + q_x \equiv 0.$$

We may multiply this through by Δ, substitute from (25), (26), (27), and (28), and obtain

$$pF_z f_p - pF_p f_z + qF_z f_q - qF_q f_z + F_y f_q - F_q f_y + F_z f_p - F_p f_x = 0.$$

When arranged in terms of derivatives of f, this becomes

$$-F_p f_x - F_q f_y - (pF_p + qF_q)f_z + (F_x + pF_z)f_p + (F_y + qF_z)f_q = 0,$$

which is a linear partial differential equation in f considered as a function of the five independent variables x, y, z, p, and q. The corresponding Lagrange equations are

$$\frac{dx}{-F_p} = \frac{dy}{-F_q} = \frac{dz}{-(pF_p + qF_q)} = \frac{dp}{F_x + pF_z} = \frac{dq}{F_y + qF_z} = \frac{df}{0}.$$

Any solution of this system, involving p or q, or both, and one arbitrary constant, such that $\Delta \not\equiv 0$, may be used with (16) to define p and q. These functions will render (17) integrable, and its complete solution

$$\psi(x, y, z, a, b) = 0 \tag{29}$$

will be the *complete solution* of (16), that is, a solution involving two arbitrary constants.

The relation (29) represents a two-parameter system of surfaces. If this system has an envelope, the equation of the envelope is called the *singular solution*. It may be found by eliminating a and b between (29) and the two derived equations

$$\psi_a(x, y, z, a, b) = 0,$$
$$\psi_b(x, y, z, a, b) = 0.$$

As in the case of one independent variable treated in Chapter III, the eliminant must not be accepted on faith, but its factors must be separately tried in (16). The singular solution may also be found by eliminating p and q from (16) and

$$F_p(x, y, z, p, q) = 0,$$
$$F_q(x, y, z, p, q) = 0,$$

and testing the eliminant by substitution in (16).

If, in the complete solution (29), we choose b as an arbitrary function of a, say $b = f(a)$, we have a one-parameter system of solutions

$$\psi(x, y, z, a, f(a)) = 0. \tag{30}$$

The envelope of this family is obtained by eliminating a between (30) and

$$\psi_a(x, y, z, a, f(a)) + \psi_b(x, y, z, a, f(a))f'(a) = 0.$$

The eliminant will involve an arbitrary function f, and is called the *general solution*. The curves of contact of the surfaces (30) and their envelope are called *characteristics* of the given equation (16) or of the system (29). We see, then, that a general solution is a locus of characteristics.

Illustration

Let us study the differential equation

$$16z^2p^2 + 25z^2q^2 + 9z^2 - 81 = 0. \tag{31}$$

This is of the form (16), with

$$F \equiv 16z^2p^2 + 25z^2q^2 + 9z^2 - 81,$$
$$F_x \equiv 0 \equiv F_y,$$
$$F_z \equiv 32zp^2 + 50zq^2 + 18z,$$
$$F_p \equiv 32z^2p,$$
$$F_q \equiv 50z^2q.$$

We wish to find a new relation

$$f(x, y, z, p, q) = 0 \tag{18}$$

such that the functions of p and q defined by (18) and (31) will make

$$dz = p\,dx + q\,dy \tag{17}$$

integrable. For such a function we look among the solutions of

$$\frac{dx}{-32z^2p} = \frac{dy}{-50z^2q} = \frac{dz}{-32z^2p^2 - 50z^2q^2}$$
$$= \frac{dp}{32zp^3 + 50zpq^2 + 18zp}$$
$$= \frac{dq}{32zqp^2 + 50zq^3 + 18zq} = \frac{df}{0}.$$

We may find a solution by using the multipliers 9, 0, 16p, 16z, 0, 0, which produce the ratio

$$\frac{9dx + 16p\,dz + 16z\,dp}{-288z^2p - 512z^2p^3 - 800z^2pq^2 + 512z^2p^3 + 800z^2pq^2 + 288z^2p}.$$

Since the denominator vanishes identically, we have

$$9dx + 16p\,dz + 16z\,dp = 0,$$

an exact equation having as solution

$$9(x - a) + 16pz = 0, \tag{32}$$

where the arbitrary constant has been called 9a. Solving (32) for p, we obtain

$$p = -\frac{9}{z}\left(\frac{x - a}{16}\right),$$

which we substitute into the given equation (31) to solve for q. We thus obtain

$$q = \pm\frac{9}{5z}\sqrt{1 - \frac{z^2}{9} - \frac{(x - a)^2}{16}}.$$

These two expressions for p and q may be substituted into (17) to obtain

$$dz = -\frac{9(x - a)dx}{16z} \pm \frac{9}{5z}\sqrt{1 - \frac{z^2}{9} - \frac{(x - a)^2}{16}}\,dy.$$

Dividing through by the coefficient of dy, we obtain

$$\pm dy = \frac{5\left\{\dfrac{z\,dz}{9} + \dfrac{x - a}{16}\,dx\right\}}{\sqrt{1 - \dfrac{z^2}{9} - \dfrac{(x - a)^2}{16}}},$$

which has the solution

$$\pm(y - b) = 5\sqrt{1 - \frac{z^2}{9} - \frac{(x - a)^2}{16}}$$

or, upon rationalization,

$$\frac{(x - a)^2}{16} + \frac{(y - b)^2}{25} + \frac{z^2}{9} = 1, \tag{33}$$

the complete solution of (31).

This complete solution represents a two-parameter system of ellipsoids, the parameters a and b defining the center $(a, b, 0)$. The ellipsoids have the over-all measurements of 8 units parallel to the x-axis, 10 units parallel to the y-axis, and 6 units parallel to the z-axis.

The envelope of the system is seen to have the equation $z^2 = 9$, but we shall go through the formal work of determining the singular solution in order to illustrate the methods. With

$$\psi \equiv \frac{(x - a)^2}{16} + \frac{(y - b)^2}{25} + \frac{z^2}{9} - 1$$

we have

$$\psi_a \equiv \frac{-(x - a)}{8}, \quad \psi_b \equiv \frac{-2(y - b)}{25},$$

so we eliminate a and b between (33) and the two equations

$$\frac{-(x - a)}{8} = 0, \quad \frac{-2(y - b)}{25} = 0.$$

We obtain

$$z^2 - 9 = 0,$$

as predicted.

Also, we may find the singular solution from the given equation (31) and the two equations

$$\begin{cases} 32z^2p = 0, \\ 50z^2q = 0, \end{cases}$$

obtained by differentiating (31) partially with respect to p and q. Since $z^2 = 0$ does not satisfy the equation, we reduce the derived equations to $p = 0$, $q = 0$, which, substituted into (31), give $z^2 - 9 = 0$, as before. The student should verify that $z^2 - 9 = 0$ actually satisfies the given differential equation.

If we set b equal to a function of a, say $b = f(a)$, we restrict the centers of the ellipsoids to the curve $y = f(x)$ in the xy-plane, and the ellipsoids thus determined generate a tubular surface whose equation is obtained by eliminating a between

$$\frac{(x - a)^2}{16} + \frac{(y - f(a))^2}{25} + \frac{z^2}{9} - 1 = 0$$

and

$$\frac{-(x - a)}{8} - \frac{2(y - f(a))f'(a)}{25} = 0.$$

This eliminant we have called the general solution of the original differential equation (31).

71. Equations involving several variables; Jacobi's method. Consider a partial differential equation of the first order in n independent variables $x_1, \cdots, x_n$, but free of the dependent variable z, as

$$F_1(x_1, x_2, \cdots, x_n, p_1, p_2, \cdots, p_n) = 0, \qquad (34)$$

where p_i represents z_{x_i}. The problem of solution becomes that of determining n functions p_i which satisfy it identically, and such that the equation

$$dz = p_1 \, dx_1 + p_2 \, dx_2 + \cdots + p_n \, dx_n \qquad (35)$$

is integrable. This equation is clearly exact if

$$\frac{\partial p_i}{\partial x_k} \equiv \frac{\partial p_k}{\partial x_i} \qquad (i, k = 1, \cdots, n),$$

and, analogous to the above treatment, we shall determine these p_i by means of (34) and $n - 1$ additional equations

$$\begin{cases} F_2(x_1, \cdots, x_n, p_1, \cdots, p_n) = a_2, \\ \cdot \cdot \cdot \cdot \cdot \cdot \cdot \cdot \cdot \cdot \cdot \cdot \cdot \cdot \cdot \cdot \cdot \\ F_n(x_1, \cdots, x_n, p_1, \cdots, p_n) = a_n, \end{cases} \qquad (36)$$

where $a_2, \cdots, a_n$ are arbitrary constants. By differentiating (34) and all of the equation (36) partially with respect to x_i, we obtain

$$\begin{cases} \dfrac{\partial F_1}{\partial x_i} + \dfrac{\partial F_1}{\partial p_1} \cdot \dfrac{\partial p_1}{\partial x_i} + \dfrac{\partial F_1}{\partial p_2} \cdot \dfrac{\partial p_2}{\partial x_i} + \cdots + \dfrac{\partial F_1}{\partial p_n} \cdot \dfrac{\partial p_n}{\partial x_i} = 0, \\[2mm] \dfrac{\partial F_2}{\partial x_i} + \dfrac{\partial F_2}{\partial p_1} \cdot \dfrac{\partial p_1}{\partial x_i} + \dfrac{\partial F_2}{\partial p_2} \cdot \dfrac{\partial p_2}{\partial x_i} + \cdots + \dfrac{\partial F_2}{\partial p_n} \cdot \dfrac{\partial p_n}{\partial x_i} = 0, \\[2mm] \cdot \cdot \cdot \cdot \cdot \cdot \cdot \cdot \cdot \cdot \cdot \cdot \cdot \cdot \cdot \cdot \cdot \cdot \cdot \cdot \\ \cdot \cdot \cdot \cdot \cdot \cdot \cdot \cdot \cdot \cdot \cdot \cdot \cdot \cdot \cdot \cdot \cdot \cdot \cdot \cdot \\ \dfrac{\partial F_n}{\partial x_i} + \dfrac{\partial F_n}{\partial p_1} \cdot \dfrac{\partial p_1}{\partial x_i} + \dfrac{\partial F_n}{\partial p_2} \cdot \dfrac{\partial p_2}{\partial x_i} + \cdots + \dfrac{\partial F_n}{\partial p_n} \cdot \dfrac{\partial p_n}{\partial x_i} = 0. \end{cases}$$

This is a system of n linear equations in the n quantities $\dfrac{\partial p_k}{\partial x_i}$ ($k = 1, \cdots, n$), whose determinant,

$$\Delta \equiv \left| \frac{\partial F_1}{\partial p_1} \ \frac{\partial F_1}{\partial p_2} \ \cdots \ \frac{\partial F_1}{\partial p_n} \right|^*,$$

---

* Here, as before, we have exhibited only the first row. To obtain the jth row, replace F_1 by F_j.

must not vanish if the n equations (34), (36) are to determine unique values of $p_1, \cdots, p_n$. The system may be solved for $\dfrac{\partial p_k}{\partial x_i}$ to obtain

$$-\Delta\, \frac{\partial p_k}{\partial x_i} = \left| \frac{\partial F_1}{\partial p_1}\ \frac{\partial F_1}{\partial p_2} \cdots \frac{\partial F_1}{\partial p_{k-1}}\ \frac{\partial F_1}{\partial x_i}\ \frac{\partial F_1}{\partial p_{k+1}} \cdots \frac{\partial F_1}{\partial p_n} \right|.$$

From the conditions for exactness we then have

$$\left| \frac{\partial F_1}{\partial p_1} \cdots \frac{\partial F_1}{\partial p_{k-1}}\ \frac{\partial F_1}{\partial x_i}\ \frac{\partial F_1}{\partial p_{k+1}} \cdots \frac{\partial F_1}{\partial p_n} \right|$$
$$\equiv \left| \frac{\partial F_1}{\partial p_1} \cdots \frac{\partial F_1}{\partial p_{i-1}}\ \frac{\partial F_1}{\partial x_k}\ \frac{\partial F_1}{\partial p_{i+1}} \cdots \frac{\partial F_1}{\partial p_n} \right|.$$

These determinants differ only in their kth and ith columns, and will certainly be equal if all corresponding two-rowed minors from those columns are equal. Hence, set

$$\left| \begin{matrix} \dfrac{\partial F_1}{\partial p_i} & \dfrac{\partial F_1}{\partial x_i} \\[2mm] \dfrac{\partial F_j}{\partial p_i} & \dfrac{\partial F_j}{\partial x_i} \end{matrix} \right| \equiv \left| \begin{matrix} \dfrac{\partial F_1}{\partial x_k} & \dfrac{\partial F_1}{\partial p_k} \\[2mm] \dfrac{\partial F_j}{\partial x_k} & \dfrac{\partial F_j}{\partial p_k} \end{matrix} \right|,$$

or

$$\frac{\partial F_1}{\partial x_k} \cdot \frac{\partial F_j}{\partial p_k} + \frac{\partial F_1}{\partial x_i} \cdot \frac{\partial F_j}{\partial p_i} - \frac{\partial F_1}{\partial p_i} \cdot \frac{\partial F_j}{\partial x_i} - \frac{\partial F_1}{\partial p_k} \cdot \frac{\partial F_j}{\partial x_k} \equiv 0.$$

This is a linear partial differential equation in the unknown function F_j, and the corresponding Lagrange system of ordinary differential equations is

$$\frac{dx_i}{-\dfrac{\partial F_1}{\partial p_i}} = \frac{dx_k}{-\dfrac{\partial F_1}{\partial p_k}} = \frac{dp_i}{\dfrac{\partial F_1}{\partial x_i}} = \frac{dp_k}{\dfrac{\partial F_1}{\partial x_k}} = \frac{dF_j}{0}.$$

Since the equations hold for all values of i and k, we have

$$\frac{dx_1}{-\dfrac{\partial F_1}{\partial p_1}} = \frac{dx_2}{-\dfrac{\partial F_1}{\partial p_2}} = \cdots = \frac{dx_n}{-\dfrac{\partial F_1}{\partial p_n}} = \frac{dp_1}{\dfrac{\partial F_1}{\partial x_1}} = \frac{dp_2}{\dfrac{\partial F_1}{\partial x_2}} = \cdots = \frac{dp_n}{\dfrac{\partial F_1}{\partial x_n}}$$
$$= \frac{dF_j}{0}\ (j = 2, 3, \cdots, n).$$

Therefore, any $n-1$ solution of this system of the form

$$\begin{cases} F_2(x_1, \cdots, x_n, p_1, \cdots, p_n) = a_2, \\ \ \cdot\ \ \cdot\ \ \cdot\ \ \cdot\ \ \cdot\ \ \cdot\ \ \cdot\ \ \cdot\ \ \cdot\ \ \cdot\ \ \cdot\ \ \cdot\ \ \cdot\ \ \cdot \\ F_n(x_1, \cdots, x_n, p_1, \cdots, p_n) = a_n, \end{cases}$$

such that $\Delta(F_1, \cdots, F_n) \not\equiv 0$, may be taken as the n functions determining $p_1, \cdots, p_n$, and these p_i will render (35) exact. Its solution introduces one additional arbitrary constant a, giving a relation

$$z = f(x_1, \cdots, x_n, a_1, \cdots, a_n) \qquad (37)$$

as the *complete* solution of (34). As before, we obtain the singular solution, if it exists, by eliminating the constants a_i from (37) and the n equations

$$f_{a_i}(x_1, \cdots, x_n, a_1, \cdots, a_n) = 0 \quad (i = 1, \cdots, n),$$

or by eliminating the p_i from (34) and the n equations

$$\frac{\partial}{\partial p_i} \cdot F_1(x_1, \cdots, x_n, p_1, \cdots, p_n) = 0 \quad (i = 1, \cdots, n).$$

If, in an equation of the first order in n independent variables, the dependent variable z appears the equation can be replaced by another equation containing $n + 1$ independent variables in which the dependent variable does not appear. Let the equation be designated by

$$F(z, x_1, \cdots, x_n, p_1, \cdots, p_n) = 0, \qquad (38)$$

and a solution be

$$y(x_1, \cdots, x_n, z) - a_0 = 0, \qquad (39)$$

By partial differentiation in (39), we obtain

$$y_{x_i} + y_z p_i = 0 \qquad (i = 1, \cdots, n),$$

or

$$p_i = -\frac{y_{x_i}}{y_z} \qquad (i = 1, \cdots, n),$$

which satisfy (38) identically. Then we have

$$F\left(z, x_1, x_2, \cdots, x_n, -\frac{y_{x_1}}{y_z}, \cdots, -\frac{y_{x_n}}{y_z}\right) \equiv 0. \qquad (40)$$

This may be written as

$$F_1(z, x_1, \cdots, x_n, y_z, y_{x_1}, \cdots, y_{x_n}) = 0 \qquad (41)$$

and may be considered as a partial differential equation in $n + 1$ independent variables $z, x_1, \cdots, x_n$, in which the dependent variable y does not appear. By the foregoing methods it may be solved in the form

$$y - a_0 = f(z, x_1, \cdots, x_n, a_1, \cdots, a_n).$$

Since this satisfies (41) identically, it satisfies the other form, (40), identically. But (40) is the result of substituting $y - a_0$ into (38), so $y - a_0 = 0$, or, what is the same thing,

$$f(z, x_1, \cdots, x_n, a_1, \cdots, a_n) = 0,$$

which satisfies (38) identically.

Exercises

Find the complete solution of each of the following:

1. $q^2 = 2p$. *Hint:* If the equation lacks x, y, and z, choose p and q as constants which satisfy the equation, and integrate $dz = p\, dx + q\, dy$. In this case $q \equiv 2a$, $p \equiv 2a^2$, a constant.

2. $p^2 = 2q - 1$.

3. $p^{2/3} + q^{2/3} = 1$

4. $p^2 + q^2 = 4$.

5. $pq = 2p - q$.

6. $p_1 + p_2 + p_3 = 0$. *Hint:* Let $p_3 \equiv a_3$, $p_2 \equiv a_2$, $p_1 \equiv -a_3 - a_2$, and solve $dz = p_1\, dx_1 + p_2\, dx_2 + p_3\, dx_3$.

7. $p_1^2 + p_2^2 + p_3^2 = 1$.

8. $p_1 p_2 - p_1 p_3 + p_2 p_3 = 0$.

9. $p^2 z + q^2 = 10$. *Hint:* If the equation is free of x and y, let $z = f(x + ay) \equiv f(s)$; then $p = \dfrac{dz}{ds} \cdot \dfrac{\partial s}{\partial x} = \dfrac{dz}{ds}$, and $q = \dfrac{dz}{ds} \cdot \dfrac{\partial s}{\partial y} = a\dfrac{dz}{ds}$, and the equation becomes an ordinary differential equation in z and s.

10. $p = z(1 - pq)$.

11. $q^2(1 + p) = p(z - 1)$.

12. $p^2 + q^2 = 5z$.

13. $pq(1 - z) = z^2$.

14. $zp^3 - zpq - 3p^2 + 3q = 0$.

15. $q^2 y^2 = z(z - px)$. *Hint:* Let $y = e^Y$, $x = e^X$.

16. $z^2 pq^2 + p^2 z^3 + pq^3 + p^2 qz = zq^3 + pqz^2 + p^3 z^2 + zp^2 q^2$.

17. $p_1^2 + zp_2^2 + z^2p_3^2 = z^3p_1p_2p_3.$

18. $z = p + pq.$

19. $p^4 - q^2z^2 = 0.$

20. $p^3 - 4qz^2 = 0.$

21. $z = q + \sqrt{1 + p^2}.$

22. $p - x^2 = q - y^2.$ *Hint:* In equations of the form $f(x, p) = g(y, q)$, set each side equal to the same constant, solve for p and q, and integrate $dz = p\,dx + q\,dy.$

23. $p^3 = q + x.$

24. $zpx - zxy = p^2z.$ Is $z = 0$ a solution? Is it a singular solution? A particular solution?

25. $p^2q = x^2y.$

26. $p(q - \sin y) = \sin x.$

27. Prove that the extended Clairaut equation $z = p_1x_1 + p_2x_2 + \cdots + p_nx_n + f(p_1, \cdots, p_n)$ is satisfied by $z = a_1x_1 + a_2x_2 + \cdots + a_nx_n + f(a_1, \cdots, a_n).$

28. $z = px + qy + 2p + 3q^2.$

29. $z = px + qy + p^2 + q^2 + 1.$

30. $z = px + qy + 5p^3 - 2p - q.$

31. $(z - px - qy)^2 = pq.$

32. $z = p_1x_1 + p_2x_2 + p_3x_3 + p_1p_2p_3.$

33. $z = p_1x_1 + p_2x_2 + p_3x_3 + p_4x_4 + p_1p_2 + p_3p_4.$

34. $z^2p^2 + z^2q^2 - z^2 = 1.$

35. $x^2yp + xy^2q - xyz + zpq = 0.$

36. $p^2x + pq(x + y + z - 1) + q^2y - pq(px + qy) - (p + q)z = 0.$

37. $z^2p^2 - z^2q^2 - z^2 = 1.$

38. $z^2p^2 + 5z^2q^2 - z^2 = 0.$

39. $z = px + qy + \log pq.$

40. $q^2 + 6x^4 + 2x^2p + 2xz = 0.$

41. $z = px + qy + \sqrt{q^{1/2} - p}.$

42. $4z^2q^2 = y + 2zp - 2x.$

43. $2zp_3 + 4z^2p_1^2 + 8z^3p_2^3 = 1.$

44. $p_1^2 - p_2p_3 = zp_2 + zp_3.$

45. $2zp_3 = 4z^2e^{x_3}(p_1e^{-x_1} + p_2e^{-x_2})^2.$

46. $2p_1x_1 + 3p_2x_2 + 6p_3x_3 - 6 = 0.$

47. $x_1p_1 + x_2p_2 + x_3p_3 + x_4p_4 - p_1p_2p_3p_4 = 0.$

48. $x_1p_1 + x_2p_2 + x_3p_3 + x_4p_4 - p_1^2p_2^2p_3^2p_4^2 = 0.$

$\underline{ex\ 35}$: Reducable to Clairauts form

If $z = \dfrac{spx}{m} + \dfrac{sqy}{n} + \dfrac{1}{z^{s-1}} \phi\left(\dfrac{z^{s-1}p}{x^{m-1}}, \dfrac{z^{s-1}q}{y^{m-1}}\right)$

then use $x^m = x,\ y^n = y,\ z^\delta = z$

$\text{I} \qquad z = mpx + nqy + \dfrac{1}{z^{n-1}} \phi(z^{n-1}p,\ z^{n-1}q)$

$\qquad\qquad\qquad\qquad$ use $x = x,\ y = y,\ z^n = z$

$\text{II} \qquad z = \dfrac{px}{n} + qy + \phi\left(\dfrac{p}{x^{m-1}},\ q\right)$ use $x^n = x$
$\qquad\qquad\qquad\qquad\qquad\qquad\qquad\qquad y = y \quad z = z$

$\text{III} \qquad z = px + \dfrac{qy}{m} + \phi\left(p,\ \dfrac{q}{y^{m-1}}\right)$ use $x = x,\ y^n = y$
$\qquad\qquad\qquad\qquad\qquad\qquad\qquad\qquad\qquad z = z$

$\underline{\text{IV}} \quad z = \dfrac{px}{n} + \dfrac{qy}{m} + \phi\left(\dfrac{p}{x^{m-1}},\ \dfrac{q}{y^{m-1}}\right)$ use $x^n = x,\ y^m = y$
$\qquad\qquad\qquad\qquad\qquad\qquad\qquad\qquad\qquad z = z$

$\underline{\text{V}} \quad z = px + qy + \dfrac{1}{z}\phi\left(\dfrac{zp}{x},\ \dfrac{zq}{y}\right)$ use $x^2 = x,\ y^2 = y$
$\qquad\qquad\qquad\qquad\qquad\qquad\qquad\qquad z^2 = z$

$\underline{\text{Form } \text{V} \text{ corresponds to } ex.\ 35}$

CHAPTER IX

Linear Partial Differential Equations
with Constant Coefficients

72. Homogeneous linear equations with constant coefficients.
In Chapter IV we made use of an operator $D \equiv \dfrac{d}{dx}$, and in an entirely analogous manner we shall employ here two operators $D_1 \equiv \dfrac{\partial}{\partial x}$ and $D_2 \equiv \dfrac{\partial}{\partial y}$. Thus,

$$D_1 z \equiv \frac{\partial z}{\partial x}, \; D_2 z \equiv \frac{\partial z}{\partial y},$$

and

$$f(D_1, D_2)z \equiv \sum_{p,\,q} a_{pq} \frac{\partial^{p+q} z}{\partial x^p \partial y^q},$$

where p and q are positive integers or zero, a_{pq} are constants, and

$$f(D_1, D_2) \equiv \sum_{p,\,q} a_{pq} D_1^p D_2^q$$

when D_1 and D_2 are regarded as variables.

We leave it as an exercise for the student to verify that the addition and multiplication of these operators obey the laws of algebra, $i.\ e.$, that

$$[f(D_1, D_2) + g(D_1, D_2)]z \equiv [g(D_1, D_2) + f(D_1, D_2)]z$$
$$\equiv f(D_1, D_2)z + g(D_1, D_2)z,$$
$$[f(D_1, D_2) \cdot g(D_1, D_2)]z \equiv [g(D_1, D_2) \cdot f(D_1, D_2)]z$$
$$\equiv f(D_1, D_2)\,[g(D_1, D_2)z],$$

if z is a function of x and y that has continuous partial derivatives of all orders called for by these operators.

By a homogeneous linear partial differential equation of order n with constant coefficients, we shall mean an equation of the form

$$a_n \frac{\partial^n z}{\partial x^n} + a_{n-1} \frac{\partial^n z}{\partial x^{n-1} \partial y} + \cdots + a_1 \frac{\partial^n z}{\partial x \partial y^{n-1}} + a_0 \frac{\partial^n z}{\partial y^n} = 0,$$

where the a's are real constants, not all zero. This can be written as

$$(a_nD_1^n + a_{n-1}D_1^{n-1}D_2 + \cdots + a_1D_1D_2^{n-1} + a_0D_2^n)z = 0. \quad (1)$$

The simplest possible equation of this kind is one of the first order, as

$$(a_1D_1 + a_0D_2)z = 0.$$

It can be written in the form

$$a_1z_x + a_0z_y = 0.$$

This falls under the treatment of first order partial differential equations given in Chapter VIII, and the general solution is

$$z = F(a_1y - a_0x).$$

Since the operator in (1) may be factored into the product of n linear factors of the form

$$\alpha_iD_1 + \beta_iD_2 \qquad (i = 1, \cdots, n),$$

where the α_i and β_i are complex numbers in general, we shall have need of the following

THEOREM I. *If* $z = F(\alpha y - \beta x)$ *is a solution of the differential equation* $\phi(D_1, D_2)z = 0$, *it is a solution of the equation* $[\psi(D_1, D_2) \cdot \phi(D_1, D_2)]z = 0$.

The truth of this theorem is evidently a direct consequence of the property of the operators which asserts that

$$[\psi(D_1, D_2) \cdot \phi(D_1, D_2)]z \equiv \psi(D_1, D_2)[\phi(D_1, D_2)z].$$

We know from algebra that the operator in (1) can be broken up into a product of linear operators in essentially only one way, so that (1) takes the form

$$(\alpha_1D_1 + \beta_1D_2)(\alpha_2D_1 + \beta_2D_2) \cdots (\alpha_nD_1 + \beta_nD_2)z = 0. \quad (2)$$

Then, by Theorem I, a solution is

$$z = F_n(\alpha_ny - \beta_nx),$$

and, since the order of factors in the operator is immaterial,

$$z = F_i(\alpha_iy - \beta_ix) \qquad (i = 1, \cdots, n - 1)$$

are also solutions. To obtain the general solution, we shall employ

THEOREM II. *If* $z = u(x, y)$ *and* $z = v(x, y)$ *are both solutions of* $f(D_1, D_2)z = 0$, *then* $z = u(x, y) + v(x, y)$ *is also a solution.*

The proof of this theorem comes directly from the properties of the operator, as the student may readily verify.

By use of Theorem II, we now see that

$$z = F_1(\alpha_1 y - \beta_1 x) + F_2(\alpha_2 y - \beta_2 x) + \cdots + F_n(\alpha_n y - \beta_n x) \quad (3)$$

is also a solution of (2), with each function F_i arbitrary in form. If the factors $\alpha_i D_1 + \beta_i D_2$ of the operator are essentially distinct, *i. e.*, if no one of them is a constant multiple of any other, (3) is what we shall call the *general solution* of (1).

In each of the n factors $\alpha_i D_1 + \beta_i D_2$, not both of α_i and β_i are zero, and, for simplicity in notation, we shall assume for the present $\alpha_i \neq 0$ $(i = 1, \cdots, n)$, so that (2) may be written in the form

$$(D_1 - m_1 D_2)(D_1 - m_2 D_2) \cdots (D_1 - m_n D_2)z = 0, \quad (4)$$

while (3) is written

$$z = F_1(y + m_1 x) + F_2(y + m_2 x) + \cdots + F_n(y + m_n x). \quad (5)$$

73. Case of complex roots. Although (5) may be called the general solution of (4), it is not the general *real* solution unless all of the numbers m_i are real. If one of these is complex, its conjugate is also present. That is, if $m_i = a + bi$ $(a, b, \text{ real})$, then $m_j = a - bi$ is present among the m's. To find real solutions, consider the equation

$$[D_1^2 - 2aD_1 D_2 + (a^2 + b^2)D_2^2]z = 0. \quad (6)$$

From the above discussion,

$$z = \Phi(y + ax, bx) \equiv F_1(y + ax + ibx) + F_1(y + ax - ibx)$$

and

$$z = \Psi(y + ax, bx) \equiv iF_2(y + ax + ibx) - iF_2(y + ax - ibx)$$

are solutions of (6) by Theorem II, and

$$z = \Phi(y + ax, bx) + \Psi(y + ax, bx) \quad (7)$$

is the desired solution. Since F_1 and F_2 are entirely arbitrary real functions, this solution is general. By means of exponential identities we can easily throw (7), which, in full, is

$$z = F_1(y + ax + ibx) + F_1(y + ax - ibx)$$
$$+ i[F_2(y + ax + ibx) - F_2(y + ax - ibx)],$$

into the form

$$z = c_1 e^{g_1 \cdot (y+ax)} \cos g_1 bx + c_2 e^{g_2 \cdot (y+ax)} \cos g_2 bx + \cdots$$
$$+ d_1 e^{h_1 \cdot (y+ax)} \sin h_1 bx + d_2 e^{h_2 \cdot (y+ax)} \sin h_2 bx + \cdots$$
$$\equiv \sum_{j=1}^{\infty} c_j e^{g_j \cdot (y+ax)} \cos g_j bx + \sum_{j=1}^{\infty} d_j e^{h_j \cdot (y+ax)} \sin h_j bx, \tag{8}$$

where c_j, d_j, g_j, h_j are any real constants such that

$$2F_1(t) \equiv c_1 e^{g_1 t} + c_2 e^{g_2 t} + c_3 e^{g_3 t} + \cdots$$

and

$$2F_2(t) \equiv d_1 e^{h_1 t} + d_2 e^{h_2 t} + d_3 e^{h_3 t} + \cdots ,$$

but it is easier to verify directly that

$$z = c \cdot e^{g \cdot (y+ax)} \cos gbx$$

and

$$z = d \cdot e^{h \cdot (y+ax)} \sin hbx$$

are solutions of (6) for any constant values of g, h, c, d, and hence apply Theorem II to obtain (8). The student should make this verification.

74. Case of multiple roots. To state our next theorem we shall need the following:

DEFINITION. *The solution*

$$z = F_i(y + m_i x)$$

is said to be the solution of (1) *corresponding to the factor* $D_1 - m_i D_2$ *of the operator in* (1) *if* m_i *is real.*

DEFINITION. *The solution* (7) *or the solution* (8) *is said to be the solution of* (1) *corresponding to the factor* $D_1^2 - 2aD_1D_2 + (a^2 + b^2)D_2^2$ *of the operator in* (1) *if* a *and* b *are real.*

In this nomenclature we can state

THEOREM III. *If* $z = f(x, y)$ *is the solution of* (1) *corresponding to a factor of the operator of multiplicity* k, *then* $z = xf(x, y)$, $\cdots$, $z = x^{k-1} f(x, y)$ *are all solutions.*

To prove this, take the equation

$$(D_1 - mD_2)^k z = 0, \tag{9}$$

where m is real, write it

$$(D_1 - mD_2)^{k-1}(D_1 - mD_2)z = 0,$$

and compute $(D_1 - mD_2)z$ with

$$z \equiv x^p F(y + mx). \tag{10}$$

We have

$$D_1 z \equiv px^{p-1} F(y + mx) + mx^p F'(y + mx)$$

and

$$D_2 z \equiv x^p F'(y + mx),$$

hence

$$(D_1 - mD_2)z \equiv px^{p-1} F(y + mx).$$

The equation (9) is satisfied by (10) if, and only if,

$$(D_1 - mD_2)^{k-2}(D_1 - mD_2)[px^{p-1}F(y + mx)] \equiv 0.$$

The operation $(D_1 - mD_2)[px^{p-1}F(y + mx)]$ reduces to

$$p(p - 1)x^{p-2}F(y + mx).$$

The equation (9) is now satisfied if, and only if,

$$(D_1 - mD_2)^{k-3}(D_1 - mD_2)[p(p - 1)x^{p-2}F(y + mx)] \equiv 0.$$

Continuing in this manner, we arrive finally at the equation

$$p(p - 1)(p - 2) \cdots (p - k + 1)x^{p-k}F(y + mx) \equiv 0.$$

which is immediately seen to be true if $p = 0, 1, 2, \cdots, k - 1$.

For the case of a factor which is a power of $[D_1^2 - 2aD_1D_2 + (a^2 + b^2)D_2^2]$, consider the equation

$$[D_1^2 - 2aD_1D_2 + (a^2 + b^2)D_2^2]^k z = 0. \tag{11}$$

Let

$$z \equiv x^p \sum_i c_i e^{g_i \cdot (y+ax)} \cos g_i bx + x^p \sum_i d_i e^{h_i \cdot (y+ax)} \sin h_i bx, \tag{12}$$

where the sums are either finite or infinite.* In evaluating the operation

$$[D_1^2 - 2aD_1D_2 + (a^2 + b^2)D_2^2]z,$$

we obtain

$$p(p - 1)x^{p-2} \left\{ \sum_i c_i e^{g_i \cdot (y+ax)} \cos g_i bx + \sum_i d_i e^{h_i \cdot (y+ax)} \sin h_i bx \right\}$$

$$- 2bpx^{p-1} \sum_i \{ g_i c_i e^{g_i \cdot (y+ax)} \sin g_i bx - h_i d_i e^{h_i \cdot (y+ax)} \cos h_i bx \}.$$

_____

* The condition that a series of differentiable functions, which converges to a function $F(x)$ in an interval, be differentiable term by term, in the interval, is shown in the Theory of Functions of a Real Variable to be, that the derived series converge uniformly in the interval.

This is seen to consist of two terms of the type of the proposed solution (12), in one of which a coefficient is p, and in the other of which a coefficient is $p(p-1)$.   If the process is repeated k times, the number of terms becomes $k+1$, with the coefficients $p(p-1)$ $\cdots$ $(p-k+1)$, $p(p-1)$ $\cdots$ $(p-k)$, $\cdots$, $p(p-1)$ $\cdots$ $(p-2k+1)$, all of which vanish if $p = 0, 1, 2, \cdots, k-1$.   The student may show, in an entirely similar manner, that

$$z = x^p\{\Phi(y + ax, bx) + \Psi(y + ax, bx)\}$$

is a solution of (11) if Φ and Ψ are defined as in (7), and $p = 0,$ $1, \cdots, k-1$.

Exercises

Find the general solution of each of the following:

1. $(D_1^2 - 7D_1D_2 + 10D_2^2)z = 0.$

2. $(D_1^2 - 2D_1D_2 - 3D_2^2)z = 0.$

3. $(D_1^3 - 6D_1^2D_2 + 11D_1D_2^2 - 6D_2^3)z = 0.$

4. $(D_1^3 + 2D_1^2D_2 - D_1D_2^2 - 2D_2^3)z = 0.$

5. $(D_1^4 - 5D_1^2D_2^2 + 4D_2^4)z = 0.$

6. $(D_1^4 + 2D_1^3D_2 - 5D_1^2D_2^2 - 6D_1D_2^3)z = 0.$

7. $(D_1^2 - 2D_1D_2 - 2D_2^2)z = 0.$

8. $(D_1^2 + 4D_1D_2 - 6D_2^2)z = 0.$

9. $(D_1^3 + D_1^2D_2 - 10D_1D_2^2 - 6D_2^3)z = 0.$

10. $(D_1^3 - 4D_1^2D_2 - 5D_1D_2^2 + 14D_2^3)z = 0.$

11. $(D_1^4 + 2D_1^3D_2 - 10D_1^2D_2^2 - 20D_1D_2^3 - 8D_2^4)z = 0.$ *Hint:* $D_1^2 - 2D_1D_2 - 4D_2^2$ is a factor of the operator.

12. $(D_1^2 + 6D_1D_2 + D_2^2)(D_1^2 - 6D_1D_2 - 5D_2^2)z = 0.$

13. $(D_1^2 + 4D_1D_2 + 4D_2^2)z = 0.$

14. $(4D_1^2 - 12D_1D_2 + 9D_2^2)z = 0.$

15. $(D_1^3 + 3D_1^2D_2 + 3D_1D_2^2 + D_2^3)z = 0.$

16. $(8D_1^3 - 12D_1^2D_2 + 6D_1D_2^2 - D_2^3)z = 0.$

17. $(2D_1^4 - 13D_1^3D_2 + 25D_1^2D_2^2 - 8D_1D_2^3 - 12D_2^4)z = 0.$

18. $(2D_1 - D_2)^2(2D_1 - 3D_2)^2z = 0.$

19. $(D_1^2 - 2D_1D_2 + 2D_2^2)z = 0.$

20. $(9D_1^2 - 6D_1D_2 + 5D_2^2)z = 0.$

21. $(3D_1^3 + 11D_1^2D_2 + 20D_1D_2^2 - 8D_2^3)z = 0.$

22. $(-2D_1^3 - 3D_1^2D_2 - 18D_1D_2^2 + 10D_2^3)z = 0.$

23. $(D_1^2 + 2D_1D_2 + 2D_2^2)^2z = 0.$

24. $(2D_1^2 - 6D_1D_2 + 5D_2^2)^2z = 0.$

75. Right-hand member not zero. We now study the case of an equation of the form

$$f(D_1, D_2)z = \phi(x, y), \tag{13}$$

where $f(D_1, D_2)$ is a homogeneous polynomial of degree n in D_1, D_2. This case is analogous to linear equations with one independent variable, treated in Chapter IV, and hence the general solution of (13) consists of the general solution of the *reduced* equation

$$f(D_1, D_2)z = 0,$$

which solution we shall call the *complementary function*, plus any particular solution of the complete equation. The problem at hand becomes, therefore, the problem of finding a particular solution of (13).

76. Special cases. Before attacking the problem in general, let us consider a few special forms of the function $\phi(x, y)$ which can be expediently handled by special methods. If, for example, z is a homogeneous polynomial of degree m, $f(D_1, D_2)z$ is a homogeneous polynomial of degree $m - n$; hence we state

NOTE I. *If $\phi(x, y)$ is a homogeneous polynomial of degree m, assume a particular solution of the form $z = A_0 x^{m+n} + A_1 x^{m+n-1}y + \cdots + A_{m+n}y^{m+n}$, operate on z by $f(D_1, D_2)$, equate coefficients of corresponding terms in $f(D_1, D_2)z$ and $\phi(x, y)$ and solve for the coefficients.*

If z is $\sin\left(\dfrac{n\pi}{2} + ay + bx\right) + \cos\left(\dfrac{n\pi}{2} + ay + bx\right)$, the homogeneous operator $f(D_1, D_2)$ of degree n reduces z to

$$f(-a, -b)\{\sin(ay + bx) + \cos(ay + bx)\}$$

and hence we deduce

NOTE II. *If $\phi(x, y) \equiv c\cos(ay + bx) + d \cdot \sin(ay + bx)$, assume a particular integral of the form*

$$z = A\cos(ay + bx) + B\sin(ay + bx),$$

operate on z by $f(D_1, D_2)$, *equate* $f(D_1, D_2)z$ *identically to* $\phi(x, y)$, *and solve for* A *and* B. (See Exercises 8 and 9 below for exception.)

If $z = e^{ax+by}$, the homogeneous operator $f(D_1, D_2)$ reduces z to $f(a, b)e^{ax+by}$, and hence

NOTE III. *If* $\phi(x, y) \equiv ce^{ax+by}$, *assume a particular solution of the form*

$$z = Ae^{ax+by},$$

operate on z by $f(D_1, D_2)$, *equate the result identically to* $\phi(x, y)$, *and solve for* A. (See Exercise 15 for exception.)

Exercises

Solve completely:

1. $(D_1^2 - 7D_1D_2 + 10D_2^2)z = 12x^2y + y^3$.

2. $(D_1^2 - 2D_1D_2 - 2D_2^2)z = x^3y^4$.

3. $(D_1^3 + D_1^2D_2 - 10D_1D_2^2 - 6D_2^3)z = x + y^2$. *Hint:* Add the particular solutions obtained for $\phi(x, y) \equiv x$ to the particular solution obtained for $\phi(x, y) \equiv y^2$.

4. $(D_1^2 + 4D_1D_2 + 2D_2^2)(D_1^2 - 2D_1D_2 - 4D_2^2)z = x^2 + x^2y^2$.

5. $(D_1^2 - 2D_1D_2 - 3D_2^2)z = 20 \cos (y + 2x)$.

6. $(D_1^4 + 2D_1^3D_2 - 5D_1^2D_2^2 - 6D_1D_2^3)z = 5 \cos (2y + 3x) - \sin (2y + 3x)$.

7. $(4D_1^2 - 12D_1D_2 + 9D_2^2)z = \cos (x + y) + \cos (2x - y)$.

8. $(D_1^2 - 5D_1D_2 + 6D_2^2)z = \cos (y + 2x)$. *Hint:* The method of the Note would be to try

$$z = A \cos (\pi + y + 2x) \equiv -A \cos (y + 2x),$$

but this must fail since

$$z = -A \cos (y + 2x)$$

is an instance of

$$z = F_1(y + 2x) + F_2(y + 3x),$$

which is the general solution of the reduced equation

$$(D_1^2 - 5D_1D_2 + 6D_2^2)z = 0.$$

Try

$$z = Ax \sin (y + 2x).$$

9. $(D_1^2 - 4D_1D_2 + 4D_2^2)z = \cos (y + 2x)$. *Hint:* Try $z = Ax^2 \cos (y + 2x) + Bx^2 \sin (y + 2x)$ for the particular integral.

10. $(D_1^2 - 5D_1D_2) + 6D_2^2)z = \sin (y + 2x)$.

11. $(D_1^2 - 5D_1D_2 + 6D_2^2)z = 3 \sin (y + 2x) + \cos (y + 3x)$.

12. $(D_1 + 2D_2)^3 z = \cos x + \sin (y - 2x)$.

13. $(D_1^2 + 4D_1D_2 + 4D_2^2)z = 5e^{2x+3y}$.

14. $(D_1^3 - 4D_1^2D_2 - 5D_1D_2^2 + 24D_2^3)z = e^{3x-y}$.

15. $(D_1^2 - 7D_1D_2 + 10D_2^2)z = e^{y+2x}$. *Hint:* The method of the Note fails, because $z = Ae^{y+2x}$ is a part of the complementary function. Try $z = Axe^{y+2x}$.

16. $(D_1^3 + 6D_1^2D_2 + 12D_1D_2^2 + 8D_2^3)z = e^{y-2x}$.

17. $(D_1^3 - 4D_1^2D_2 + 5D_1D_2^2 - 2D_2^3)z = e^{y+x} + e^{y+2x} + e^{y+3x}$.

77. Inverse operators; factoring. If we were to treat the operator $f(D_1, D_2)$ as an algebraic quantity, the equation

$$f(D_1, D_2)z = \phi(x, y) \tag{13}$$

would reduce to

$$z = \frac{1}{f(D_1, D_2)} \phi(x, y). \tag{14}$$

No such operator as $\dfrac{1}{f(D_1, D_2)}$ has been defined, but it is clear that if equation (14) is to mean the same as (13), then

$$f(D_1, D_2)z = f(D_1, D_2) \cdot \frac{1}{f(D_1, D_2)} \phi(x, y) \equiv \phi(x, y).$$

Now if

$$f(D_1, D_2) \equiv (D_1 - m_1D_2)(D_1 - m_2D_2) \cdots (D_1 - m_nD_2)$$
$$\equiv \prod_{i=1}^{n} (D_1 - m_iD_2),*$$

then

$$z = \frac{1}{\prod\limits_{i=1}^{n} (D_1 - m_iD_2)} \phi(x, y),$$

---

* The symbol $\prod$ stands for repeated multiplication; thus, $\prod\limits_{i=1}^{4} x_i \equiv x_1 x_2 x_3 x_4$. As used here, the index runs from 1 to n, unless it appears as $\prod\limits_{i \neq r}$, when it runs from 1 to n, excepting the value r.

and this can be written as

$$z = \frac{1}{\overset{i \neq n}{\Pi}\,(D_1 - m_i D_2)} \left[\frac{1}{D_1 - m_n D_2} \cdot \phi(x, y)\right],$$

since

$$f(D_1, D_2) \equiv (D_1 - m_n D_2) \left[\overset{i \neq n}{\Pi}\,(D_1 - m_i D_2)\right];$$

and hence

$$f(D_1, D_2)z \equiv (D_1 - m_n D_2) \left[\overset{i \neq n}{\Pi}\,(D_1 - m_i D_2) \cdot \frac{1}{\overset{i \neq n}{\Pi}\,(D_1 - m_i D_2)}\right.$$
$$\left.\left\{\frac{1}{(D_1 - m_n D_2)} \cdot \phi(x, y)\right\}\right]$$
$$\equiv (D_1 - m_n D_2) \left[\frac{1}{D_1 - m_n D_2} \cdot \phi(x, y)\right] \equiv \phi(x, y).$$

Then we may evaluate the expression $\dfrac{1}{f(D_1, D_2)}\, \phi(x, y)$ by factoring the operator and applying one factor at a time; this gives

$$\frac{1}{D_1 - m_1 D_2} \left[\frac{1}{D_1 - m_2 D_2} \left[\frac{1}{D_1 - m_3 D_2} \left[\cdots \right.\right.\right.$$
$$\left.\left.\left.\left[\frac{1}{D_1 - m_n D_2} \cdot \phi(x, y)\right] \cdots \right]\right]\right].$$

For example, consider the equation

$$(D_1^3 - D_1^2 D_2 - 4D_1 D_2^2 + 4D_2^3)z = \cos(3y + 2x),$$

or

$$(D_1 - D_2)(D_1 - 2D_2)(D_1 + 2D_2)z = \cos(3y + 2x).$$

The general solution is expressible as

$$z = F_1(y + x) + F_2(y + 2x) + F_3(y - 2x)$$
$$+ \frac{1}{D_1 - D_2}\left[\frac{1}{D_1 - 2D_2}\left\{\frac{1}{D_1 + 2D_2}\cos(3y + 2x)\right\}\right], \quad (15)$$

where $F_1(y + x) + F_2(y + 2x) + F_3(y - 2x)$ is the complementary function, *i. e.*, the solution of $(D_1 - D_2)(D_1 - 2D_2)(D_1 + 2D_2)z = 0$.

To effect the operation $\dfrac{1}{D_1 + 2D_2} \cdot \cos(3y + 2x)$, call the result u, and write

$$(D_1 + 2D_2)u = \cos(3y + 2x).$$

This can be put into the form

$$u_x + 2u_y = \cos(3y + 2x),$$

and the corresponding Lagrange system is

$$\frac{dx}{1} = \frac{dy}{2} = \frac{du}{\cos(3y + 2x)}. \tag{16}$$

A solution of (16) is $y - 2x = a$, and if we substitute $a + 2x$ for y, the system (16) gives

$$\frac{dx}{1} = \frac{du}{\cos(8x + 3a)},$$

a solution of which is $u = \frac{1}{8}\sin(8x + 3a)$.   When a is replaced by $y - 2x$, this becomes

$$u = \frac{1}{8}\sin(3y + 2x).$$

The solution (15) now takes the form

$$z = F_1(y + x) + F_2(y + 2x) + F_3(y - 2x)$$
$$+ \frac{1}{D_1 - D_2}\left[\frac{1}{D_1 - 2D_2} \cdot \frac{1}{8}\sin(3y + 2x)\right].$$

Evaluation of the quantity $\dfrac{1}{D_1 - 2D_2} \cdot \dfrac{1}{8}\sin(3y + 2x)$ reduces the solution to

$$z = F_1(y + x) + F_2(y + 2x) + F_3(y - 2x)$$
$$+ \frac{1}{D_1 - D_2} \cdot \frac{1}{32}\cos(3y + 2x).$$

This, finally, reduces to

$$z = F_1(y + x) + F_2(y + 2x) + F_3(y - 2x) - \frac{1}{32}\sin(3y + 2x).$$

78. Partial fractions.   We may write

$$\frac{1}{f(D_1, D_2)} \equiv \frac{1}{D_2^n} \cdot \left[\frac{1}{\prod\limits_{i=1}^{n}\left(\dfrac{D_1}{D_2} - m_i\right)}\right], \tag{17}$$

and resolve the second factor into partial fractions such that

$$\frac{1}{\prod\limits_{i=1}^{n}\left(\dfrac{D_1}{D_2}-m_i\right)} \equiv \frac{A_1}{\dfrac{D_1}{D_2}-m_1} + \frac{A_2}{\dfrac{D_1}{D_2}-m_2} + \cdots + \frac{A_n}{\dfrac{D_1}{D_2}-m_n}$$

$$\equiv \sum_{i=1}^{n}\frac{A_i}{\dfrac{D_1}{D_2}-m_i},$$

where the A_i are constants such that

$$\sum_{i=1}^{n}\left[A_i\,\overset{j\neq i}{\prod}\left(\frac{D_1}{D_2}-m_j\right)\right] \equiv 1,$$

when $\dfrac{D_1}{D_2}$ is considered as a variable.   This can be written

$$\sum_{i=1}^{n}A_i\,\overset{j\neq i}{\prod}\,(D_1-m_jD_2) \equiv D_2^{n-1}.$$

To show that the operator $\dfrac{1}{f(D_1,\,D_2)}$ may be replaced by this sum of partial operators, form the expression

$$\left\{\frac{1}{D_2^{n}}\sum_{i=1}^{n}\left[\frac{A_i}{\dfrac{D_1}{D_2}-m_i}\right]\right\}\phi(x,\,y) \equiv \frac{1}{D_2^{n-1}}\sum_{i=1}^{n}\left[\frac{A_i}{D_1-m_iD_2}\cdot\phi(x,\,y)\right],$$

and operate on it by $f(D_1,\,D_2)$, obtaining

$$f(D_1,\,D_2)\cdot\frac{1}{D_2^{n-1}}\sum_{i=1}^{n}\left[\frac{A_i}{D_1-m_iD_2}\cdot\phi(x,\,y)\right]$$

$$\equiv \frac{1}{D_2^{n-1}}\sum_{i=1}^{n}f(D_1,\,D_2)\cdot\left[\frac{A_i}{D_1-m_iD_2}\cdot\phi(x,\,y)\right]$$

$$\equiv \frac{1}{D_2^{n-1}}\sum_{i=1}^{n}\left[A_i\,\overset{j\neq i}{\prod}\,(D_1-m_jD_2)\right]\cdot\phi(x,\,y)$$

$$\equiv \left[\frac{1}{D_2^{n-1}}\cdot D_2^{n-1}\right]\phi(x,\,y) \equiv \phi(x,\,y).$$

In the example just demonstrated we have

$$\frac{1}{(D_1 - D_2)(D_1 - 2D_2)(D_1 + 2D_2)} \cos (3y + 2x)$$

$$\equiv \frac{1}{D_2^3} \cdot \frac{1}{\left(\dfrac{D_1}{D_2} - 1\right)\left(\dfrac{D_1}{D_2} - 2\right)\left(\dfrac{D_1}{D_2} + 2\right)} \cdot \cos (3y + 2x)$$

$$\equiv \frac{1}{D_2^3} \left[\frac{-\frac{1}{3}}{\dfrac{D_1}{D_2} - 1} + \frac{\frac{1}{4}}{\dfrac{D_1}{D_2} - 2} + \frac{\frac{1}{12}}{\dfrac{D_1}{D_2} + 2} \right] \cos (3y + 2x)$$

$$\equiv \frac{1}{D_2^2} \left[\frac{1}{-3D_1 + 3D_2} + \frac{1}{4D_1 - 8D_2} + \frac{1}{12D_1 + 24D_2} \right] \cos (3y + 2x)$$

$$\equiv \frac{1}{D_2^2} \left[\frac{1}{3} \sin (3y + 2x) - \frac{1}{16} \sin (3y + 2x) + \frac{1}{96} \sin (3y + 2x) \right]$$

$$\equiv \frac{1}{D_2^2} \left[\frac{9}{32} \sin (3y + 2x) \right] \equiv \frac{1}{D_2} \left[-\frac{3}{32} \cos (3y + 2x) \right]$$

$$\equiv -\frac{1}{32} \sin (3y + 2x).$$

79. Case of α_i not all different from zero. The assumption made on page 244, that no α_i is zero, has been in effect throughout all the intervening pages. Suppose now that an equation

$$f(D_1, D_2)z = \phi(x, y)$$

is given, in which some of the α's are zero. It may be written as

$$(\alpha_1 D_1 + \beta_1 D_2)(\alpha_2 D_1 + \beta_2 D_2) \cdots (\alpha_j D_1 + \beta_j D_2)$$
$$\cdot D_2^{n-i} \cdot z = \phi(x, y),$$

where $\alpha_i \neq 0 \ (i = 1, 2, \cdots, j)$. We may define w by the equation

$$D_2^{n-i} z = w,$$

and obtain

$$(\alpha_1 D_1 + \beta_1 D_2)(\alpha_2 D_1 + \beta_2 D_2) \cdots (\alpha_j D_1 + \beta_j D_2)w = \phi(x, y).$$

The solution of this may be found by any of the methods already discussed, and then we may obtain

$$z = \int \int \cdots \int w \, (dy)^{n-i},$$

where each quadrature is performed with x regarded as constant, and an arbitrary function of x is introduced with each quadrature in place of an arbitrary constant.

Exercises

1. Find the general solution of each of the following equations:

(a) $(D_1^2 - 7D_1D_2 + 10D_2^2)z = \dfrac{1}{x^3}$.

(b) $(D_1^2 - 2D_1D_2 + D_2^2)z = xe^{3x+5y}$.

(c) $(D_1^3 + 2D_1^2D_2 - D_1L_2^2 - 2D_2^3)z = \sqrt{3x - 2y}$.

(d) $(D_1^3 + 3D_1^2D_2 + 3D_1L_2^2 + D_2^3)z = \phi(y - x)$.

(e) $(8D_1^3 - 12D_1^2D_2 + 6D_1D_2^2 - D_2^3)z = f(2y + x) + x^3y$.

(f) $(D_1^2 + 6D_1D_2 + D_2^2)(L_1^2 - 6D_1D_2 - 5D_2^2)z =$
$x \cos (y - 3x)$.

(g) $(D_1^2 - D_1D_2 - 6D_2^2)z = (x^2 + y^2)$.

(h) $(D_1^3 - 6D_1^2D_2 + 11D_1L_2^2 - 6D_2^3)z = \sin (x + y) +$
$\cos (2x + y) + e^{3x+y}$.

(i) $(D_1^3 + 2D_1^2D_2 - D_1L_2^2 - 2D_2^3)z = x^2 \sin (2x - 3y) +$
$(x + y)^{2/3}$.

(j) $(D_1^2 + 4D_1D_2 - 6D_2^2)z = (x - 5y)e^{x+y}$.

(k) $(D_1^4 - 5D_1^2D_2^2 + 4D_2^4)z = x(y^2 - 4x^2) + e^x(y^2 - x^2)$.

(l) $(9D_1^2 - 6D_1D_2 + 5D_2^2)z = e^x(4 \cos y + 6 \sin y)$.

2. If a and b are two constants, and f is a homogeneous function of degree n of two arguments such that $f(a, b) \neq 0$, show that a particular integral of

$$f(D_1, D_2)z = \phi(ax + by)$$

is

$$z = \frac{1}{f(a, b)} \int_{c_n}^{ax+by} \int_{c_{n-1}}^{u} \int_{c_{n-2}}^{u} \cdots \int_{c_1}^{u} \phi(u)(du)^n,$$

where c_i are arbitrary constants.

3. Employ the result of Exercise 2 to find particular integrals of:

(a) $(D_1^4 - 6D_1^3D_2 + 5D_1^2D_2^2 - 4D_1D_2^3 + D_2^4)z = (2x + y)^{1/2}$.

(b) $(D_1^6 + 3D_2^6)z = (4x + 3y)^3 + e^{x-y}$.

(c) $(D_1^3 - 2D_1^2D_2 + 4D_1D_2^2)z = \cos (2x) + \sin (x - y)$.

4. Show that the equation $(bD_1 - aD_2)^n z = \phi(ax + by)$ has as particular integral $z = \dfrac{x^n}{n! b^n} \phi(ax + by)$ if $b \neq 0$.

5. By use of Exercise 4, find particular solutions of:

(a) $(D_1 - 3D_2)^4 z = (3x + y)e^{(3x+y)}$.

(b) $(D_1^3 + 3D_1^2D_2 + 3D_1D_2^2 + D_2^3)z = \cosh (y - x)$.

(c) $(D_1 + 2D_2)^2 z = \sqrt{y - 2x}$.

6. If $D_1^n z \equiv \dfrac{\partial^n z}{\partial x_1^n}$, $D_2^n z \equiv \dfrac{\partial^n z}{\partial x_2^n}$, $D_3^n z \equiv \dfrac{\partial^n z}{\partial x_3^n}$ $(n = 0, 1, 2, \cdots)$, show that $(D_1 + aD_2 + bD_3)z = 0$ has the general solution

$$z = \phi(x_3 - bx_1, x_2 - ax_1).$$

7. Find the general solution of

$$(D_1 + a_1D_2 + b_1D_3)(D_1 + a_2D_2 + b_2D_3)z = 0.$$

8. Find the general solution of

$$(D_1 - 2D_2 + 3D_3)(D_1 + D_2 - 2D_3)z = e^{3x_1 + x_2 - x_3}.$$

9. Find the general solution of

$$(D_1 - D_2 + D_3)(D_1 + 2D_2 + 2D_3)z = \sin x_1 + \cos (x_2 - x_3).$$

80. Non-homogeneous equations. Let us now consider equations of the form

$$f(D_1, D_2)z = \phi(x, y), \tag{18}$$

where the function $f(D_1, D_2)$ is no longer homogeneous in D_1 and D_2. We divide the discussion into two parts, as above, the first being the problem of finding the *complementary function, viz.*, the general solution of the *reduced* equation

$$f(D_1, D_2)z = 0, \tag{19}$$

and the second being the problem of finding a particular integral of (18). As before, the general solution of (18) is the sum of a particular integral and the complementary function.

81. Right-hand member zero. If the function $f(D_1, D_2)$ is the product of n linear factors $D_1 + a_iD_2 + b_i$, we have, as a solution of (19),

$$z = z_1 + z_2 + \cdots + z_n,$$

where $z = z_i(x, y)$ is the general solution of

$$(D_1 + a_iD_2 + b_i)z = 0.$$

This equation, which can be written in the form

$$z_x + a_i z_y + b_i z = 0, \tag{20}$$

is of the first order and degree, and the corresponding Lagrange system is

$$\frac{dx}{1} = \frac{dy}{a_i} = \frac{dz}{-b_i z},$$

of which a solution is

$$\begin{cases} y - a_i x = c_1, \\ \log z + b_i x = c_2. \end{cases}$$

Hence the general solution of (20) is

$$\phi(\log z + b_i x, \, y - a_i x) = 0,$$

where ϕ is an arbitrary function. This can be solved for $\log z + b_i x$, and put into the form

$$z = e^{-b_i x} f(y - a_i x),$$

where $f(y - a_i x)$ is an arbitrary function. We have, then, the conclusion that a solution of (19) is

$$z = \sum_{i=1}^{n} e^{-b_i x} f_i(y - a_i x),$$

where $f_1, \cdots, f_n$ are n arbitrary functions.

82. Particular integrals. As we have found on previous occasions, certain forms of the function $\phi(x, y)$ lend themselves to solution by inspection. For example, if $\phi(x, y) \equiv e^{ax+by} v(x, y)$, we have

$$D_1 \phi \equiv a e^{ax+by} v(x, y) + e^{ax+by} D_1 v(x, y) \equiv e^{ax+by}(D_1 + a) v(x, y),$$

and similarly,

$$D_2 \phi \equiv e^{ax+by}(D_2 + b) v(x, y).$$

From these we can readily establish, by induction,

$$f(D_1, D_2) e^{ax+by} v(x, y) \equiv e^{ax+by} f(D_1 + a, D_2 + b) v(x, y). \quad (21)$$

Formula (21) also holds for inverse operators, as we can see if we let

$$f(D_1 + a, D_2 + b) v(x, y) \equiv g(x, y).$$

Then,

$$v(x, y) \equiv \frac{1}{f(D_1 + a, D_2 + b)} g(x, y),$$

and substitution into (21) gives

$$f(D_1, D_2) \left[e^{ax+by} \cdot \frac{1}{f(D_1 + a, D_2 + b)} \cdot g(x, y) \right]$$
$$\equiv e^{ax+by} \cdot [f(D_1 + a, D_2 + b)] \left[\frac{1}{f(D_1 + a, D_2 + b)} \cdot g(x, y) \right]$$
$$\equiv e^{ax+by} g(x, y);$$

hence, upon operating by $\dfrac{1}{f(D_1, D_2)}$, we have

$$\frac{1}{f(D_1, D_2)} e^{ax+by} g(x, y) \equiv e^{ax+by} \cdot \frac{1}{f(D_1 + a, D_2 + b)} \cdot g(x, y). \quad (22)$$

The formula holds for any function $g(x, y)$ having continuous partial derivatives of all orders called for by the operator.

If $\phi(x, y) \equiv e^{ax+by}$, then we may apply (22) to obtain

$$\frac{1}{f(D_1, D_2)} \phi(x, y) \equiv e^{ax+by} \frac{1}{f(D_1 + a, D_2 + b)} \cdot 1 \equiv e^{ax+by} \cdot \frac{1}{f(a, b)}.$$

This result may be checked by direct use of the operator $f(D_1, D_2)$ and is correct if defined, *i. e.*, if $f(a, b) \neq 0$. In case $f(a, b) = 0$, consider e^{ax+by} as the limit of $e^{ax+hx+by}$ as h approaches zero. We thus obtain the equation

$$\frac{1}{f(D_1, D_2)} e^{ax+by+hx} \equiv \frac{1}{f(a + h, b)} \cdot e^{ax+hx+by} \equiv \frac{1}{f(a + h, b)} e^{ax+by} \cdot e^{hx}$$

$$\equiv \frac{1}{f(a + h, b)} e^{ax+by} \left(1 + hx + \frac{h^2 x^2}{2!} + \frac{h^3 x^3}{3!} + \cdots \right)$$

$$\equiv \frac{e^{ax+by}}{f(a + h, b)} + \frac{h e^{ax+by}}{f(a + h, b)} \cdot \left(x + \frac{hx^2}{2!} + \frac{h^2 x^3}{3!} + \cdots \right).$$

Here we must recall that we seek a particular integral of the equation

$$f(D_1, D_2)z = e^{ax+by+hx}, \quad (23)$$

and that the term $\dfrac{e^{ax+by}}{f(a + h, b)}$ is included in the complementary function. Therefore, a particular integral of (23) is

$$\frac{h e^{ax+by}}{f(a + h, b)} \left(x + \frac{hx^2}{2!} + \frac{h^2 x^3}{3!} + \cdots \right).$$

Now,

$$\lim_{h \to 0} \frac{hx e^{ax+by}}{f(a + h, b) - f(a, b)} \equiv \frac{x e^{ax+by}}{f_a(a, b)},$$

and we may insert the term $-f(a, b)$ in the denominator because its value is zero. By repetition of this process we may show that, if $f_a(a, b) = 0$, we have

$$z = \frac{1}{f(D_1, D_2)} e^{ax+by} \equiv \frac{x^2}{2 f_{aa}(a, b)} e^{ax+by}$$

as a particular integral.

In case $\varphi(x, y) \equiv A \sin (ax + by) + B \cos (ax + by)$, let

$$\frac{1}{f(D_1, D_2)} \varphi(x, y) \equiv A_1 \sin (ax + by) + B_1 \cos (ax + by),$$

operate by $f(D_1, D_2)$, and equate coefficients of $\sin (ax + by)$ and $\cos (ax + by)$. If the equations are inconsistent, then try

$$A_1 x \sin (ax + by) + B_1 x \cos (ax + by),$$

and so on.

It is, of course, permissible to factor the inverse operator and to apply one factor at a time if the evaluation can be carried out. An important case of this type arises when $\varphi(x, y)$ is a polynomial. We then write

$$\frac{1}{f(D_1, D_2)} \varphi(x, y) \equiv \left(\frac{1}{D_1 + a_1 D_2 + b_1} \right) \cdots \left(\frac{1}{D_1 + a_n D_2 + b_n} \right) \varphi(x, y),$$

and evaluate the expression one factor at a time. If $b_n = 0$,

$$\frac{1}{D_1 + a_n D_2 + b_n} \cdot \varphi(x, y)$$

can be reduced to $\int \varphi(x, c + a_n x) dx$ by the methods of Chapter VIII, with c replaced by $y - a_n x$ after integration. The result is another polynomial. If b_n is not zero, we can write

$$\frac{1}{D_1 + a_n D_2 + b_n} \equiv \frac{1}{b_n} \left[1 + \frac{D_1 + a_n D_2}{b_n} \right]^{-1}$$

$$\equiv \frac{1}{b_n} \left[1 - \frac{D_1 + a_n D_2}{b_n} + \left(\frac{D_1 + a_n D_2}{b_n} \right)^2 - \cdots \right],$$

and, since there are only a finite number of the derivatives of a polynomial which are different from zero, $\dfrac{1}{D_1 + a_n D_2 + b_n} \varphi(x, y)$ reduces to another polynomial.

Exercises

Find general solutions of the following:

1. $(D_1 + 2D_2 - 3)(D_1 D_2 + D_2^2 - D_2)z = 0$.

2. $(D_1 + 2D_2 - 3)(D_1 D_2 + D_2^2 - D_2)z = x^2 - 2xy$.

3. $(D_1^3 - 4D_1^2 D_2 + 5D_1^2)z = 0$.

4. of even No's.

4. $(D_1^3 - 4D_1^2D_2 + 5D_1^2)z = e^{2x+y}(x - y)$.

5. $(D_1^3D_2 + 2D_1^2D_2^2 - D_1^2D_2)z = 0$.

6. $(D_1^3D_2 + 2D_1^2D_2^2 - D_1^2D_2)z = \sin (x - 7y)$.

7. $(D_1 + D_2 + 1)(D_1 + D_2 + 2)(D_1 + D_2)z = 0$.

8. $(D_1 + D_2 + 1)(D_1 + D_2 + 2)(D_1 + D_2)z = e^{5x-y} \sinh (x - y)$.

9. $(D_1^2 - 4D_2^2 + D_1 + 2D_2)z = 0$.

10. $(D_1^2 - 4D_2^2 + D_1 + 2D_2)z = x^2 + y^3 + e^{x-4y}$.

11. $(D_1 + 2D_2 - 1)(D_1 - D_2 - 3)(D_1 + D_2 - 5)z = 0$.

12. $(D_1 + 2D_2 - 1)(D_1 - D_2 - 3)(D_1 + D_2 - 5)z = \cosh (x + 5y + 6)$.

13. $(D_1^2 + D_1D_2 + D_2)z = z$.

14. $(D_1^2 + D_1D_2 + D_2)z = z + e^{3x-y+1}$.

83. Other forms of $f(D_1, D_2)$. To solve the equation

$$f(D_1, D_2)z = \varphi(x, y)$$

in case $f(D_1, D_2)$ is not the product of linear factors, let us first assume $z = ce^{ax+by}$ to be a solution of the reduced equation

$$f(D_1, D_2)z = 0.$$

Substituting this value into the equation, we obtain

$$f(a, b)e^{ax+by} = 0,$$

which is true if, and only if, $f(a, b) = 0$. Now the equation

$$f(a, b) = 0$$

is satisfied by an infinity of pairs of numbers (a, b), and hence we may write as our complementary function

$$z = \sum_i c_i e^{a_i x + b_i y}, \qquad f(a_i, b_i) = 0.$$

In finding a particular integral, we employ special methods to evaluate the operation $\dfrac{1}{f(D_1, D_2)} \cdot \varphi(x, y)$. If $\varphi(x, y) \equiv e^{ax+by} \cdot g(x, y)$, we may employ formula (22) to reduce $\dfrac{1}{f(D_1, D_2)} e^{ax+by}g(x, y)$ to $e^{ax+by} \cdot \dfrac{1}{f(D_1 + a, D_2 + b)} g(x, y)$. If $\varphi(x, y) \equiv e^{ax+\beta y}$, we have, as before,

$$\frac{1}{f(D_1,\, D_2)}\, e^{\alpha x + \beta y} \equiv \frac{1}{f(\alpha,\, \beta)}\, e^{\alpha x + \beta y},$$

unless $f(\alpha,\, \beta) = 0$. In the latter case we have, again,

$$\frac{1}{f(D_1,\, D_2)}\, e^{\alpha x + \beta y} \equiv \frac{x e^{\alpha x + \beta y}}{f_\alpha(\alpha,\, \beta)},$$

unless $f_\alpha(\alpha,\, \beta) = 0$, and so on. If $\varphi(x,\, y) \equiv A \sin(ax + by) + B \cos(ax + by)$, let

$$\frac{1}{f(D_1,\, D_2)}\, \varphi(x,\, y) \equiv A' x^n \sin(ax + by) + B' x^n \cos(ax + by),$$

where n is zero if the resulting equations can be solved for A' and B', and where otherwise it is the smallest positive integer for which the equations can be solved.

If $\varphi(x,\, y)$ is a polynomial, the expression

$$\frac{1}{f(D_1,\, D_2)}\, \varphi(x,\, y)$$

may be evaluated by expanding $\dfrac{1}{f(D_1,\, D_2)}$ into an infinite series.

84. Equations reducible to linear equations with constant coefficients. We shall close the treatment of linear partial differential equations of any order with the observation that an equation of the form

$$\sum_{r,\, s} a_{rs} x^r y^s \frac{\partial^{r+s} z}{\partial x^r\, \partial y^s} = \psi(x,\, y)$$

can be reduced to one of the form

$$\sum_{r,\, s} b_{rs} \frac{\partial^{r+s} z}{\partial \xi^r \partial \eta^s} = \varphi(\xi,\, \eta)$$

by the transformation $x = e^\xi$, $y = e^\eta$. After reduction, the equation thus becomes one with constant coefficients and may be treated by the methods of the preceding section. In its solution we may replace ξ by $\log x$, and η by $\log y$, to obtain a solution of the given equation.

Exercises

1. Solve the following:

    (a) $(D_1^3 - 2D_1 D_2 + D_2^2 - D_1 + 8)z = e^{2x-y}$.

    (b) $(D_1^2 + D_1 D_2 - D_2^2 + D_1 - D_2)z = \sin(x - y) + \cos(x - 2y)$.

(c) $(D_1^3 + 3D_2^2 + D_1 - 8)z = e^{4x-5y+6} \cos (x + 2y)$.

(d) $(D_1^2 + 2D_1D_2^2 - 3D_2 + 5)z = x^2 + y^3$.

(e) $(D_1^3 + 3D_2^3 + D_1 - 5D_2)z = \sinh (3x - y) +$ cosh $(3x - y)$.

(f) $(D_1^2 + D_1D_2 + D_1 - D_2 + 1)z = e^{2x}(x^2 - 3xy^2)$.

(g) $(D_1^3 + 3D_2^3 + 3)z = e^{3x-2y}$.

(h) $(D_1^2 + D_1D_2 + D_2^2 + 2D_1 - 3D_2 + 9)z = \sin (3x + 2y)$.

(i) $x^2z_{xx} - 2xyz_{xy} - y^2z_{yy} - xz_x + yz_y - 5z = 7x - 5y$.

2. Show that the equation $F(D_1, D_2)z = 0$ is satisfied by

$$z = \frac{\partial}{\partial a} (e^{ax+f(a)y}) \equiv e^{ax+f(a)y}[x + f'(a)y],$$

where $F(a, f(a)) = 0$. *Hint:* Since $z = \dfrac{e^{ax+f(a)y}}{\Delta a}$ and

$$z = \frac{e^{(a+\Delta a)x+f(a+\Delta a)y}}{\Delta a}$$

are both solutions, their difference, $z = \dfrac{e^{(a+\Delta a)x+f(a+\Delta a)y} - e^{ax+f(a)y}}{\Delta a}$

is a solution, and the limit of this difference as $\Delta a \to 0$ is the solution proposed.

85. Laplace's equation. We conclude this chapter with a few remarks on a celebrated equation, bearing the name of Laplace* and which the student will meet frequently in mathematical physics, *viz.*,

$$v_{xx} + v_{yy} = 0 \tag{24}$$

or

$$v_{xx} + v_{yy} + v_{zz} = 0, \tag{25}$$

in the cases, respectively, of two, or three, independent variables. These equations are satisfied, at a point (x, y) in the plane, or (x, y, z) in space, by the function v which represents the potential due to a gravitational, or an electric, or a magnetic, field of force, or again, the temperature due to a steady flow of heat, in a plane lamina or in a solid.

Equation (24), put in the form $(D_1^2 + D_2^2)v = 0$, has been disposed of in the treatment of Equation (6), Section 73, and its solu-

---

* Pierre Simon Laplace (1749–1827), great French mathematician and astronomer.

tion is given by (8) of that article as

$$v = \sum_{j=1}^{\infty} (c_j e^{g_j y} \cos g_j x + d_j e^{h_j y} \sin h_j x).\qquad(26)$$

A classical problem in the study of heat flow is that of determining the temperature at any point in a thin rectangular plate of width π and of infinite length, subject to the conditions that the temperature be unity along the short edge, zero along the long edges, and that, further, the temperature decrease continuously as one recedes from the short edge. The plate is supposed to be insulated so that there is no loss of heat. The temperature, v, is, then, represented by (26), subject to the conditions (under proper choice of axes)

$$v = 0 \text{ when } x = 0,\qquad\text{(I)}$$
$$v = 0 \text{ when } x = \pi.\qquad\text{(II)}$$
$$v = 0 \text{ for } y = \infty.\qquad\text{(III)}$$
$$v = 1 \text{ when } y = 0.\qquad\text{(IV)}$$

Conditions (I) and (II) will, evidently, be met by choosing $c_j = 0$, and (III) by choosing $h_1 = -1$, $h_2 = 0$, $h_3 = -1$, $h_4 = 0$, $\cdots$, so that we get

$$v = d_1 e^{-y} \sin x + d_3 e^{-3y} \sin 3x + d_5 e^{-5y} \sin 5x + \cdots.$$

To fulfill (IV), now, note the expansion, valid for $0 < x < \pi$,

$$1 = \frac{4}{\pi} \left(\sin x + \frac{1}{3} \sin 3x + \frac{1}{5} \sin 5x + \cdots \right).\text{*}$$

Hence, if we choose $d_1 = \frac{4}{\pi}$, $d_3 = \frac{4}{3\pi}$, $d_5 = \frac{4}{5\pi}$, $\cdots$ and obtain

$$v = \frac{4}{\pi} \left(e^{-y} \sin x + \frac{1}{3} e^{-3y} \sin 3x + \frac{1}{5} e^{-5y} \sin 5x + \cdots \right),\qquad(27)$$

we have the desired function, v.

To solve (25), transform it to cylindrical coördinates, by the substitutions

$$x = r \cos \theta,$$
$$y = r \sin \theta,$$
$$z = z.$$

---

* *Fourier Series and Spherical Harmonics*, by W. E. Byerly, p. 39.

We leave it to the student, as an exercise (Exercise 2 below) to derive the new form of (25) as

$$v_{rr} + \frac{v_{\theta\theta}}{r^2} + \frac{v_r}{r} + v_{zz} = 0.$$

Assume now a solution in the form

$$v(r, \theta, z) = f(r) \cdot g(\theta) \cdot h(z).$$

Then the last equation takes the form

$$\frac{f''(r)}{f(r)} + \frac{g''(\theta)}{r^2 g(\theta)} + \frac{f'(r)}{r f(r)} = - \frac{h''(z)}{h(z)},$$

since $v_{rr} = f''(r) \cdot g(\theta) \cdot h(z)$, $v_{\theta\theta} = f(r) \cdot g''(\theta) \cdot h(z)$, and so forth. The left-hand member is, evidently, independent of z. Hence, so is the right-hand member. Consequently, $- \dfrac{h''(z)}{h(z)}$ is a constant, say $-k^2$ (and, of course, the left-hand member equals $-k^2$). The equation $\dfrac{h''(z)}{h(z)} = k^2$, or $(D^2 - k^2)h = 0$, gives at once

$$h(z) = c_1 e^{kz} + c_2 e^{-kz}.$$

Turning to the left-hand member, set equal to $-k^2$, we obtain

$$\frac{r^2 f''(r)}{f(r)} + \frac{r f'(r)}{f(r)} + k^2 r^2 = - \frac{g''(\theta)}{g(\theta)},$$

and, as a while ago, we conclude that $- \dfrac{g''(\theta)}{g(\theta)}$, being independent of θ, as is the left-hand side, must equal a constant, say m^2. Thus

$$\frac{g''(\theta)}{g(\theta)} = -m^2,$$

and

$$r^2 f''(r) + r f'(r) + k^2 r^2 f(r) = m^2 f(r).$$

The first of these gives

$$g(\theta) = c_3 \cos m\theta + c_4 \sin m\theta.$$

The second may be revised, by setting $kr = R$ (hence, $f(r) = F(R)$, $f'(r) = kF'(R)$, $f''(r) = k^2 F''(R)$) to yield

$$R^2 F''(R) + R F'(R) + (R^2 - m^2) F(R) = 0.$$

This is a Bessel Equation [see (29) Section 50], and has for its solution

$$F(R) = c_5 J_m(R) + c_6 J_{-m}(R),$$

or

$$f(r) = c_5 J_m(kr) + c_6 J_{-m}(kr).$$

It thus develops that a solution of (25) is

$$v(r, \theta, z) = (c_1 e^{kz} + c_2 e^{-kz})(c_3 \cos m\theta + c_4 \sin m\theta)$$
$$(c_5 J_m(kr) + c_6 J_{-m}(kr)), \quad (28)$$

and, by the linearity of the equation, the sum of any finite (or infinite) number of such values of v is a solution.

A sufficient number of initial conditions must, of course, be provided in a given problem, to fix the arbitrary constants as well as the values of k and m.

Exercises

1. Solve (24) by assuming $v = f(x) \cdot g(y)$. *Hint:* The equation becomes $\dfrac{f''(x)}{f(x)} = -\dfrac{g''(y)}{g(y)}$. Hence, each side is a constant, say $-g^2$. Solve and obtain $f(x) = c_1 \cos gx + c_2 \sin gx$, $g(y) = c_3 e^{gy} + c_4 e^{-gy}$.

Hence, $v = \displaystyle\sum_{j=1}^{\infty} (c_{1j} \cos g_j x + c_{2j} \sin g_j x)(c_{3j} e^{g_j y} + c_{4j} e^{-g_j y})$ is a solution, by the linearity of (24). Assume, without proof, that the summation from $j = 1$ to $j = \infty$ is also a solution. Identify this solution with (26) of the text by setting $c_{1j}c_{3j} = c_j$, $c_{2j}c_{3j} = 0$, $h_j = -g_j$, $c_{1j}c_{4j} = 0$, $c_{2j}c_{4j} = -d_j$.

2. Solve (24) by transforming to polar coördinates. *Hint:* By $x = r \cos \theta$, $y = r \sin \theta$, and $v_x = v_r r_x + v_\theta \theta_x$, $v_y = v_r r_y + v_\theta \theta_y$, and so forth, obtain

$$v_{xx} = v_r \frac{\sin^2 \theta}{r} + 2v_\theta \frac{\sin \theta \cos \theta}{r^2} + v_{rr} \cos^2 \theta - 2v_{r\theta} \frac{\sin \theta \cos \theta}{r}$$
$$+ v_{\theta\theta} \frac{\sin^2 \theta}{r^2},$$

$$v_{yy} = v_r \frac{\cos^2 \theta}{r} - 2v_\theta \frac{\sin \theta \cos \theta}{r^2} + v_{rr} \sin^2 \theta + 2v_{r\theta} \frac{\sin \theta \cos \theta}{r}$$
$$+ v_{\theta\theta} \frac{\cos^2 \theta}{r^2},$$

thus reducing (24) to

$$\frac{v_r}{r} + v_{rr} + \frac{v_{\theta\theta}}{r^2} = 0.$$

Assume as a solution, $v = f(r) \cdot g(\theta)$, and derive,

$$v = \sum_k (c_{1k} r^k + c_{2k} r^{-k})(c_{3k} \cos k\theta + c_{4k} \sin k\theta),$$

or, what is the same,

$$v = \sum_k [r^k(A_k \cos k\theta + B_k \sin k\theta) + r^{-k}(C_k \cos k\theta + D_k \sin k\theta)].$$

3. For the illustration in the text, compute the temperature, to three decimal places,

(a) at the point $\left(\dfrac{\pi}{2}, 1\right)$ of the plate;

(b) at the point $\left(\dfrac{\pi}{4}, 2\right)$ of the plate.

4. (a) Transform Equation (25) to spherical coördinates, *i. e.*, by $x = \rho \sin \varphi \cos \theta$, $y = \rho \sin \varphi \sin \theta$, $z = \rho \cos \varphi$.

(b) Solve the equation obtained in (a) under the hypothesis that v is independent of θ, *i. e.*, v is a function of ρ and φ only.

Hint: The equation becomes

$$\rho^2 v_{\rho\rho} + v_{\varphi\varphi} + 2\rho v_\rho + \cot \varphi \cdot v_\varphi = 0.$$

Assume as a solution $v = f(\rho) \cdot g(\varphi)$, and derive

$$\frac{\rho^2 f''(\rho)}{f(\rho)} + \frac{2\rho f'(\rho)}{f(\rho)} = \frac{-g''(\varphi)}{g(\varphi)} - \cot \varphi \frac{g'(\varphi)}{g(\varphi)}.$$

Set each equal to a constant, say k^2. From the left-hand member, set equal to k^2, obtain

$$f(\rho) = c_1 \rho^{\frac{-1+\sqrt{1+4k^2}}{2}} + c_2 \rho^{\frac{-1-\sqrt{1+4k^2}}{2}}.$$

Let $m = \dfrac{-1 + \sqrt{1 + 4k^2}}{2}$; hence $-m - 1 = \dfrac{-1 - \sqrt{1 + 4k^2}}{2}$, $k^2 = m^2 + m$, and obtain,

$$f(\rho) = c_1 \rho^m + \frac{c_2}{\rho^{m+1}}.$$

The right-hand member, set equal to k^2, yields

$$g''(\varphi) + \cot \varphi \cdot g'(\varphi) + k^2 g(\varphi) = 0,$$

or

$$g''(\varphi) + \cot \varphi \cdot g'(\varphi) + (m^2 + m)g(\varphi) = 0.$$

Revise this by setting $u = \cos \varphi$, whence $g(\varphi) = h(u)$, $g'(\varphi) = -\sin \varphi \cdot h'(u)$, $g''(\varphi) = h''(u) \cdot \sin^2 \varphi - h'(u) \cdot \cos \varphi$, and reduce the last equation to

$$(1 - u^2)h''(u) - 2uh'(u) + m(m + 1)h(u) = 0,$$

a Legendre equation [see (23), Section 49], which has for a solution, if m is taken as a positive integer,

$$h(u) \equiv P_m(u), \qquad (P_m(u) \text{ a Legendre Polynomial of degree } m),$$

i. e.,
$$g(\varphi) = P_m(\cos \varphi),$$

and the final result is

$$v = \left[c_1\rho^m + \frac{c_2}{\rho^{m+1}} \right] P_m(\cos \varphi), \text{ where } m \text{ is a positive integer.}$$

Again, by the linearity of the equation, we get as a value of v satisfying the equation

$$v = \sum_{m=0}^{\infty} \left[A_m\rho^m + \frac{B_m}{\rho^{m+1}} \right] P_m(\cos \varphi).$$

CHAPTER X

Partial Differential Equations of Order Two

86. Introduction. In this chapter we shall consider z as a function of two independent variables x and y, and employ the notation

$$z_x \equiv p, \ z_y \equiv q,$$
$$z_{xx} \equiv r, \ z_{xy} \equiv s, \ z_{yy} \equiv t.$$

Any partial differential equation of order two, involving two independent variables, may be expressed in the form

$$F(x, y, z, p, q, r, s, t) = 0. \tag{1}$$

A relation as

$$u(x, y, z, p, q) = 0$$

which satisfies (1) identically, is called an *intermediate* integral of (1), and a relation as

$$f(x, y, z) = 0 \tag{2}$$

for which $f_z \not\equiv 0$ and which satisfies (1) identically, is called a *solution* of (1). Since, given an equation of the form (1), our ultimate purpose is to find solutions (2) for which $f_z \not\equiv 0$, we may feel free at any time to divide by x, y, dx, or dy, because $x = c$, a constant, or $y = c$, a constant, cannot yield (2).

We shall treat only certain special cases of (1), and these by special methods:

1. Equations of the form

$$Rr + Ss + Tt = V,$$

where R, S, T, V are functions of x, y, z, p, q, will be treated by Monge's method.

2. Equations of the form

$$Rr + Ss + Tt + U(rt - s^2) = V,$$

where R, S, T, U, V are functions of x, y, z, p, q, will be treated by Monge's method.

3. Equations of the form

$$Rr + Ss + Tt + Pp + Qq + Zz = W,$$

where R, S, T, P, Q, Z, W are functions of x and y, will be dealt with by Laplace's transformations.

None of these methods is adequate to solve every equation of the type to which it applies; nevertheless, they are possessed of considerable generality.

87. Intermediate integrals of a second order differential equation. Let u and v be determined functions of x, y, z, p, q; and let

$$\varphi(u, v) = 0 \tag{3}$$

be an arbitrary relation between u and v. Differentiation of (3) with respect to x and y yields

$$\begin{cases} \varphi_u(u_x + pu_z + ru_p + su_q) + \varphi_v(v_x + pv_z + rv_p + sv_q) = 0, \\ \varphi_u(u_y + qu_z + su_p + tu_q) + \varphi_v(v_y + qv_z + sv_p + tv_q) = 0, \end{cases}$$

and, in order that these equations may be satisfied by values of φ_u and φ_v not both zero, it is necessary and sufficient that

$$\begin{vmatrix} u_x + pu_z + ru_p + su_q & u_y + qu_z + su_p + tu_q \\ v_x + pv_z + rv_p + sv_q & v_y + qv_z + sv_p + tv_q \end{vmatrix} = 0.$$

This condition may be written in the form

$$Rr + Ss + Tt + U(rt - s^2) = V, \tag{4}$$

where

$$U \equiv \begin{vmatrix} u_p & u_q \\ v_p & v_q \end{vmatrix}, \quad R \equiv \begin{vmatrix} u_p & u_y + qu_z \\ v_p & v_y + qv_z \end{vmatrix}, \quad T \equiv \begin{vmatrix} u_x + pu_z & u_q \\ v_x + pv_z & v_q \end{vmatrix},$$

$$S \equiv \begin{vmatrix} u_x + pu_z & u_p \\ v_x + pv_z & v_p \end{vmatrix} + \begin{vmatrix} u_q & u_y + qu_z \\ v_q & v_y + qv_z \end{vmatrix}, \quad V \equiv \begin{vmatrix} u_y + qu_z & u_x + pu_z \\ v_y + qv_z & v_x + pv_z \end{vmatrix},$$

and is a partial differential equation of the second order and second degree which is satisfied identically by (3). The relation (3) is said to be an *intermediate integral* of (4), and in the ensuing sections we shall discuss means of obtaining these intermediate integrals from given partial differential equations of order and degree two. It may be observed, in passing, that if a partial differential equation of the second order and second degree cannot be put into the form (4), it can have no intermediate integral of the form (3). It should also be noticed that these five functions R, S, T, U, and V are all determined in a highly special way by two given functions u and v, and hence it is not to be expected that they should be entirely independent. In other words, we cannot expect that every equation of the form (4) will have an intermediate integral of the form (3).

88. Monge's method for $Rr + Ss + Tt = V$. Let us first consider an equation of the form (4), with $U \equiv 0$; that is, an equation

$$Rr + Ss + Tt = V, \tag{5}$$

where R, S, T, and V are given functions of x, y, z, p, and q. Since we wish to determine z as a function of x and y satisfying (5), we have p and q as functions of x and y, and, hence, the relations

$$\begin{cases} dp = r\,dx + s\,dy, \\ dq = s\,dx + t\,dy. \end{cases} \tag{6}$$

If, now, we multiply (5) by $dx \cdot dy$, (6₁) by $R \cdot dy$, and (6₂) by $T \cdot dx$, and add, we obtain

$$(R\,dp\,dy + T\,dq\,dx - V\,dx\,dy) - (R\,dy^2 - S\,dx\,dy + T\,dx^2)s = 0, \tag{7}$$

an equation free of r and t. If both of the equations

$$\begin{cases} R\,dy^2 - S\,dx\,dy + T\,dx^2 = 0 \\ R\,dp\,dy + T\,dq\,dx - V\,dx\,dy = 0 \end{cases} \tag{8}$$

called *Monge's equations* after Gaspard Monge (1746–1818), are satisfied by the simultaneous pair

$$\begin{cases} u(x,\,y,\,z,\,p,\,q) = a, \\ v(x,\,y,\,z,\,p,\,q) = b, \end{cases}$$

(a and b arbitrary constants) either identically, or in view of the equation

$$dz = p\,dx + q\,dy, \tag{9}$$

then certainly (7), and therefore (5), is satisfied by that pair. If such is the case, we can take

$$\varphi(u,\,v) = 0$$

as an intermediate integral of (5).

The equation (8₁) can always be factored into the two equations

$$\begin{aligned} N_1\,dx + M_1\,dy = 0, \\ N_2\,dx + M_2\,dy = 0, \end{aligned} \tag{10}$$

and we then have available the system

$$\begin{cases} N_1\, dx + M_1\, dy = 0, \\ R\, dp\, dy + T\, dq\, dx - V\, dx\, dy = 0, \\ p\, dx + q\, dy - dz = 0, \end{cases} \tag{11}$$

of three ordinary differential equations in the five variables x, y, z, p, and q, and another such system

$$\begin{cases} N_2\, dx + M_2\, dy = 0, \\ R\, dp\, dy + T\, dq\, dx - V\, dx\, dy = 0, \\ p\, dx + q\, dy - dz = 0, \end{cases} \tag{12}$$

which employs (10_2) in place of (10_1). Since four equations are required to form a determinate system in five variables, either one or both of the above systems may be non-integrable. If $S^2 = 4RT$, the two systems are identical, because, in that case, (10_1) is the same as (10_2). If both systems are integrable and different, they lead to two different intermediate integrals of the form

$$\varphi(u, v) = 0. \tag{3}$$

Illustration

Consider the equation

$$(x - y)(xz_{xx} - xz_{xy} - yz_{xy} + yz_{yy}) = (x + y)(z_x - z_y). \tag{13}$$

In the above notation, we have

$$R \equiv x(x - y), \quad S \equiv -(x - y)(x + y), \quad T \equiv y(x - y),$$
$$V \equiv (x + y)(p - q),$$

and hence the equations (8) become

$$\begin{cases} x(x - y)dy^2 + (x - y)(x + y)dx\, dy + y(x - y)dx^2 = 0, \\ x(x - y)dp\, dy + y(x - y)dq\, dx - (x + y)(p - q)dx\, dy = 0. \end{cases}$$

The first of these yields the two equations

$$dy + dx = 0, \quad x\, dy + y\, dx = 0,$$

and the two systems of equations corresponding to (11) and (12) are

$$\begin{cases} dy + dx = 0, \\ x(x - y)dp\, dy + y(x - y)dq\, dx - (x + y)(p - q)dx\, dy = 0, \\ dz = p\, dx + q\, dy, \end{cases} \tag{14}$$

and

$$\begin{cases} x\, dy + y\, dx = 0, \\ x(x - y)dp\, dy + y(x - y)dq\, dx - (x + y)(p - q)dx\, dy = 0, \\ dz = p\, dx + q\, dy. \end{cases} \tag{15}$$

Equation (14₁) has the solution

$$y + x = a, \tag{16}$$

and if we substitute $-dx$ for dy and $a - x$ for y in (14₂), the latter becomes, after dx is divided out,

$$-x(2x - a)dp + (a - x)(2x - a)dq + a(p - q)dx = 0,$$

an integrable equation whose solution is

$$\frac{xp - (a - x)q}{2x - a} = b,$$

or, if we change a to $x + y$,

$$\frac{xp - yq}{x - y} = b. \tag{17}$$

Equations (16) and (17) now furnish the intermediate integral

$$\varphi_1\left(\frac{xp - yq}{x - y}, \; x + y\right) = 0. \tag{18}$$

Taking up the system (15) in the same way, we find

$$xy = c$$

as the solution of (15₁), and by means of it we reduce (15₂) to

$$-x(x^2 - c)dp + x(x^2 - c)dq + (x^2 + c)(p - q)dx = 0,$$

the solution of which is

$$\frac{(p - q)x}{x^2 - c} = d,$$

or, since $c = xy$,

$$\frac{p - q}{x - y} = d.$$

Thus we have built up another intermediate integral of (13), in the form

$$\varphi_2\left(\frac{p - q}{x - y}, \; xy\right) = 0. \tag{19}$$

To solve these intermediate integrals, note that (18) may be solved for $\dfrac{xp - yq}{x - y}$ to obtain

$$\frac{xp - yq}{x - y} = f_1(x + y), \tag{20}$$

and that (19) may be put into the form

$$\frac{p - q}{x - y} = f_2(xy). \tag{21}$$

Equations (20) and (21) may now be solved for p and q to obtain

$$\begin{cases} p = f_1(x + y) - yf_2(xy) \\ q = f_1(x + y) - xf_2(xy). \end{cases}$$

If these values of p and q are substituted into (9), the equation becomes

$$dz = [f_1(x + y) - yf_2(xy)]dx + [f_1(x + y) - xf_2(xy)]dy, \tag{22}$$

which is integrable and has, as solution,

$$z = \int f_1(x + y) \cdot d(x + y) - \int f_2(xy) \cdot d(xy)$$
$$= F_1(x + y) + F_2(xy).$$

89. Integrability of $dz = p\,dx + q\,dy$. It might appear to have been especially fortunate that the equation (22) was found integrable, but we shall prove that (9) is always integrable when systems (11) and (12) are different and both integrable. To show this, let us assume that

$$F(x, y, z, p, q) = 0 \tag{23}$$

is an intermediate integral of (5) coming from (11), and that

$$f(x, y, z, p, q) = 0 \tag{24}$$

is an intermediate integral of (5) coming from (12). By differentiating (23) partially with respect to x and y, we obtain

$$F_x + pF_z + rF_p + sF_q = 0 \tag{25}$$

and

$$F_y + qF_z + sF_p + tF_q = 0. \tag{26}$$

If we eliminate r and t between (5), (25), and (26), we obtain

$$RF_xF_q + pRF_zF_q + TF_yF_p + qTF_zF_p + VF_pF_q$$
$$+ s(RF_q^2 - SF_pF_q + TF_p^2) = 0.$$

If this relation is true identically in s, then the two relations

$$R(F_q)^2 - SF_pF_q + T(F_p)^2 = 0, \tag{27}$$
$$R(F_x + pF_z)F_q + T(F_y + qF_z)F_p + VF_pF_q = 0, \tag{28}$$

must hold. From (27) we see that $\dfrac{F_q}{F_p}$ is one of the roots of the quadratic equation

$$Rm^2 - Sm + T = 0, \tag{29}$$

say,

$$\frac{F_q}{F_p} \equiv m_1. \tag{30}$$

Similarly, since $f(x, y, z, p, q) = 0$ is an intermediate integral, we have

$$\frac{f_q}{f_p} \equiv m_2, \tag{31}$$

where m_2 is the other root of (29). From (30), let us now substitute $m_1 F_p$ for F_q into (28) and divide out F_p, obtaining

$$Rm_1(F_x + pF_z) + T(F_y + qF_z) + m_1 VF_p = 0.$$

If, here, we change m_1 to $\dfrac{T}{Rm_2}$, since $m_1 m_2 \equiv \dfrac{T}{R}$, and multiply through by $\dfrac{m_2}{T}$, we have

$$(F_x + pF_z) + m_2(F_y + qF_z) + \frac{V}{R} F_p = 0. \tag{32}$$

Similarly, by working with the intermediate integral (24) and the relation (31), we obtain

$$(f_x + pf_z) + m_1(f_y + qf_z) + \frac{V}{R} f_p = 0. \tag{33}$$

Between (32) and (33) we may eliminate $\dfrac{V}{R}$, obtaining

$$(F_x + pF_z)f_p - (f_x + pf_z)F_p + m_2(F_y + qF_z)f_p - m_1(f_y + qf_z)F_p = 0,$$

from which, by use of (30) and (31), we draw

$$(F_x + pF_z)f_p - (f_x + pf_z)F_p + (F_y + qF_z)f_q - (f_y + qf_z)F_q = 0.$$

This can be written in the form

$$-F_p f_x - F_q f_y - (pF_p + qF_q)f_z + (F_x + pF_z)f_p + (F_y + qF_z)f_q = 0,$$

which is precisely the condition of Chapter VIII that the equation

$$dz = p\,dx + q\,dy \tag{9}$$

should be integrable, where p and q are determined in terms of x, y, and z, by two equations like (23) and (24).

90. Monge's method for $Rr + Ss + Tt + U(rt - s)^2 = V$.   If we follow the plan of Section 87 and eliminate r and t from

$$Rr + Ss + Tt + U(rt - s^2) = V \tag{4}$$

and

$$\begin{cases} dp = r\,dx + s\,dy, \\ dq = s\,dx + t\,dy, \end{cases} \tag{6}$$

we obtain

$$s(R\,dy^2 - S\,dx\,dy + T\,dx^2 + U\,dp\,dx + U\,dq\,dy) \\ + R\,dp\,dy + T\,dq\,dx + U\,dp\,dq - V\,dx\,dy = 0. \tag{34}$$

We see, as before, that this equation will be satisfied if both of the equations

$$\begin{cases} R\,dy^2 - S\,dx\,dy + T\,dx^2 + U\,dp\,dx + U\,dq\,dy = 0, \\ R\,dp\,dy + T\,dq\,dx + U\,dp\,dq - V\,dx\,dy = 0, \end{cases} \tag{35}$$

are satisfied.   These correspond to the Monge equations for the case $U \equiv 0$, the first of which was factorable.   In this case neither equation is immediately factorable, so we add an arbitrary multiple of the first to the second and try to select the multiplier in such a way that the resulting equation

$$\lambda(R\,dy^2 - S\,dy\,dx + T\,dx^2 + U\,dp\,dx + U\,dq\,dy) \\ + (R\,dp\,dy + T\,dq\,dx + U\,dp\,dq - V\,dx\,dy) = 0 \tag{36}$$

can be factored.   Since the equation is linear in dp, it is apparent that dp can come into only one factor.   The same statement holds for dq, and, since the product $dp \cdot dq$ does appear, dp is in one factor, while dq is in the other.   If we assume factors as $(a\,dy + b\,dx + c\,dp)(l\,dy + m\,dx + n\,dq) = 0$, we must have

$$al \equiv R\lambda,\ bm \equiv T\lambda,\ cn \equiv U, \\ am + bl \equiv -S\lambda - V,\ an \equiv U\lambda, \\ cm \equiv U\lambda,\ bn \equiv T,\ cl \equiv R.$$

If we take $a \equiv \lambda$ and $l \equiv R$, we find

$$b \equiv \frac{T}{U},\ m \equiv U\lambda,$$

$$c \equiv l,\ n \equiv U,$$

and the condition $am + bl \equiv -S\lambda - V$ reduces to

$$U^2\lambda^2 + SU\lambda + TR + UV = 0, \tag{37}$$

which is a quadratic equation in λ, since $U \not\equiv 0$. Then, in general, (36) factors for two distinct values of λ, say λ_1 and λ_2, the roots of the quadratic (37). In the respective cases, (36) reduces to

$$(\lambda_1 U \, dy + T \, dx + U \, dp)(R \, dy + U\lambda_1 \, dx + U \, dq) = 0 \quad (38)$$

and

$$(\lambda_2 U \, dy + T \, dx + U \, dp)(R \, dy + U\lambda_2 \, dx + U \, dq) = 0. \quad (39)$$

The student may show that if (36) vanishes for two distinct values of λ, then both of the equations (35) are satisfied, and that, hence, (34) is satisfied. To solve, therefore, we will equate to zero one factor of (38) and one of (39), and solve simultaneously. However, we can obtain no solution by equating the first factors of each or the second factors of each, so we employ simultaneously

$$\begin{cases} \lambda_1 U \, dy + T \, dx + U \, dp = 0, \\ R \, dy + \lambda_2 U \, dx + U \, dq = 0, \end{cases} \quad (40)$$

or

$$\begin{cases} \lambda_2 U \, dy + T \, dx + U \, dp = 0, \\ R \, dy + \lambda_1 U \, dx + U \, dq = 0. \end{cases} \quad (41)$$

If $S^2 = 4(RT + UV)$, (39) has only the one root $\lambda = -\dfrac{S}{2U}$, and both (40) and (41) are supplanted by

$$\begin{cases} -\dfrac{S}{2} \, dy + T \, dx + U \, dp = 0, \\[2mm] R \, dy - \dfrac{S}{2} \, dx + U \, dq = 0, \end{cases} \quad (42)$$

either one of which is sufficient to cause (36) to vanish when λ is replaced by $-\dfrac{S}{2U}$. When we substitute

$$\begin{cases} dp = \dfrac{S}{2U} \, dy - \dfrac{T}{U} \, dx \\[2mm] dq = \dfrac{S}{2U} \, dx - \dfrac{R}{U} \, dy \end{cases}$$

from (42) into (34), we find that it vanishes identically, and hence a solution of (42) yields an integral of (34); that is, an intermediate integral of the given equation (4).

If, where possible, we employ two first integrals, one from (40) and one from (41), we find that they may be solved simultaneously for p and q in such a way that

$$dz = p\, dx + q\, dy \qquad (9)$$

is integrable. To prove this, let us assume that

$$F(x, y, z, p, q) = 0 \qquad (43)$$

is a solution of (40), and that

$$f(x, y, z, p, q) = 0$$

is a solution of (41). Then each is an intermediate integral of (4). From (43) we obtain

$$F_x + pF_z + rF_p + sF_q = 0$$

and

$$F_y + qF_z + sF_p + tF_q = 0.$$

If we eliminate r and t between (4) and these two equations, we obtain

$$-R(F_x + pF_z)F_q - T(F_y + qF_z)F_p + U(F_x + pF_z)(F_y + qF_z)$$
$$- VF_pF_q - s\{R(F_q)^2 - SF_qF_p + T(F_p)^2 - U(F_y + qF_z)F_q$$
$$- U(F_x + pF_z)F_p\} = 0.$$

Now, since (43) is an intermediate integral of (4), this equation must hold identically in s, and hence the equations

$$R(F_q)^2 - SF_qF_p + T(F_p)^2 - U(F_y + qF_z)F_q$$
$$- U(F_x + pF_z)F_p = 0 \qquad (44)$$

and

$$-R(F_x + pF_z)F_q - T(F_y + qF_z)F_p$$
$$+ U(F_x + pF_z)(F_y + qF_z) - VF_pF_q = 0 \qquad (45)$$

both hold. Therefore, the equation obtained by adding λ times (44) to (45) holds for all values of λ, and, in particular, for the two roots of

$$U^2\lambda^2 + SU\lambda + TR + UV = 0. \qquad (37)$$

But if λ is taken as the root λ_1, we find the equation factoring into the form

$$[\lambda_1 UF_q + TF_p - U(F_x + pF_z)][RF_q + U\lambda_1 F_p$$
$$- U(F_y + qF_z)] = 0, \qquad (46)$$

and if $\lambda = \lambda_2$, it factors into

$$[\lambda_2 UF_q + TF_p - U(F_x + pF_z)][RF_q + U\lambda_2 F_p$$
$$- U(F_y + qF_z)] = 0. \qquad (47)$$

Since $F(x, y, z, p, q) = 0$ satisfies both (44) and (45), it causes one factor in (46) to vanish, and one factor of (47) to vanish. The two first factors cannot vanish simultaneously, since $\lambda_1 \neq \lambda_2$, nor can the two second factors vanish simultaneously. Thus we have

$$\lambda_1 U F_q + T F_p - U(F_x + p F_z) = 0 \qquad (48)$$

and

$$R F_q + U \lambda_2 F_p - U(F_y + q F_z) = 0. \qquad (49)$$

Similarly, since $f(x, y, z, p, q) = 0$ is an intermediate integral of (4) and a solution of (41), we obtain

$$\lambda_2 U f_q + T f_p - U(f_x + p f_z) = 0 \qquad (50)$$

and

$$R f_q + U \lambda_1 f_p - U(f_y + q f_z) = 0. \qquad (51)$$

Eliminating T between (48) and (50) and dividing by U, since $U \neq 0$, we have

$$\lambda_1 f_p F_q - \lambda_2 F_p f_q + F_p(f_x + p f_z) - f_p(F_x + p F_z) = 0, \qquad (52)$$

and eliminating R between (49) and (51), we have

$$\lambda_1 f_p F_q - \lambda_2 F_p f_q + f_q(F_y + q F_z) - F_q(f_y + q f_z) = 0. \qquad (53)$$

From (52) and (53) both λ_1 and λ_2 are eliminated by subtraction, giving, upon rearrangement,

$$-F_p f_x - F_q f_y - (p F_p + q F_q) f_z + (F_x + p F_z) f_p + (F_y + q F_z) f_q = 0,$$

which is the condition obtained in Chapter VIII for the integrability of

$$dz = p\, dx + q\, dy, \qquad (9)$$

p and q being determined simultaneously by $F(x, y, z, p, q) = 0$ and $f(x, y, z, p, q) = 0$.

Illustration 1

To solve the equation

$$xq(z - yq)r + 2xypqs + yp(z - xp)t + xyz(rt - s^2)$$
$$= pq(px + qy - z),$$

we have

$$R \equiv xq(z - yq), \ S \equiv 2xypq, \ T \equiv yp(z - xp)$$
$$U \equiv xyz, \ V \equiv pq(px + qy - z),$$

and hence equation (37) for the determination of λ becomes, after division by $x^2 y^2$,

$$z^2 \lambda^2 + 2pqz\lambda + p^2 q^2 = 0,$$

with the unique solution

$$\lambda = -\frac{pq}{z}.$$

The use of this value of λ in (42) gives the system

$$\begin{cases} -xpq\,dy + p(z - xp)dx + xz\,dp = 0, \\ q(z - yq)dy - pqy\,dx + yz\,dq = 0. \end{cases}$$

If we eliminate dy between the first of these and

$$dz = p\,dx + q\,dy, \tag{9}$$

and eliminate dx between the second and (9), we obtain the system

$$\begin{cases} pz\,dx - xp\,dz + xz\,dp = 0, \\ qz\,dy - yq\,dz + yz\,dq = 0. \end{cases}$$

The first of these has the solution

$$\frac{xp}{z} = a, \tag{54}$$

while the second has the solution

$$\frac{yq}{z} = b. \tag{55}$$

We may, then, take

$$\frac{xp}{z} = f\left(\frac{yq}{z}\right), \tag{56}$$

where the function f is arbitrary, as the general intermediate integral of the given equation. We illustrate two methods of further integration:

First Method. Solve (54) for p and (55) for q, substitute the results in (9), and integrate. This method gives

$$dz = \frac{az}{x}\cdot dx + \frac{bz}{y}\cdot dy,$$

of which the general solution is

$$z = cx^a y^b.$$

Second Method. Let us take a linear function as the arbitrary function f in (56), and write

$$\frac{xp}{z} = m\left(\frac{yq}{z}\right) + n.$$

or

$$xp = myq + nz. \tag{57}$$

(To 57) corresponds the Lagrange system

$$\frac{dx}{x} = \frac{dy}{-my} = \frac{dz}{nz}.$$

From the equation

$$\frac{dx}{x} = \frac{dy}{-my}$$

we obtain the solution

$$x^m y = k,$$

and from the equation

$$\frac{dx}{x} = \frac{dz}{nz}$$

we obtain the solution

$$z = x^n l.$$

If we set l equal to an arbitrary function of k and replace k by $x^m y$, we have

$$z = x^n \phi(x^m y).$$

Illustration 2

To solve the equation

$$2r - 5s + 2t + (rt - s^2) = 2,$$

which is of the form (4) with $R \equiv T \equiv V \equiv 2$, $U \equiv 1$, and $S \equiv -5$, note that (39) reduces to

$$\lambda^2 - 5\lambda + 6 = 0,$$

from which we have $\lambda_1 = 2$, $\lambda_2 = 3$, and the two systems (40) and (41) reduce to

$$\begin{cases} 2dy + 2dx + dp = 0, \\ 2dy + 3dx + dq = 0, \end{cases} \tag{58}$$

and

$$\begin{cases} 3dy + 2dx + dp = 0, \\ 2dy + 2dx + dq = 0, \end{cases} \tag{59}$$

As the solution of (58) we have

$$\begin{cases} p + 2y + 2x = a, \\ q + 2y + 3x = b, \end{cases}$$

or the intermediate integral

$$p + 2y + 2x = f(q + 2y + 3x). \tag{60}$$

Similarly, the system (59) has the solution

$$\begin{cases} p + 3y + 2x = c, \\ q + 2y + 2x = d, \end{cases}$$

and yields the intermediate integral

$$p + 3y + 2x = g(q + 2y + 2x). \tag{61}$$

As means of further integrating these intermediate integrals, we shall employ three methods.

First Method. Let us replace the arbitrary function f of (60) by a linear function, and obtain

$$p + 2y + 2x = m(q + 2y + 3x) + n.$$

This may be solved by employing Lagrange's system

$$\frac{dx}{1} = \frac{dy}{-m} = \frac{dz}{n + 3mx + 2my - 2x - 3y},$$

and its solution is thus found to be

$$z = nx - x^2 - 2xy - y^2 + \frac{m}{2} x^2 + \phi(y + mx), \tag{62}$$

where m and n are arbitrary constants and ϕ is an arbitrary function. If we treat the intermediate integral (61) by the same method we obtain

$$z = nx - x^2 - 3xy - y^2 - \frac{m}{2} x^2 + \phi(y + mx). \tag{63}$$

Second Method. If we regard α and β as parameters, the intermediate integral (60) can be expressed by the equations

$$\begin{cases} p + 2y + 2x = \alpha, \\ q + 2y + 3x = f(\alpha), \end{cases} \tag{64}$$

and (61) can be expressed as

$$\begin{cases} p + 3y + 2x = \beta, \\ q + 2y + 2x = g(\beta). \end{cases} \tag{65}$$

Subtracting (64_1) from (65_1), we obtain

$$y = \beta - \alpha,$$

and subtracting (65_2) from (64_2) we obtain

$$x = -g(\beta) + f(\alpha).$$

If we substitute the value of p from (64_1) and that of q from (65_2) into

$$dz = p \, dx + q \, dy, \tag{9}$$

we obtain

$$
\begin{aligned}
dz &\equiv \{\alpha - 2(x + y)\}dx + \{g(\beta) - 2(x + y)\}dy \\
&\equiv -2(x + y)(dx + dy) + \alpha \, dx + g(\beta)dy \\
&\equiv -d(x + y)^2 + \alpha\{f'(\alpha)d\alpha - g'(\beta)d\beta\} + g(\beta)\{d\beta - d\alpha\} \\
&\equiv -d(x + y)^2 + \alpha f'(\alpha)d\alpha - \alpha g'(\beta)d\beta - g(\beta)d\alpha + g(\beta)d\beta \\
&\equiv -d(x + y)^2 + d[\alpha \cdot f(\alpha)] - f(\alpha)d\alpha - d[\alpha g(\beta)] + g(\beta)d\beta
\end{aligned}
$$

$\therefore$

$$z = -(x + y)^2 + \alpha f(\alpha) - \int f(\alpha)d\alpha - \alpha g(\beta) + \int g(\beta)d\beta.$$

If, now, we write $\int f(\alpha)d\alpha \equiv F(\alpha)$ and $\int g(\beta)d\beta \equiv G(\beta)$, we have the solution expressed parametrically in the form

$$
\begin{aligned}
z &= -(x + y)^2 + \alpha F'(\alpha) - \alpha G'(\beta) - F(\alpha) + G(\beta), \\
x &= F'(\alpha) - G'(\beta), \\
y &= \beta - \alpha.
\end{aligned}
$$

We may express this by a single equation as

$$z = -(x + y)^2 + \alpha x - F(\alpha) + G(\alpha + y),$$

or

$$z = -x^2 - 2xy + \alpha x + \phi(y),$$

where we have dropped the terms $F(\alpha)$ and $-y^2$ by assuming them to be absorbed into the arbitrary function ϕ, which may involve α as an arbitrary constant. This solution, we note, is an instance of (62), obtained by the first method, with $m = 0$.

If, in the above, we had chosen to employ $p = \beta - 2x - 3y$ from (65_1) and $q = f(\alpha) - 2y - 3x$ from (64_2), we would have obtained

$$dz = (\beta - 2x - 3y)dx + [f(\alpha) - 2y - 3x]dy,$$

whose general solution can be reduced to $z = -x^2 - 3xy + \beta x + F(y)$, an instance of (63) with $m = 0$.

Third Method. This method affords results comparable in generality to those of the second method. We begin with the equation

$$p + 2y + 2x = \alpha, \tag{66}$$

an instance of (60), and obtain

$$p + 3y + 2x = \alpha + y.$$

If, now, we solve (61) for $q + 2y + 2x$, we obtain

$$q + 2y + 2x = \phi(p + 3y + 2x) = \phi(\alpha + y), \qquad (67)$$

where ϕ is quite arbitrary. If we substitute for p from (66) and for q from (67) into

$$dz = p\, dx + q\, dy, \qquad (9)$$

we have

$$dz = (\alpha - 2x - 2y)dx + [\phi(\alpha + y) - 2x - 2y]dy,$$

which has, as solution,

$$z = \alpha x - x^2 - 2xy - y^2 + \psi(\alpha + y),$$

or

$$z = \alpha x - x^2 - 2xy - y^2 + G(y) = \alpha x - x^2 - 2xy + H(y).$$

This same method may be applied again, by setting

$$p + 3y + 2x = \alpha$$

and

$$q + 2y + 3x = f(\alpha - y),$$

and drawing therefrom the solution

$$z = -x^2 - 3xy + \alpha x + F(y).$$

Exercises

Solve the following equations:

1. $r - a^2t = 0.$

2. $qs - pt = 0.$

3. $r + 2s + t = 0.$

4. $y^2(s - t) = x.$

5. $r \sin^3 y - t \sin y = -q \cos y.$

6. $r \operatorname{sech}^2 x - t \operatorname{sech}^2 y + q \operatorname{sech}^2 y \tanh y - p \operatorname{sech}^2 x \tanh x = 0.$

7. $x^2 r + 2xys + y^2 t = 0.$

8. $(x + y)(r - t) + 4p = 0.$

9. $(2 + 3q)^2 r - 2(2 + 3q)(1 + 3p)s + (1 + 3p)^2 t = 0.$

10. $2x(x - 2y)r + (4y^2 - x^2)s + y(x - 2y)t = (x + 2y)(2p - q)$.

11. $3r - 6s + 4t - (rt - s^2) = 3$.

12. $5r + 2s + 5t - 4(rt - s^2) = 6$.

13. $4r - 3s - 3t + 2(rt - s^2) = 4$.

14. $2r + 5s + 3t + 6(rt - s^2) = 0$.

15. $xqr - (x + y)s + ypt + xy(rt - s^2) = 1 - pq$.

16. $2x^2y\,qr + 2(px + qy)s + 2xy^2\,pt + (x^2y^2 - 1)(rt - s^2) + 4xy\,pq = 0$.

17. $xq(2xy - 1)r + (px^2 + qy^2)s + yp(2xy - 1)t + xy(xy - 1)(rt - s^2) = pq(1 - 4xy)$.

91. Laplace's transformation. We shall first follow through an illustration afforded by the second order partial differential equation

$$r + 3s + 2t = x + y. \tag{68}$$

Monge's auxiliary equation

$$R(dy)^2 - S\,dy\,dx + T(dx)^2 = 0 \tag{8_1}$$

becomes

$$(dy)^2 - 3\,dy\,dx + 2(dx)^2 = 0, \qquad (dy - dx)(dy - 2dx)$$

and has as solutions

$$y - 2x = c_1,\ y - x = c_2.$$

If we now employ new independent variables defined by

$$\xi = y - 2x,\ \eta = y - x,$$

we find

$$
\begin{aligned}
p &\equiv z_x = -2z_\xi - z_\eta,\\
q &\equiv z_y = z_\xi + z_\eta,\\
r &\equiv p_x = 4z_{\xi\xi} + 4z_{\xi\eta} + z_{\eta\eta},\\
s &\equiv p_y \equiv q_x = -2z_{\xi\xi} - 3z_{\xi\eta} - z_{\eta\eta},\\
t &\equiv q_y = z_{\xi\xi} + 2z_{\xi\eta} + z_{\eta\eta},
\end{aligned}
$$

and, if we substitute these values into (68), the latter becomes

$$z_{\xi\eta} = 2\xi - 3\eta.$$

Integration with respect to η gives

$$z_\xi = 2\xi\eta - \frac{3}{2}\eta^2 + \phi'(\xi),$$

where $\phi'(\xi)$ is an arbitrary function of ξ, and this in turn may be integrated with respect to ξ, which gives the solution

$$z = \xi^2\eta - \frac{3}{2}\xi\eta^2 + \phi(\xi) + f(\eta).$$

Returning now to the original variables, we have

$$z = (y - 2x)^2(y - x) - \frac{3}{2}(y - 2x)(y - x)^2 + \phi(y - 2x) + f(y - x),$$

or

$$z = -\frac{1}{2}y^3 + y^2x + \frac{1}{2}yx^2 - x^3 + \phi(y - 2x) + f(y - x),$$

which reduces to

$$z = \frac{1}{2}yx^2 - \frac{1}{3}x^3 + \phi(y - 2x) + f(y - x),$$

where $\frac{1}{6}(y - 2x)^3$ is absorbed by ϕ, and $-\frac{2}{3}(y - x)^3$ is absorbed by f. Let us now consider the equation

$$Rr + Ss + Tt + Pp + Qq + Zz = W, \tag{69}$$

in which R, S, T, P, Q, Z, and W are functions of x and y. This equation is of the form (5), with $R \equiv R$, $S \equiv S$, $T \equiv T$, $V \equiv W - Pp - Qq - Zz$, and the auxiliary equation

$$R(dy)^2 - S\,dy\,dx + T(dx)^2 = 0 \tag{8_1}$$

gives two equations

$$\begin{cases} N_1\,dx + M_1\,dy = 0, \\ N_2\,dx + M_2\,dy = 0. \end{cases} \tag{10}$$

If $S^2 \neq 4RT$, the two equations are distinct and have distinct solutions

$$\xi(x, y) = a,$$
$$\eta(x, y) = b.$$

In this case we employ the transformation to new independent variables, defined by

$$\begin{cases} \xi = \xi(x, y), \\ \eta = \eta(x, y), \end{cases}$$

given by Laplace in 1773.   By differentiation we find

$$p \equiv z_x = z_\xi \cdot \xi_x + z_\eta \cdot \eta_x,$$
$$q \equiv z_y = z_\xi \cdot \xi_y + z_\eta \cdot \eta_y,$$
$$r = z_{\xi\xi}(\xi_x)^2 + 2z_{\xi\eta} \cdot \xi_x\eta_x + z_{\eta\eta}(\eta_x)^2 + z_\xi \cdot \xi_{xx} + z_\eta \cdot \eta_{xx},$$
$$s = z_{\xi\xi}\xi_x\xi_y + z_{\xi\eta}(\xi_x\eta_y + \xi_y\,\eta_x) + z_{\eta\eta} \cdot \eta_x\eta_y + z_\xi \cdot \xi_{xy} + z_\eta \cdot \eta_{xy},$$
$$t = z_{\xi\xi}(\xi_y)^2 + 2z_{\xi\eta} \cdot \xi_y\eta_y + z_{\eta\eta}(\eta_y)^2 + z_\xi \cdot \xi_{yy} + z_\eta \cdot \eta_{yy},$$

and if these be substituted into (69), we note that the coefficient of $z_{\xi\xi}$ is

$$R(\xi_x)^2 + S\xi_x\xi_y + T(\xi_y)^2,$$

which is zero identically because $\xi(x, y) = a$ is a solution of (8). Similarly, the coefficient of $z_{\eta\eta}$ is given by

$$R(\eta_x)^2 + S\eta_x\eta_y + T(\eta_y)^2,$$

which also vanishes identically.   The equation will therefore be of the form

$$z_{\xi\eta} + Lz_\xi + Mz_\eta + Nz = V, \tag{70}$$

where L, M, N, and V are functions of ξ and η.

In the above illustration the functions L, M, and N were all zero, and the equation was solved by quadratures.   Such will not always be the case, but the equation can always be written in the form

$$\left(\frac{\partial}{\partial\xi} + M\right)\left(\frac{\partial}{\partial\eta} + L\right)z + \left(N - LM - \frac{\partial L}{\partial\xi}\right)z = V. \tag{71}$$

In case $N - LM - \frac{\partial L}{\partial\xi}$ happens to be zero identically, we can solve as follows.   Let

$$\left(\frac{\partial}{\partial\eta} + L\right)z = \zeta, \tag{72}$$

and thus obtain from (71)

$$\left(\frac{\partial}{\partial\xi} + M\right)\zeta = V. \tag{73}$$

Solve (73) for $\zeta = \varphi(\xi, \eta)$, substitute the solution in (72), and solve for z.   Equation (70) can also be written as

$$\left(\frac{\partial}{\partial\eta} + L\right)\left(\frac{\partial}{\partial\xi} + M\right)z + \left(N - LM - \frac{\partial M}{\partial\eta}\right)z = V,$$

and hence if the quantity $N - LM - \dfrac{\partial M}{\partial \eta}$ vanishes, we may come immediately to a solution.　If neither of the quantities $N - LM - \dfrac{\partial L}{\partial \xi}$, $N - LM - \dfrac{\partial M}{\partial \eta}$ is found to be zero, we may change the dependent variable as follows.　Let

$$\left(\frac{\partial}{\partial \eta} + L \right) z = \zeta, \tag{72}$$

and substitute in (71) to obtain

$$\left(\frac{\partial}{\partial \xi} + M \right) \zeta + \left(N - LM - \frac{\partial L}{\partial \xi} \right) z = V,$$

from which we have

$$z = \frac{1}{N - LM - \dfrac{\partial L}{\partial \xi}} \left[V - M\zeta - \frac{\partial \zeta}{\partial \xi} \right].$$

If we substitute this into (72), we obtain a new equation which reduces to the form

$$\zeta_{\xi\eta} + \mathcal{L}\,\zeta_{\xi} + \mathcal{M}\zeta_{\eta} + \mathcal{N}\,\zeta = \mathcal{U}, \tag{74}$$

where $\mathcal{L}$, $\mathcal{M}$, $\mathcal{N}$, and $\mathcal{U}$ are new functions of ξ and η.　In the same way it is possible to begin with the substitution

$$\left(\frac{\partial}{\partial \xi} + M \right) z = \zeta$$

and derive an equation like (74).　If, in either of the new equations, one of the relations

$$\mathcal{N} - \mathcal{L}\mathcal{M} - \frac{\partial \mathcal{L}}{\partial \xi} \equiv 0, \quad \mathcal{N} - \mathcal{L}\mathcal{M} - \frac{\partial \mathcal{M}}{\partial \eta} \equiv 0,$$

holds, the equation may be solved, as before.　If such is not the case, one may again pass to new equations of similar form.　Unfortunately the process will sometimes prove unfruitful, as will certainly be the case for the equation

$$z_{\xi\eta} + z_{\xi} + z_{\eta} + 2z = 0,$$

since it is left unaltered in form by the above transformations.

If $S^2 \equiv 4RT$, the auxiliary equation (8_1) reduces to

$$(N_1 dx + M_1 dy)^2 = 0,$$

which has the solution

$$\xi(x, y) = a. \tag{75}$$

Since (75) is a solution of (8_1), we have

$$R(\xi_x)^2 + S\xi_x\xi_y + T(\xi_y)^2 = 0,$$

or, taking the square root,

$$2R\xi_x + S\xi_y = 0,$$

or

$$S\xi_x + 2T\xi_y = 0.$$

If we now transform the dependent variables by the transformation

$$\begin{cases} \xi = \xi(x, y), \\ \eta = y, \end{cases}$$

we obtain the equation

$$z_{\eta\eta} + Lz_\xi + Mz_\eta + Nz = V.$$

In case L should vanish, we may look upon this as an ordinary linear differential equation determining z as a function of η, and in its solution employ arbitrary functions of ξ rather than arbitrary constants.

Exercises

Solve the following:

1. $2r - 3s + t - 4p + q - 6z + 2x + 2y = 0.$

2. $(2y - x)(2x - 3y)(6r + 7s + 2t) + (5x - 6y)p + (2x - 2y)q = 4(2x - 3y)^3(2y - x) + 2(2y - x)^3(2x - 3y) - 2z.$

3. $z_{xx} - y^2 z_{xy} + 2y^2 z_y - 4z = x - \dfrac{1}{y}.$

4. $r - t \cosh^2 x - p \tanh x = 0.$

5. $x(x + y)r + (x^2 - y^2)s - y(x + y)t - (x - y)(p + q) = 0.$

6. $xy(t - r) + (x^2 - y^2)(s - 2) = py - qx.$

7. $z_{xx} + 2z_{xy} + z_{yy} + 5z_x + 5z_y + 6z = 6.$

8. $xz_{xx} - 2xz_{xy} + xz_{yy} - (1 + 12x^2)(z_x - z_y) + 20x^3[z - 2(x + y)^2] = 0.$

9. $25y^2 z_{xx} + 10y^2 z_{xy} + y^2 z_{yy} + 35yz_x + 7yz_y = 10x - 50y - 5z.$

10. $r - 2s + t = y + \varphi(x + y).$

11. $x^2 r + 2xys + y^2 t + xp + yq - 9z = \log x - \log y.$

12. $x(4 + y)^2(x^2 z_{xx} + 2xyz_{xy} + y^2 z_{yy}) - 2xy(4 + y)(xz_x + yz_y) + 2xy^2 z = 2y^2(x + y)(4 + y)^3.$

Table of Integrals

1. $\displaystyle\int (ax + b)^n dx = \frac{1}{a}\frac{(ax + b)^{n+1}}{n + 1}, \; n \neq -1.$

2. $\displaystyle\int \frac{dx}{(ax + b)} = \frac{1}{a}\log(ax + b).$

3. $\displaystyle\int x^m(ax + b)^n \, dx$

$\displaystyle = \frac{1}{a(m + n + 1)}\left[x^m(ax + b)^{n+1} - mb \int x^{m-1}(ax + b)^n dx \right],$

$\displaystyle = \frac{1}{m + n + 1}\left[x^{m+1}(ax + b)^n + nb \int x^m(ax + b)^{n-1} dx \right],$

$$m > 0, \; m + n + 1 \neq 0.$$

4. $\displaystyle\int \frac{dx}{x(ax + b)} = \frac{1}{b}\log\frac{x}{ax + b}.$

5. $\displaystyle\int \frac{dx}{x(ax + b)^2} = \frac{1}{b(ax + b)} + \frac{1}{b^2}\log\frac{x}{ax + b}.$

6. $\displaystyle\int \frac{dx}{x^2(ax + b)} = -\frac{1}{bx} + \frac{a}{b^2}\log\frac{ax + b}{x}.$

7. $\displaystyle\int \frac{dx}{x^2(ax + b)^2} = -\frac{b + 2ax}{b^2 x(ax + b)} + \frac{2a}{b^3}\log\frac{ax + b}{x}.$

8. $\displaystyle\int \frac{x\,dx}{(ax + b)^2} = \frac{b}{a^2(ax + b)} + \frac{1}{a^2}\log(ax + b).$

9. $\displaystyle\int \frac{x^2\, dx}{(ax + b)^3} = \frac{1}{a^3}\left[\log(ax + b) + \frac{2b}{ax + b} - \frac{b^2}{2(ax + b)^2} \right].$

10. $\displaystyle\int \frac{\sqrt{ax + b}}{x}\, dx = 2\sqrt{ax + b} + b\int \frac{dx}{x\sqrt{ax + b}}.$

11(a). $\displaystyle\int \frac{dx}{x\sqrt{ax + b}} = \frac{1}{\sqrt{b}}\log\frac{\sqrt{ax + b} - \sqrt{b}}{\sqrt{ax + b} + \sqrt{b}}, \text{ for } b > 0.$

(b). $\displaystyle\int \frac{dx}{x\sqrt{ax + b}} = \frac{2}{\sqrt{-b}}\tan^{-1}\sqrt{\frac{ax + b}{-b}}, \text{ for } b < 0.$

12. $\displaystyle\int \frac{dx}{x^2\sqrt{ax+b}} = -\frac{\sqrt{ax+b}}{bx} - \frac{a}{2b}\int \frac{dx}{x\sqrt{ax+b}}.$

13. $\displaystyle\int \frac{x^m dx}{\sqrt{ax+b}} = \frac{2x^m\sqrt{ax+b}}{(2m+1)a} - \frac{2mb}{(2m+1)a}\int \frac{x^{m-1}dx}{\sqrt{ax+b}}.$

14. $\displaystyle\int \frac{dx}{x^n\sqrt{ax+b}} = \frac{-\sqrt{ax+b}}{(n-1)bx^{n-1}}$

$$-\frac{(2n-3)a}{(2n-2)b}\int \frac{dx}{x^{n-1}\sqrt{ax+b}}.$$

15. $\displaystyle\int \frac{dx}{a^2-x^2} = \frac{1}{2a}\log\frac{a+x}{a-x}.$

16. $\displaystyle\int \sqrt{a^2-x^2}\,dx = \frac{x}{2}\sqrt{a^2-x^2} + \frac{a^2}{2}\sin^{-1}\frac{x}{a}.$

17. $\displaystyle\int \frac{\sqrt{a^2-x^2}}{x}\,dx = \sqrt{a^2-x^2} - a\log\frac{a+\sqrt{a^2-x^2}}{x}.$

18. $\displaystyle\int \frac{\sqrt{a^2-x^2}}{x^2}\,dx = -\frac{\sqrt{a^2-x^2}}{x} - \sin^{-1}\frac{x}{a}.$

19. $\displaystyle\int x\sqrt{a^2-x^2}\,dx = -\tfrac{1}{3}(\sqrt{a^2-x^2})^3.$

20. $\displaystyle\int \frac{dx}{\sqrt{a^2-x^2}} = \sin^{-1}\frac{x}{a}.$

21. $\displaystyle\int \frac{x\,dx}{\sqrt{a^2-x^2}} = -\sqrt{a^2-x^2}.$

22. $\displaystyle\int \frac{x^2\,dx}{\sqrt{a^2-x^2}} = -\frac{x}{2}\sqrt{a^2-x^2} + \frac{a^2}{2}\sin^{-1}\frac{x}{a}.$

23. $\displaystyle\int \frac{x^3\,dx}{\sqrt{a^2-x^2}} = \frac{(a^2-x^2)^{3/2}}{3} - a^2\sqrt{a^2-x^2}.$

24. $\displaystyle\int (a^2-x^2)^{3/2}\,dx = \tfrac{1}{4}x(a^2-x^2)^{3/2} + \tfrac{3}{8}a^2x\sqrt{a^2-x^2}$

$$+ \tfrac{3}{8}a^4\sin^{-1}\frac{x}{a}.$$

25. $\displaystyle\int \frac{dx}{x\sqrt{x^2-a^2}} = -\frac{1}{a}\sin^{-1}\frac{a}{x}.$

26. $\displaystyle\int \frac{dx}{x^2\sqrt{a^2-x^2}} = -\frac{1}{a^2x}\sqrt{a^2-x^2}.$

27. $\int \sqrt{x^2 \pm a^2}\, dx = \frac{1}{2}x\, \sqrt{x^2 \pm a^2} \pm \frac{1}{2}a^2 \log\,(x + \sqrt{x^2 \pm a^2}).$

28. $\int \dfrac{dx}{\sqrt{x^2 \pm a^2}} = \log\,(x + \sqrt{x^2 \pm a^2}).$

29. $\int \dfrac{dx}{x\,\sqrt{a^2 \pm x^2}} = \dfrac{1}{a} \log \dfrac{x}{a + \sqrt{a^2 \pm x^2}}.$

30. $\int \dfrac{\sqrt{a^2 \pm x^2}}{x}\, dx = \sqrt{a^2 \pm x^2} + a \log \dfrac{x}{a + \sqrt{a^2 \pm x^2}}.$

31. $\int \dfrac{\sqrt{x^2 - a^2}}{x}\, dx = \sqrt{x^2 - a^2} + a \sin^{-1} \dfrac{a}{x}.$

32. $\int \dfrac{x\, dx}{\sqrt{x^2 \pm a^2}} = \sqrt{x^2 \pm a^2}.$

33. $\int \dfrac{x^2\, dx}{\sqrt{x^2 \pm a^2}} = \dfrac{x}{2}\, \sqrt{x^2 \pm a^2} \mp \dfrac{a^2}{2} \log\,(x + \sqrt{x^2 \pm a^2}).$

34. $\int \dfrac{dx}{x^2\,\sqrt{x^2 \pm a^2}} = \mp \dfrac{\sqrt{x^2 \pm a^2}}{a^2 x}.$

35. $\int \dfrac{dx}{(\sqrt{a^2 - x^2})^3} = \dfrac{x}{a^2\,\sqrt{a^2 - x^2}}.$

36. $\int \dfrac{dx}{(\sqrt{x^2 \pm a^2})^3} = \dfrac{\pm x}{a^2\,\sqrt{x^2 \pm a^2}}.$

37(a). $\int \dfrac{dx}{ax^2 + bx + c} =$

$$\dfrac{1}{\sqrt{b^2 - 4ac}} \log \dfrac{2ax + b - \sqrt{b^2 - 4ac}}{2ax + b + \sqrt{b^2 - 4ac}},\ b^2 > 4ac.$$

(b). $\int \dfrac{dx}{ax^2 + bx + c} = \dfrac{2}{\sqrt{4ac - b^2}} \tan^{-1} \dfrac{2ax + b}{\sqrt{4ac - b^2}},$

$$b^2 < 4ac.$$

(c). $\int \dfrac{dx}{ax^2 + bx + c} = -\dfrac{2}{2ax + b},\ b^2 = 4ac.$

38. $\int \dfrac{x\,dx}{ax^2 + bx + c} = \dfrac{1}{2a} \log\,(ax^2 + bx + c) -$

$$\dfrac{b}{2a} \int \dfrac{dx}{ax^2 + bx + c}.$$

39. $\int \dfrac{x^2 dx}{ax^2 + bx + c} = \dfrac{x}{a} - \dfrac{b}{2a^2} \log (ax^2 + bx + c)$

$$+ \frac{b^2 - 2ac}{2a^2} \int \frac{dx}{ax^2 + bx + c}.$$

40. $\int \dfrac{dx}{x(ax^2 + bx + c)} = \dfrac{1}{2c} \log \dfrac{x^2}{ax^2 + bx + c}$

$$- \frac{b}{2c} \int \frac{dx}{(ax^2 + bx + c)}.$$

41. $\int \dfrac{dx}{x^2(ax^2 + bx + c)} = \dfrac{b}{2c^2} \log \left(\dfrac{ax^2 + bx + c}{x^2} \right) - \dfrac{1}{cx}$

$$+ \left(\frac{b^2}{2c^2} - \frac{a}{c} \right) \int \frac{dx}{(ax^2 + bx + c)}.$$

42(a). $\int \dfrac{dx}{\sqrt{ax^2 + bx + c}} = \dfrac{1}{\sqrt{a}} \log (2ax + b$

$$+ 2\sqrt{a}\sqrt{ax^2 + bx + c}), \, a > 0.$$

(b). $\int \dfrac{dx}{\sqrt{ax^2 + bx + c}} = \dfrac{1}{\sqrt{-a}} \sin^{-1} \dfrac{-2ax - b}{\sqrt{b^2 - 4ac}}, \, a < 0.$

43. $\int \dfrac{x \, dx}{\sqrt{ax^2 + bx + c}} = \dfrac{\sqrt{ax^2 + bx + c}}{a}$

$$- \frac{b}{2a} \int \frac{dx}{\sqrt{ax^2 + bx + c}}.$$

44. $\int \sqrt{ax^2 + bx + c} \, dx = \dfrac{2ax + b}{4a} \sqrt{ax^2 + bx + c}$

$$+ \frac{4ac - b^2}{8a} \int \frac{dx}{\sqrt{ax^2 + bx + c}}.$$

45. $\int x \sqrt{ax^2 + bx + c} \, dx = \dfrac{(ax^2 + bx + c)^{3/2}}{3a}$

$$- \frac{b}{2a} \int \sqrt{ax^2 + bx + c} \, dx.$$

46. $\int \dfrac{dx}{x \sqrt{ax^2 + bx + c}} = - \dfrac{1}{\sqrt{c}} \log \left(\dfrac{\sqrt{ax^2 + bx + c} + \sqrt{c}}{x} \right.$

$$\left. + \frac{b}{2\sqrt{c}} \right), \, c > 0.$$

47. $\int \dfrac{dx}{x \sqrt{ax^2 + bx + c}} = \dfrac{1}{\sqrt{-c}} \sin^{-1} \dfrac{bx + 2c}{x \sqrt{b^2 - 4ac}}, \, c < 0.$

48. $\int \sin x \, dx = -\cos x, \int \cos x \, dx = \sin x.$

49. $\int \sin^2 x \, dx = \frac{1}{2}x - \frac{1}{2}\sin x \cos x = \frac{1}{2}x - \frac{1}{4}\sin 2x.$

50. $\int \cos^2 x \, dx = \frac{1}{2}x + \frac{1}{2}\sin x \cos x = \frac{1}{2}x + \frac{1}{4}\sin 2x.$

51. $\int \sin^3 x \, dx = -\frac{1}{3}(\sin^2 x + 2)\cos x.$

52. $\int \cos^3 x \, dx = \frac{1}{3}(\cos^2 x + 2)\sin x.$

53. $\int \sin^n x \, dx = -\frac{\sin^{n-1} x \cos x}{n} + \frac{n-1}{n}\int \sin^{n-2} x \, dx.$

54. $\int \cos^n x \, dx = \frac{\cos^{n-1} x \sin x}{n} + \frac{n-1}{n}\int \cos^{n-2} x \, dx.$

55. $\int \sin^2 x \cos^2 x \, dx = -\frac{1}{8}(\frac{1}{4}\sin 4x - x).$

56(a). $\int \cos^m x \sin^n x \, dx = \frac{\cos^{m-1} x \sin^{n+1} x}{m+n}$

$$+ \frac{m-1}{m+n}\int \cos^{m-2} x \sin^n x \, dx.$$

(b). $\int \cos^m x \sin^n x \, dx = -\frac{\sin^{n-1} x \cos^{m+1} x}{m+n}$

$$+ \frac{n-1}{m+n}\int \cos^m x \sin^{n-2} x \, dx.$$

57. $\int \tan x \, dx = -\log \cos x, \int \text{ctn } x \, dx = \log \sin x.$

58. $\int \tan^2 x \, dx = \tan x - x, \int \text{ctn}^2 x \, dx = -\text{ctn } x - x.$

59. $\int \tan^n x \, dx = \frac{\tan^{n-1} x}{n-1} - \int \tan^{n-2} x \, dx.$

60. $\int \text{ctn}^n x \, dx = -\frac{\text{ctn}^{n-1} x}{n-1} - \int \text{ctn}^{n-2} x \, dx.$

61. $\int \sec x \, dx = \log (\sec x + \tan x).$

62. $\displaystyle\int \csc x\, dx = \log\,(\csc x - \operatorname{ctn} x).$

63. $\displaystyle\int \sec^2 x\, dx = \tan x, \quad \int \csc^2 x\, dx = -\cot x.$

64. $\displaystyle\int \sec^3 x\, dx = \frac{\sin x}{2\cos^2 x} + \frac14 \log \frac{1+\sin x}{1-\sin x}.$

65. $\displaystyle\int \csc^3 x\, dx = -\frac{\cos x}{2\sin^2 x} + \frac14 \log \frac{1-\cos x}{1+\cos x}.$

66. $\displaystyle\int \sec^n x\, dx = \frac{\tan x \sec^{n-2} x}{n-1} + \frac{n-2}{n-1} \int \sec^{n-2} x\, dx.$

67. $\displaystyle\int \csc^n x\, dx = -\frac{\cot x \csc^{n-2} x}{n-1} + \frac{n-2}{n-1} \int \csc^{n-2} x\, dx.$

68. $\displaystyle\int x \sin x\, dx = \sin x - x \cos x.$

69. $\displaystyle\int x \cos x\, dx = \cos x + x \sin x.$

70. $\displaystyle\int x^2 \sin x\, dx = 2\,x \sin x - (x^2 - 2) \cos x.$

71. $\displaystyle\int x^2 \cos x\, dx = 2\,x \cos x + (x^2 - 2) \sin x.$

72. $\displaystyle\int x^n \sin x\, dx = -x^n \cos x + n \int x^{n-1} \cos x\, dx.$

73. $\displaystyle\int x^n \cos x\, dx = x^n \sin x - n \int x^{n-1} \sin x\, dx.$

74. $\displaystyle\int x \sin^n x\, dx = \frac{\sin^{n-1} x(\sin x - nx \cos x)}{n^2}$
$$+ \frac{n-1}{n} \int x \sin^{n-2} x\, dx.$$

75. $\displaystyle\int x \cos^n x\, dx = \frac{\cos^{n-1} x(\cos x + nx \sin x)}{n^2}$
$$+ \frac{n-1}{n} \int x \cos^{n-2} x\, dx.$$

76. $\displaystyle\int \frac{\sin x\, dx}{x^m} = -\frac{1}{m-1} \frac{\sin x}{x^{m-1}} + \frac{1}{m-1} \int \frac{\cos x\, dx}{x^{m-1}}.$

77. $\int \dfrac{\cos x \, dx}{x^m} = -\dfrac{1}{m-1}\dfrac{\cos x}{x^{m-1}} - \dfrac{1}{m-1}\int \dfrac{\sin x \, dx}{x^{m-1}}.$

78. $\int \sin mx \sin nx \, dx = \dfrac{\sin (m-n)x}{2(m-n)} - \dfrac{\sin (m+n)x}{2(m+n)}.$

79. $\int \sin mx \cos nx \, dx = -\dfrac{\cos (m-n)x}{2(m-n)} - \dfrac{\cos (m+n)x}{2(m+n)}.$

80. $\int \cos mx \cos nx \, dx = \dfrac{\sin (m-n)x}{2(m-n)} + \dfrac{\sin (m+n)x}{2(m+n)}.$

81. $\int \sin^{-1} x \, dx = x \sin^{-1} x + \sqrt{1-x^2}.$

82. $\int \cos^{-1} x \, dx = x \cos^{-1} x - \sqrt{1-x^2}.$

83. $\int \tan^{-1} x \, dx = x \tan^{-1} x - \tfrac{1}{2} \log (1 + x^2).$

84. $\int x^n \sin^{-1} x \, dx = \dfrac{x^{n+1} \sin^{-1} x}{n+1} - \dfrac{1}{n+1} \int \dfrac{x^{n+1} dx}{\sqrt{1-x^2}}.$

85. $\int x^n \cos^{-1} x \, dx = \dfrac{x^{n+1} \cos^{-1} x}{n+1} + \dfrac{1}{n+1} \int \dfrac{x^{n+1} dx}{\sqrt{1-x^2}}.$

86. $\int x^n \tan^{-1} x \, dx = \dfrac{x^{n+1} \tan^{-1} x}{n+1} - \dfrac{1}{n+1} \int \dfrac{x^{n+1} dx}{1+x^2}.$

87. $\int e^{ax} \, dx = \dfrac{e^{ax}}{a}, \quad \int a^x \, dx = \dfrac{a^x}{\log a}.$

88. $\int xe^{ax} \, dx = \dfrac{e^{ax}}{a^2} (ax - 1).$

89. $\int x^n e^{ax} \, dx = \dfrac{x^n e^{ax}}{a} - \dfrac{n}{a} \int x^{n-1} e^{ax} \, dx.$

90. $\int \dfrac{e^{ax}}{x^n} \, dx = \dfrac{1}{n-1}\left[-\dfrac{e^{ax}}{x^{n-1}} + a \int \dfrac{e^{ax}}{x^{n-1}} \, dx \right], \; n \neq 1.$

91. $\int e^{ax} \sin bx \, dx = \dfrac{e^{ax}(a \sin bx - b \cos bx)}{a^2 + b^2}.$

92. $\int e^{ax} \cos bx \, dx = \dfrac{e^{ax}(b \sin bx + a \cos bx)}{a^2 + b^2}.$

93. $\displaystyle\int e^{ax} \cos^n x \, dx = \frac{e^{ax} \cos^{n-1} x (a \cos x + n \sin x)}{a^2 + n^2}$

$$+ \frac{n(n-1)}{a^2 + n^2} \int e^{ax} \cos^{n-2} x \, dx.$$

94. $\displaystyle\int e^{ax} \sin^n x \, dx = \frac{e^{ax} \sin^{n-1} x (a \sin x - n \cos x)}{a^2 + n^2}$

$$+ \frac{n(n-1)}{a^2 + n^2} \int e^{ax} \sin^{n-2} x \, dx.$$

95. $\displaystyle\int \log x \, dx = x \log x - x.$

96. $\displaystyle\int x^n \log x \, dx = x^{n+1} \left[\frac{\log x}{n+1} - \frac{1}{(n+1)^2} \right].$

97. $\displaystyle\int x^n (\log x)^m \, dx = \frac{x^{n+1}}{n+1} (\log x)^m - \frac{m}{n+1} \int x^n (\log x)^{m-1} \, dx.$

98. $\displaystyle\int \frac{x^n dx}{(\log x)^m} = -\frac{x^{n+1}}{(m-1)(\log x)^{m-1}} + \frac{n+1}{m-1} \int \frac{x^n dx}{(\log x)^{m-1}}.$

99. $\displaystyle\int e^{ax} \log x \, dx = \frac{e^{ax} \log x}{a} - \frac{1}{a} \int \frac{e^{ax}}{x} \, dx.$

NATURAL LOGARITHMS—0.00 TO 10.09

		0	1	2	3	4	5	6	7	8	9
0.0			5.395	6.088	6.493	6.781	7.004	7.187	7.341	7.474	7.592
0.1		7.697	7.793	7.880	7.960	8.034	8.103	8.167	8.228	8.285	8.339
0.2		8.391	8.439	8.486	8.530	8.573	8.614	8.653	8.691	8.727	8.762
0.3		8.796	8.829	8.861	8.891	8.921	8.950	8.978	9.006	9.032	9.058
0.4		9.084	9.108	9.132	9.156	9.179	9.201	9.223	9.245	9.266	9.287
0.5		9.307	9.327	9.346	9.365	9.384	9.402	9.420	9.438	9.455	9.472
0.6		9.489	9.506	9.522	9.538	9.554	9.569	9.584	9.600	9.614	9.629
0.7		9.643	9.658	9.671	9.685	9.699	9.712	9.726	9.739	9.752	9.764
0.8		9.777	9.789	9.802	9.814	9.826	9.837	9.849	9.861	9.872	9.883
0.9		9.895	9.906	9.917	9.927	9.938	9.949	9.959	9.970	9.980	9.990
1.0	0.0	0000	0995	1980	2956	3922	4879	5827	6766	7696	8618
1.1		9531	*0436	*1333	*2222	*3103	*3976	*4842	*5700	*6551	*7395
1.2	0.1	8232	9062	9885	*0701	*1511	*2314	*3111	*3902	*4686	*5464
1.3	0.2	6236	7003	7763	8518	9267	*0010	*0748	*1481	*2208	*2930
1.4	0.3	3647	4359	5066	5767	6464	7156	7844	8526	9204	9878
1.5	0.4	0547	1211	1871	2527	3178	3825	4469	5108	5742	6373
1.6		7000	7623	8243	8858	9470	*0078	*0682	*1282	*1879	*2473
1.7	0.5	3063	3649	4232	4812	5389	5962	6531	7098	7661	8222
1.8		8779	9333	9884	*0432	*0977	*1519	*2058	*2594	*3127	*3658
1.9	0.6	4185	4710	5233	5752	6269	6783	7294	7803	8310	8813
2.0		9315	9813	*0310	*0804	*1295	*1784	*2271	*2755	*3237	*3716
2.1	0.7	4194	4669	5142	5612	6081	6547	7011	7473	7932	8390
2.2		8846	9299	9751	*0200	*0648	*1093	*1536	*1978	*2418	*2855
2.3	0.8	3291	3725	4157	4587	5015	5442	5866	6289	6710	7129
2.4		7547	7963	8377	8789	9200	9609	*0016	*0422	*0826	*1228
2.5	0.9	1629	2028	2426	2822	3216	3609	4001	4391	4779	5166
2.6		5551	5935	6317	6698	7078	7456	7833	8208	8582	8954
2.7		9325	9695	*0063	*0430	*0796	*1160	*1523	*1885	*2245	*2604
2.8	1.0	2962	3318	3674	4028	4380	4732	5082	5431	5779	6126
2.9		6471	6815	7158	7500	7841	8181	8519	8856	9192	9527
3.0		9861	*0194	*0526	*0856	*1186	*1514	*1841	*2168	*2493	*2817
3.1	1.1	3140	3462	3783	4103	4422	4740	5057	5373	5688	6002
3.2		6315	6627	6938	7248	7557	7865	8173	8479	8784	9089
3.3		9392	9695	9996	*0297	*0597	*0896	*1194	*1491	*1788	*2083
3.4	1.2	2378	2671	2964	3256	3547	3837	4127	4415	4703	4990
3.5		5276	5562	5846	6130	6413	6695	6976	7257	7536	7815
3.6		8093	8371	8647	8923	9198	9473	9746	*0019	*0291	*0563
3.7	1.3	0833	1103	1372	1641	1909	2176	2442	2708	2972	3237
3.8		3500	3763	4025	4286	4547	4807	5067	5325	5584	5841
3.9		6098	6354	6609	6864	7118	7372	7624	7877	8128	8379
4.0		8629	8879	9128	9377	9624	9872	*0118	*0364	*0610	*0854
4.1	1.4	1099	1342	1585	1828	2070	2311	2552	2792	3031	3270
4.2		3508	3746	3984	4220	4456	4692	4927	5161	5395	5629
4.3		5862	6094	6326	6557	6787	7018	7247	7476	7705	7933
4.4		8160	8387	8614	8840	9065	9290	9515	9739	9962	*0185
4.5	1.5	0408	0630	0851	1072	1293	1513	1732	1951	2170	2388
4.6		2606	2823	3039	3256	3471	3687	3902	4116	4330	4543
4.7		4756	4969	5181	5393	5604	5814	6025	6235	6444	6653
4.8		6862	7070	7277	7485	7691	7898	8104	8309	8515	8719
4.9		8924	9127	9331	9534	9737	9939	*0141	*0342	*0543	*0744
5.0	1.6	0944	1144	1343	1542	1741	1939	2137	2334	2531	2728
5.1		2924	3120	3315	3511	3705	3900	4094	4287	4481	4673
5.2		4866	5058	5250	5441	5632	5823	6013	6203	6393	6582
5.3		6771	6959	7147	7335	7523	7710	7896	8083	8269	8455
5.4		8640	8825	9010	9194	9378	9562	9745	9928	*0111	*0293
5.5	1.7	0475	0656	0838	1019	1199	1380	1560	1740	1919	2098
5.6		2277	2455	2633	2811	2988	3166	3342	3519	3695	3871
5.7		4047	4222	4397	4572	4746	4920	5094	5267	5440	5613
5.8		5786	5958	6130	6302	6473	6644	6815	6985	7156	7326
5.9		7495	7665	7834	8002	8171	8339	8507	8675	8842	9009

Tabular value —10

	0	1	2	3	4	5	6	7	8	9

TABLE OF

NATURAL LOGARITHMS—0.00 TO 10.09

	0	1	2	3	4	5	6	7	8	9
6.0	1.7 9176	9342	9509	9675	9840	*0006	*0171	*0336	*0500	*0665
6.1	1.8 0829	0993	1156	1319	1482	1645	1808	1970	2132	2294
6.2	2455	2616	2777	2938	3098	3258	3418	3578	3737	3896
6.3	4055	4214	4372	4530	4688	4845	5003	5160	5317	5473
6.4	5630	5786	5942	6097	6253	6408	6563	6718	6872	7026
6.5	7180	7334	7487	7641	7794	7947	8099	8251	8403	8555
6.6	8707	8858	9010	9160	9311	9462	9612	9762	9912	*0061
6.7	1.9 0211	0360	0509	0658	0806	0954	1102	1250	1398	1545
6.8	1692	1839	1986	2132	2279	2425	2571	2716	2862	3007
6.9	3152	3297	3442	3586	3730	3874	4018	4162	4305	4448
7.0	4591	4734	4876	5019	5161	5303	5445	5586	5727	5869
7.1	6009	6150	6291	6431	6571	6711	6851	6991	7130	7269
7.2	7408	7547	7685	7824	7962	8100	8238	8376	8513	8650
7.3	8787	8924	9061	9198	9334	9470	9606	9742	9877	*0013
7.4	2.0 0148	0283	0418	0553	0687	0821	0956	1089	1223	1357
7.5	1490	1624	1757	1890	2022	2155	2287	2419	2551	2683
7.6	2815	2946	3078	3209	3340	3471	3601	3732	3862	3992
7.7	4122	4252	4381	4511	4640	4769	4898	5027	5156	5284
7.8	5412	5540	5668	5796	5924	6051	6179	6306	6433	6560
7.9	6686	6813	6939	7065	7191	7317	7443	7568	7694	7819
8.0	7944	8069	8194	8318	8443	8567	8691	8815	8939	9063
8.1	9186	9310	9433	9556	9679	9802	9924	*0047	*0169	*0291
8.2	2.1 0413	0535	0657	0779	0900	1021	1142	1263	1384	1505
8.3	1626	1746	1866	1986	2106	2226	2346	2465	2585	2704
8.4	2823	2942	3061	3180	3298	3417	3535	3653	3771	3889
8.5	4007	4124	4242	4359	4476	4593	4710	4827	4943	5060
8.6	5176	5292	5409	5524	5640	5756	5871	5987	6102	6217
8.7	6332	6447	6562	6677	6791	6905	7020	7134	7248	7361
8.8	7475	7589	7702	7816	7929	8042	8155	8267	8380	8493
8.9	8605	8717	8830	8942	9054	9165	9277	9389	9500	9611
9.0	9722	9834	9944	*0055	*0166	0276	*0387	*0497	*0607	*0717
9.1	2.2 0827	0937	1047	1157	1266	1375	1485	1594	1703	1812
9.2	1920	2029	2138	2246	2354	2462	2570	2678	2786	2894
9.3	3001	3109	3216	3324	3431	3538	3645	3751	3858	3965
9.4	4071	4177	4284	4390	4496	4601	4707	4813	4918	5024
9.5	* 5129	5234	5339	5444	5549	5654	5759	5863	5968	6072
9.6	6176	6280	6384	6488	6592	6696	6799	6903	7006	7109
9.7	7213	7316	7419	7521	7624	7727	7829	7932	8034	8136
9.8	8238	8340	8442	8544	8646	8747	8849	8950	9051	9152
9.9	9253	9354	9455	9556	9657	9757	9858	9958	*0058	*0158
10.0	2.3 0259	0358	0458	0558	0658	0757	0857	0956	1055	1154
	0	1	2	3	4	5	6	7	8	9

NATURAL LOGARITHMS—10 TO 99

	0	1	2	3	4	5	6	7	8	9
1	2.30259	39790	48491	56495	63906	70805	77259	83321	89037	94444
2	99573	*04452	*09104	*13549	*17805	*21888	*25810	*29584	*33220	*36730
3	3.40120	43399	46574	49651	52636	55535	58352	61092	63759	66356
4	68888	71357	73767	76120	78419	80666	82864	85015	87120	89182
5	91202	93183	95124	97029	98898	*00733	*02535	*04305	*06044	*07754
6	4.09434	11087	12713	14313	15888	17439	18965	20469	21951	23411
7	24850	26268	27667	29046	30407	31749	33073	34381	35671	36945
8	38203	39445	40672	41884	43082	44265	45435	46591	47734	48864
9	49981	51086	52179	53260	54329	55388	56435	57471	58497	59512

NATURAL LOGARITHMS—100 TO 499

	0	1	2	3	4	5	6	7	8	9
10	4.6 0517	1512	2497	3473	4439	5396	6344	7283	8213	9135
11	4.7 0048	0953	1850	2739	3620	4493	5359	6217	7068	7912
12	8749	9579	*0402	*1218	*2028	*2831	*3628	*4419	*5203	*5981
13	4.8 6753	7520	8280	9035	9784	*0527	*1265	*1998	*2725	*3447
14	4.9 4164	4876	5583	6284	6981	7673	8361	9043	9721	*0395
15	5.0 1064	1728	2388	3044	3695	4343	4986	5625	6260	6890
16	7517	8140	8760	9375	9987	*0595	*1199	*1799	*2396	*2990
17	5.1 3580	4166	4749	5329	5906	6479	7048	7615	8178	8739
18	9296	9850	*0401	*0949	*1494	*2036	*2575	*3111	*3644	*4175
19	5.2 4702	5227	5750	6269	6786	7300	7811	8320	8827	9330
20	9832	*0330	*0827	*1321	*1812	*2301	*2788	*3272	*3754	*4233
21	5.3 4711	5186	5659	6129	6598	7064	7528	7990	8450	8907
22	9363	9816	*0268	*0717	*1165	*1610	*2053	*2495	*2935	*3372
23	5.4 3808	4242	4674	5104	5532	5959	6383	6806	7227	7646
24	8064	8480	8894	9306	9717	*0126	*0533	*0939	*1343	*1745
25	5.5 2146	2545	2943	3339	3733	4126	4518	4908	5296	5683
26	6068	6452	6834	7215	7595	7973	8350	8725	9099	9471
27	9842	*0212	*0580	*0947	*1313	*1677	*2040	*2402	*2762	*3121
28	5.6 3479	3835	4191	4545	4897	5249	5599	5948	6296	6643
29	6988	7332	7675	8017	8358	8698	9036	9373	9709	*0044
30	5.7 0378	0711	1043	1373	1703	2031	2359	2685	3010	3334
31	3657	3979	4300	4620	4939	5257	5574	5890	6205	6519
32	6832	7144	7455	7765	8074	8383	8690	8996	9301	9606
33	9909	*0212	*0513	*0814	*1114	*1413	*1711	*2008	*2305	*2600
34	5.8 2895	3188	3481	3773	4064	4354	4644	4932	5220	5507
35	5793	6079	6363	6647	6930	7212	7493	7774	8053	8332
36	8610	8888	9164	9440	9715	9990	*0263	*0536	*0808	*1080
37	5.9 1350	1620	1889	2158	2426	2693	2959	3225	3489	3754
38	4017	4280	4542	4803	5064	5324	5584	5842	6101	6358
39	6615	6871	7126	7381	7635	7889	8141	8394	8645	8896
40	9146	9396	9645	9894	*0141	*0389	*0635	*0881	*1127	*1372
41	6.0 1616	1859	2102	2345	2587	2828	3069	3309	3548	3787
42	4025	4263	4501	4737	4973	5209	5444	5678	5912	6146
43	6379	6611	6843	7074	7304	7535	7764	7993	8222	8450
44	8677	8904	9131	9357	9582	9807	*0032	*0256	*0479	*0702
45	6.1 0925	1147	1368	1589	1810	2030	2249	2468	2687	2905
46	3123	3340	3556	3773	3988	4204	4419	4633	4847	5060
47	5273	5486	5698	5910	6121	6331	6542	6752	6961	7170
48	7379	7587	7794	8002	8208	8415	8621	8826	9032	9236
49	9441	9644	9848	*0051	*0254	*0456	*0658	*0859	*1060	*1261
	0	1	2	3	4	5	6	7	8	9

Answers to Exercises

Answers to Exercises

Section 3, page 7

1. (a) $xy' - 2y + x = 0$.

(b) $xy' - y = 0$.

(c) $y'^2 + xy' = y$.

(d) $y'' = 0$.

(e) $x^2y'' - 2xy' + 2y = 0$.

(f) $xyy'' - 2xy'^2 + 2yy' = 0$.

(g) $y'' - 2y' + y = 0$.

(h) $y'' + a^2y = 0$.

(i) $y''' - 2y'' + 2y' = \frac{1}{2}$.

(j) $y''' - 2y'' + y' = 2x - 4$.

2. $x + yy' = 0$.

3. $2xy' - y = 0$.

4. $y'' = 0$.

5. $xy'^2 - yy' + 1 = 0$.

Section 4, page 10

3. $8y = 2x - x^2 - 1$.

4. $x^2 + y^2 = c^2$.

5. $(x + 2)^2 + (y - 3)^2 = c^2$.

Section 6, page 12

2. (a) $2xz_x + yz_y = 2z$.

(b) $xz_x + yz_y = 2z$.

(c) $2xz_x + yz_y = z$.

(d) $xz_x - xz_y = 2z$.

(e) $(2y - 1)z_x - z_y = 0$.

3. (a) $y'^2 - 2xy' + 2y = 0$.

(b) $xy'' = y' + y'^3$.

(c) $(xy' - y)(x + yy') = y'a^2$.

(e) $[y''(y - 2) + (1 + y'^2)]^2 = (1 + y'^2)^3$.

(f) $y' = -2$.

4. (a) $y + 7x = 20$.

(b) $2x + 2y = \pi$.

(c) $R = \frac{1}{4}(10)^{3/2}$.

(d) $2x + y = 0, R = -\frac{(5)^{3/2}}{2}$,

$3x + y = 1, R = -\frac{(10)^{3/2}}{4}$.

6. (a) $y = 1 + 2x + \frac{7x^2}{2!} + \frac{14x^3}{3!} + \cdots$.

(b) $y = -1 + 2x - \dfrac{3x^2}{2!} + \dfrac{4x^3}{3!} + \cdots$.

(c) $y = 3 - \dfrac{x^2}{2} - \dfrac{x^4}{8} + \cdots$.

8. (a) $y = 2 + \dfrac{2(x-1)^3}{3!} + \cdots$.

   (b) $y = 3 + (x-1) - \dfrac{5(x-1)^2}{2!} - \dfrac{6(x-1)^3}{3!} + \cdots$.

11. (a) Minimum points: $x = 0$, $y < \dfrac{2}{3}$.

      Maximum points: $x = 0$, $y > \dfrac{2}{3}$.

      Points of inflection: $3x^2 = 1$.

   (b) Minimum points: $y = -e^x$.

      Points of inflection: $y = -2e^x$.

Section 7, page 18

1. (a) $x - 2y = c$.

   (b) $y = cxe^{y + \frac{1}{x}}$.

   (c) $e^{-y}(1 + x^2)^{5/2} = cx^5(y - 1)$.

   (d) $(x^2 + 2)^8(y + 2)^3 = cy^2(y - 2)$.

   (e) $e^{\frac{x^3}{3} - x^2} = c(1 + y)^{-1}$.

   (f) $x\sqrt{y^2 - 1} + \sqrt{1 - x^2} = cy$.

   (g) $2s + \sin 2t = c$.

   (h) $2e^{x^3} + 3e^{y^2} = c$.

2. $x^2 + y^2 = c^2$.

3. $s = 1 - e^{-2}$.

Section 8, page 22

1. (a) Not exact.

   (b) $2xy + 3x^2 = c$.

   (c) Not exact.

   (d) $ax^3 + 3bx^2y + 3cxy^2 + gy^3 = k$.

   (e) $x^4 + 10x^2y^2 + 2y^4 = c$.

   (f) Not exact.

   (g) $7x^2 - 6xy + 4y^2 + 4x - 10y = c$.

   (h) $5x^2y^4 + x^2 - 2y^3 - 4y = c$.

   (i) $e^{-\frac{1}{xy}} + \dfrac{1}{xy} = c$.

   (j) $\tan x \tan y = c$.

   (k) $x^2y - \sin x - y = c$.

   (l) $x \tan y - x^3 = c$.

   (m) $ye^x = c$.

   (n) Not exact.

(o) $\sinh x \cosh y - \sinh x + \cosh y = c.$

(p) $x^2 \tan y + x \sin 2y - e^y = c.$

4. $b = -5.$

Section 9, page 26

1. (a) $\dfrac{1}{x^2};\ \tan^{-1}\dfrac{y}{x} + y = c.$

(b) $\dfrac{1}{x^2 + y^2};\ \log(x^2 + y^2) + \tan^{-1}\dfrac{x}{y} = c.$

(c) $\dfrac{1}{x^2 y^2};\ \dfrac{x}{y} - \dfrac{1}{x} = c.$

(d) $x;\ x^2 - xy^3 = c.$

(e) $\dfrac{1}{x(x^2 + y^2)};\ \log x + \tan^{-1}\left(\dfrac{x}{y}\right) = c.$

(f) $\dfrac{1}{x^2 y^2};\ xy^2 - 1 = cxy.$

(g) $\dfrac{1}{x^3 y^3};\ 2(x + y) + \dfrac{1}{2x^2 y^2} = c.$

(h) $\dfrac{1}{y^2};\ \dfrac{2x}{y} + \dfrac{\log y}{y} = c.$

(i) $\dfrac{1}{x^2 y^2};\ \dfrac{x}{y} + \dfrac{y}{x} + \log x + \log y = c.$

(j) $\dfrac{1}{xy};\ 2ax + 3\log x + 3a \log y = c.$

(k) $\dfrac{1}{x^4};\ \sin x - \dfrac{py^2}{x^2} = c$

(l) $\cosh x;\ y \sinh x + x \sinh y = c.$

(m) $3x^2 y^2 - 6xy^2 + 2y^3 = c.$

(n) $x + y - \sqrt{x^2 + y^2} = c.$

2. $N\mu_x - M\mu_y = \mu(M_y - N_x).$

4. $\log xy^3 = c + xy.$

5. $x^{-2}y^{-2} + 4x^{-1}y^{-1} + 2\log x = c.$

6. $\dfrac{6}{(xy)^{\frac{1}{2}}} - \dfrac{2}{(xy)^{\frac{3}{2}}} + \log \dfrac{x^3}{y^6} = c.$

7. $\log xy^4 + \cos xy = c.$

8. $1/Mx.$

9. $xy = c.$

12. $x^{-2}y^{-2} - x^{-1}y^{-1} + \log x = c.$

15. $x^3 = cy^2$.

16. $x^5 y^{-1} = c$.

18. $3x^{2\frac{1}{8}} y^{\frac{1}{4}} + 7x^{-\frac{3}{8}} y^{\frac{3}{4}} = c$.

19. $3x^{-1} y^2 + \log xy = c$.

20. $2x^{-3} y^3 - x^{-6} y^3 = c$.

21. $bx + a \log \dfrac{x^3}{y} = c$.

22. $x^{-1} y^{-1} (mx^r y^s + \mu x^\rho y^\sigma)^{-1}$.

23. $x^4 y^3 = c$.

24. $y^2 = cx^3$.

26. $e^{\int g(y)\,dy}$.

27. $10xy(y^3 - 5)^2 + 2y^5 - 25y^2 = c$.

28. $3x^4 + 8x^3 y + 6x^2 y^2 = c$.

29. $12x^3 y - 84x^2 y + 3x^4 + 192xy - 8x^3 - 144y = c$.

30. $x^2(2y^2 + 1) = c$.

31. $4x^3 y - x^4 = c$.

Section 10, page 29

1. $y^2 + 4xy - x^2 = c$.

2. $cx^{4\sqrt{3}} = \dfrac{x\sqrt{3} - 2y}{x\sqrt{3} + 2y}$.

3. $\log x + \dfrac{y}{2x} + \dfrac{1}{4} \sin \dfrac{2y}{x} + c = 0$.

4. $(x^2 - 2y^2)(x^2 + y^2)^2 = c$.

5. $e^{\frac{y}{x}} = \dfrac{cx}{1 - cx}$.

6. $cx^2 = y + \sqrt{x^2 + y^2}$.

11. (a) $x^3 + y^3 = cxy$.

    (b) $x^2 \sinh \dfrac{y}{x} = c$.

    (c) $\csc \dfrac{y}{x} - \operatorname{ctn} \dfrac{y}{x} + \log x = c$.

12. $\dfrac{1}{Mx}$.

14. (a) $x^2 + xy - y^2 = c.$

(b) $3x^3 - 3x^2y + 3xy^2 - y^3 = c.$

15. The constant equals 1.

19. (a) $e^{\frac{2y}{x}} - x^2 = c.$

(b) $4y^3 + (6xy^2 - 3x^3) \sin\left(\dfrac{2y}{x}\right) + 6x^2y \cos\left(\dfrac{2y}{x}\right) + 12x = cx^3.$

(c) $\dfrac{x}{y} \sqrt{\dfrac{3y - x}{x}} + 3 \tan^{-1} \sqrt{\dfrac{3y - x}{x}} = x + c.$

20. $x^2 + y^2 = cy.$

Section 11, page 32

1. $(x - 3y + 1)(x - 2y + 2) = c.$

2. $(4x - y + 2)^3(x + 2y - 5)^{-1} = c.$

3. $\log (3x^2 + 3y^2 + 3xy - 6x - 9y + 7) =$
$$c - \frac{6}{\sqrt{3}} \tan^{-1} \frac{3x + 3y - 5}{(x - y + 1)\sqrt{3}}.$$

5. $(3x + 3y - 2)(3x - y)^3(2y - 1)^{-3} = c.$

6. $4x - 8y + 5 = ce^{4x+8y}.$

7. $(2 - 15x + 5y)^4 = ce^{10y-5x}.$

8. $3x - 3y = 2 \log (3x + 6y - 1) + c.$

10. $7x - 28y + 2 \log (28x^2 - 28xy + 7y^2 - 16x + 8y + 2)$
$$+ \frac{9}{2\sqrt{2}} \log \frac{14x - 7y - 4 - \sqrt{2}}{14x - 7y - 4 + \sqrt{2}} = c.$$

11. $x^2 + 4xy^3 = c.$

12. $(x + y + 1)^2(7x - 2y + 4)(3x + 2)^{-1} = c.$

13. $14y + 7x + 6 \log (21y - 14x - 9) = c.$

Section 12, page 35

1. (a) $ye^{\sin x} = x + c.$

(b) $y = \dfrac{2x^3}{7} + \dfrac{c}{\sqrt{x}}.$

(c) $y = e^{\frac{-3x^2}{2}} \left[\int e^{\frac{3x^2}{2}} \sin 2x \, dx + c \right].$

(d) $y^2 e^{\frac{1}{x}} = e^x + c.$

(e) $\tan y = \dfrac{x^2 + 1}{3} + \dfrac{c}{\sqrt{x^2 + 1}}.$

(f) $(2y + 1)e^{x^2} = 2x + c.$

(g) $xy = 2x \log x + c_1 + c_2 x.$

2. (a) $x = e^{-\int P\,dy}\left[\int Q(y)e^{\int P\,dy}\,dy + c\right].$

(b) $x = e^y \int e^{-y} \log y\,dy + ce^y.$

(c) $\sin x + \dfrac{y^2}{4} + \dfrac{y}{8} + \dfrac{1}{32} = ce^{4y}.$

(d) $x = e^{(x+c)\cos y}.$

(e) $x = (y + c)e^{\cos^{-1} y}.$

3. (a) $4x \sin y + 2x \cos 2x = c + \sin 2x.$

(b) $256y^3 \tan x = 32y^4 + (32y^3 - 12y) \sin 4y +$
$(24y^2 - 3) \cos 4y + c.$

8. $v = \int \dfrac{Q(x)}{f(x)}\,dx \ \therefore\ y = f(x)\left[\int \dfrac{Q(x)}{f(x)}\,dx + c\right].$

Section 13, page 38

1. (a) $cy + (y + 3)e^{\frac{3x^2}{2}} = 0.$

(b) $2x = -2t^2x^2 \log x + t^2x^2 + ct^2.$

(c) $2y^2 - 2y + \log (2y + 1) + \dfrac{8}{x(2y + 1)} = c.$

(d) $y^2 = \dfrac{2x + c}{\sin^2 x}.$

(e) $\dfrac{1}{y} = \dfrac{2 + x}{2 - x}[c - \log (2 + x)].$

(f) $xy \log x + 1 = cxy.$

2. $2 \csc y + \sin x + \cos x = ce^{-x}.$

3. $\cot^2 u + 2e^{x^2} \int e^{-x^2}\,dx = ce^{x^2}.$

Section 14, page 41

1. $\cos \theta\,ds = \sqrt{a^2 \tan^2 \theta + b^2 \sec^2 \theta}\,d\theta.$

2. $y = \tan x + \dfrac{c}{\cos^2 xe^{\cos^2 x}\left(1 - c\displaystyle\int \sec^2 xe^{-\cos^2 x}\,dx\right)}.$

4. $y(1 - x) = c(y - x^2)$.

5. $\left(\dfrac{\log^2 x}{x} - \dfrac{\log x}{x^2} + \dfrac{2}{x} - 2x \log^2 x + 4x^2 \log x - 4x \right) \dfrac{dy}{dx} +$

$\left(2 - \dfrac{\log x}{x^2} + \dfrac{4}{x} - \dfrac{1}{x^2} - 2 \log x \right) y^2 +$

$\left(\dfrac{\log^2 x}{x^2} - \dfrac{2}{x^2} + 2 \log^2 x - 4x - 4 + \dfrac{1}{x^3} \right) y +$

$\left(-\dfrac{4 \log^2 x}{x} + 4 \log x + 4 + \dfrac{2 \log x}{x^2} - \dfrac{2}{x^2} \right) = 0$.

6. 1, 1, 1.

7. 3, b.

8. $y = \tan x + \dfrac{e^{-\int \left(\frac{2 \tan x}{\cos x - 1} + \csc x \right) dx}}{\displaystyle\int \dfrac{e^{-\int \left(\frac{2 \tan x}{\cos x - 1} + \csc x \right) dx}}{\cos x - 1} \, dx + c}$.

Section 15, page 44

1. $y = c(x - 2) - 4$.

2. $y^2 = c(2x + 1)$.

3. $(3 + \pi - 3\theta)\rho^2 = 3$.

4. $x^2 + y^2 = 10x$.

5. $\dfrac{x}{y - x} - \log(y - x) = c$.

6. $y^2 - x^2 = c$.

7. $N \, dx - M \, dy = 0$.

8. $x^2 + 2x - 2y + 2 \log(x - 1) - 2 \log(y - 1) = c$.

9. $(3x - 2y + 5)^3(4x + y + 1) = c$.

10. (a) $x^2 + 2y^2 = c^2$.
(b) $2x^2 + y^2 + 4x = c$.

11. $y = ce^{\frac{x}{2}} + c^{-1}e^{-\frac{x}{2}}$.

12. $x^2 - y^2 = c$.

13. $y^{1-e^2} = cx$.

14. $x^2 + y^2 = 2a^2 \log cx$.

15. $2cy = c^2x^2 - 1$.

16. $s = 2e^t - 1$.

17. $s = 10(t + 1) \log (t + 1) - 8t + 3$.

18. $s = 2k \sqrt{t} - \cos t + c$.

19. $\dfrac{1 + bv + b^2v^2}{(1 - bv)^2 e^{-2\sqrt{3}\,\tan^{-1}\frac{1+2bv}{\sqrt{3}}}} = ce^{6gbt}$.

20. $(mg - kv)e^{\frac{k}{m}(t-t_0)} = mg + kv_0$.

21. $q = q_0 e^{\frac{1}{RC}(t_0 - t)}$.

22. $i = i_0 e^{\frac{R}{L}(t_0 - t)}$.

23. $i = \dfrac{et}{L} + k$.

24. $q = CE + (q_0 - CE)e^{\frac{1}{RC}(t_0 - t)}$.

25. $i = \dfrac{1}{RC}(CE - q_0)e^{\frac{1}{RC}(t_0 - t)}$.

26. $Ri = v + (Ri_0 - v)e^{\frac{R}{L}(t_0 - t)}$.

28. 158 minutes.

29. $\dfrac{ds}{dt} = ks;\ s = ce^{kt};\ s = 6e^{-\frac{t \log 6}{2}}$.

31. $t = 15(7 + 2\sqrt{10})$ minutes.

32. $h_0 = \dfrac{49}{81}$ feet; $\dfrac{625}{1296}$ feet.

33. $t = c - 960\sqrt{h} - 1920 \log | \sqrt{h} - 2 |$; $h = 4$ feet.

34. (a) 11 minutes; (b) 8 minutes.

35. $t = \dfrac{4 \log 25}{\log 2}$ hours.

36. $s = 5(3^{\frac{3}{8}})$ pounds; $t = 8 + \dfrac{8 \log 5}{\log 3}$.

37. 16 hours.

38. 5 lbs. of 1st substance remain; 1.47 lbs. of 1st substance and 18.82 lbs. of 2nd.

39. $x = \dfrac{ak_1}{k_1 + k_2}[1 - ce^{(k_1 + k_2)t}]$.

41. $s = 9125 \, (e^{2/5} - 1)$ dollars = \$4487.90.

42. $n = n_0 e^{\frac{t \log 2}{50}}$.

43. $n = 20,000 + \dfrac{50,000}{\log 2} = 92,134$.

44. $\theta = \dfrac{kr^3}{8} + c_1 r + \dfrac{c_2}{r}$.

45. 40.2 pounds.

46. 30.7 pounds.

47. $(.044)\%$.

Section 16, page 50

1. $xy = ce^{\frac{x}{y} - y^2}$.

2. $r \sin \theta = c$.

3. $x = ce^{\arctan \frac{y}{x}}$.

4. $13x^{-25}y^{-15} - 5x^{-26}y^{-13} = c$.

5. $(x^2 - 3y^2)^2 = cx$.

6. $\log y - \sinh^{-1}\left(\dfrac{x}{y}\right) = c$.

7. $30y + 12x + 5 = cx^6$.

8. $(u^2 - 1)e^{v^2} = c$.

9. $x^{-1}z^{-1} = 2x^{-1}(\log x + 1) + c$.

10. $3v^4 - 36uv + 4u^3 = c$.

11. $y^2 = x \log x + cx$.

12. $\cos x \cos y = c$.

13. $y = \dfrac{x^2}{2} + c_1 \log \tan \dfrac{x}{2} + c_2$.

14. $x^{1/6}y^{7/18}(x - 7) = c$.

15. $y = -x + c_1 e^x + c_2$.

16. $x - \sin y = c \cos y$.

17. $\dfrac{1}{r^3} + \sin \theta + 2 \sin \theta \cos^2 \theta = c \cos^3 \theta$.

18. $y = c_1 x^2 + c_2$.

19. $u + ve^{\frac{u}{v}} = c.$

20. $\log (x^2 + y^2 + 6x + 4y + 13) + \text{arc tan } \dfrac{x + 2y + 7}{2x - y + 4} = c.$

21. $5y + 15x + 11 \log (10y + 5x - 12) = c.$

22. $x = cye^{\frac{1}{2xy}}.$

23. $s = cte^{\frac{2}{\sqrt{st}}}.$

24. $\log x + 3e^{xy} - 2e^{-xy} = c.$

25. $4x^3y + xy^2 = c.$

26. $\pi x + x^2y - 6xy^2 + 12y^3 = c.$

27. $y^2e^{2x} + 4x^2e^{2x} = c.$

28. $\csc \theta = ce^{3/10 \sec^2 \phi}.$

29. $x^{-3/2}y^{-3} + 3x^{1/2}y^{-5} = c.$

30. $r \sqrt{\dfrac{1 + \sin \theta}{1 - \sin \theta}} + \log \dfrac{1 + \sin \theta}{1 - \sin \theta} - 2 \log \cos \theta - \sin \theta = c.$

31. $2ue^v + e^v - 4u = c.$

32. $e^{\frac{y^2}{2}}(1 - 4x + 2xy^2) = c.$

33. $\log y = \dfrac{x^2}{8y^2} + c.$

34. $x \sin \dfrac{y}{x} = c.$

35. $(4x - y - 6)^5(-x + 4y - 9)^5 = c(5x - 5y + 3).$

36. $3 \log x - 4 \log (1 + x^2y^2) - 2 \log y = c + \text{arc tan } xy.$

37. $3x^2ye^{2x} - y^3e^{2x} + e^{3x} = c.$

38. $y \sqrt{1 + x^2} + 2 \log \dfrac{1 + \sqrt{1 + x^2}}{x} = c.$

39. $y^2 = 4 + ce^{-x^2}.$

40. $ax^3 + 3bx^2y + 3cxy^2 + gy^3 = k.$

41. $M = ax^3 + 3bx^2y + 3cxy^2 + gy^3; N = bx^3 + 3cx^2y + 3gxy^2 + hy^3.$

42. $x^4 + 3x^3y + 3x^2y^2 - xy^3 + 5y^4 = c.$

43. $xy = c.$

44. $t = 10(\sqrt{7} - 1)(\sqrt{10} + 3)$ minutes.

45. $(m + n - 1)x^{1-m} = k(m - 1)y^n + cy^{1-m}.$

46. $i = i_0 + \dfrac{V}{L\omega} (\cos \omega t_0 - \cos \omega t).$

47. $q = \dfrac{V}{1 + R^2 c^2 \omega^2} \{c \sin \omega t - Rc^2 \omega \cos \omega t\} + Ke^{-\frac{t}{Rc}}.$

48. $i = \dfrac{V\omega}{1 + R^2 c^2 \omega^2} \{c \cos \omega t + Rc^2 \omega \sin \omega t\} - \dfrac{K}{Rc} e^{-\frac{t}{Rc}}.$

49. $i = \dfrac{V}{R} + \left(i_0 - \dfrac{V}{R}\right) e^{\frac{R}{L}(t_0 - t)}.$

50. $i = \dfrac{V}{R^2 + L^2 \omega^2} (R \sin \omega t - L\omega \cos \omega t) + ke^{-\frac{Rt}{L}}.$

51. Paraboloid of revolution.

53. $M_x + N_y \equiv 0.$

55. (a) $4x^2 - 4y^2.$
  (b) $0.$

63. $y(1 + c \cos x) = c \sin x + \sin x \cos x.$

64. 202.7 cu. ft.

Section 18, page 56

1. $y = ce^{3x}; y = x^2 + c.$

2. $cy^2 + 6xy^2 + 1 = 0; x(y + c) = 2.$

3. $2y = \cos^{-1}\dfrac{2}{x} + c; 2y = -\cos^{-1}\dfrac{2}{x} + c.$

4. $\log x + \displaystyle\int_c^{\frac{y}{x}} \dfrac{v \, dv}{v^2 + 1 \pm \sqrt{1 + 9v^2}} = 0.$

5. $r \sec \theta = c.$

6. $3y - x^3 = c; 2 + x^2 y = cy; 1 + 3xy^3 = cy^3.$

7. $y^2 - x^2 = c; y = c; x^4 = c(x^2 - y^2).$

8. $(y - ce^{2x})(2y - x^2 - c) = 0.$

9. $(2y + \cos 2x - c)(\sin 2y - ce^{-2x}) = 0.$

Section 19, page 57

1. $x = 2 \log p + 6p + c$, $y = 2p + 3p^2$.

2. $3y = 3xc - c^2$, $4y = 3x^2$.

3. $(5x - y)^2 = c(x^2 - 1)$.

4. $4y^2 = c(4x - 5) - c^2$; $16y^2 = (4x - 5)^2$.

5. $y = c(n^2 + p^2)^{-\frac{1}{2}}$, $x = c(n^2 + p^2 + p\sqrt{n^2 + p^2})^{-1}$.

6. $4(9 + cx^2) = c^2 y^2$.

7. $x = \dfrac{p}{2\sqrt{1 + p^2}} \log(p + \sqrt{1 + p^2}) + \dfrac{cp}{\sqrt{1 + p^2}}$,

$y = \dfrac{p}{2} - \dfrac{1}{2\sqrt{1 + p^2}} \log(p + \sqrt{1 + p^2}) - \dfrac{c}{\sqrt{1 + p^2}}$.

8. $x = c + \displaystyle\int \dfrac{3dp}{(5 - p)\sqrt{1 - p^2}}$, $y = 3\cos^{-1} p + 5x$.

9. $y = \dfrac{2(c - 2p)}{p} + 2\log p - \log 4$, $x = \dfrac{c - 2p}{p^2}$.

10. $y^2 = c(2x + 1)$.

11. $xy = \left(\dfrac{x^2}{3} + c\sqrt{x}\right)^2$; $y = 0$.

Section 20, page 58

1. $y^2 + cx - c^2 = 0$.

2. $x = 2p - p^2$, $y = p^2 - \dfrac{2p^3}{3} + c$.

3. $256c^3 y = 64c^2 x^2 - 16cx + 1$; $y = \dfrac{8x^3}{27}$.

4. $y = c^{\frac{3}{2}} p^{\frac{3}{2}}$, $x = 3c^{\frac{3}{2}} p^{\frac{1}{2}} + \dfrac{1}{3c}$; $64y = x^6$.

5. $y = \dfrac{p^2}{2} + p\cos p - \sin p + c$, $x = p + \cos p$.

6. $\log y - \dfrac{p}{y} - \dfrac{p^2}{2y^2} = c$, $x = \dfrac{p}{y} + \log p - \log y$.

7. $\tan^2 y = c^2 + 2cx$.

8. $\begin{cases} x = -2p - 2\log(p - 1) + c, \\ y = -p^2 - 2p - 2\log(p - 1) + c. \end{cases}$

9. $\begin{cases} x = \dfrac{p(c + \sin^{-1} p)}{\sqrt{1 - p^2}}, \\[3mm] y = -p + \dfrac{c + \sin^{-1} p}{\sqrt{1 - p^2}}. \end{cases}$

Section 24, page 64

1. (a) $y = cx + \dfrac{a^2}{c};\ y^2 = 4a^2 x.$

   (b) $y = cx + 2c^2 - c;\ (x - 1)^2 + 8y = 0.$

   (c) $y = cx + \sqrt{c^3 - c^2 + c - 1};\ \begin{cases} x = \dfrac{-1 + 2p - 3p^2}{2(p^3 - p^2 + p - 1)^{1/2}}, \\[3mm] y = \dfrac{-p^3 + p - 2}{2(p^3 - p^2 + p - 1)^{1/2}}. \end{cases}$

   (d) $y = (x - 5)c + c^2;\ (x - 5)^2 + 4y = 0.$

   (e) $y = cx + \log c;\ xe^{y+1} + 1 = 0.$

   (f) $(y - cx)(3c - 1) = 5c^2;\ \begin{cases} y = \dfrac{5p^2}{(3p - 1)^2}, \\[3mm] x = \dfrac{-5p(3p - 2)}{(3p - 1)^2}. \end{cases}$

   (g) $e^{y-cx} = c^2;\ 4 - x^2 e^{y+2} = 0.$

   (h) $\log y = cx + c^2;\ y = e^{\frac{-x^2}{4}}.$

2. $y^2 = 4 + 4x^2.$

3. $4y^3 - 27x^2 = 0.$

4. $27y - 2x^3 = 0.$

5. $4y = x^2.$

6. $x^2 + y^2 = 25.$

7. $(x - 5 \cos c)^2 + (y - 5 \sin c)^2 = 1;\ (p^2 + 1)(x^4 + 2x^2 y^2 + y^4 + 576) + 8xyp - 4(13x^2 p^2 + 12y^2 p^2 + 12x^2 + 13y^2) = 0;$
   $x^2 + y^2 = 26 \pm 10.$

9. $3y = e^{\frac{x^2}{4}}.$

11. $y = 0;\ y = \dfrac{2x^3}{27}.$

12. Particular.

13. Singular.

14. $3y^2 = x^2.$

17. $y^2 = cx.$

18. $y = c(1 + p^2)^{-\frac{1}{2}}(p + \sqrt{1 + p^2})^{-1/a}(p + a\sqrt{1 + p^2});$

$x = c(1 + p^2)^{-\frac{1}{2}}(p + \sqrt{1 + p^2})^{-1/a}.$

19. $x^5y^2 + cy + cyx^6 + c^2x = 0.$

20. $x^2 + y^2 - 2xy + 2c(x + y) + c^2 = 0.$

21. $y^{1-\frac{n}{i}} - x^{1-\frac{n}{i}} = c.$

26. (a) $(c - 4y)^2 - 48x = 0.$

(b) $y^2 - 2cy - cx^2y + c^2(x^2 + 1) = 0.$

(c) $x = \dfrac{2y - 4p}{p^2}; \; y = px + \dfrac{4p \log p - cp}{p - 2}.$

(d) $4y = 2p(5p + \sqrt{1 + 4p^2}) - \log(2p + \sqrt{1 + 4p^2}) + c;$
$x = 5p + \sqrt{1 + 4p^2}.$

(e) $\sqrt{x - x^2} - \tan^{-1}\sqrt{\dfrac{1 - x}{x}} = \pm y + c.$

(f) $y = cxe^{1/x}.$

28. (a) $x^2y^2 - y^2 + 2cxy + c^2 = 0.$

(b) $(x^2 - 9)c^2 - 2xyc + y^2 - 9 = 0; \; x^2 + y^2 = 9.$

(c) $e^{2y-2c} - 2xe^{y-c} + 1 = 0.$

(d) $y + \displaystyle\int \sqrt[3]{\dfrac{x \pm a}{x}}\, dx = c.$

(e) $x = c + \log\dfrac{p + \sqrt{p^2 + 9}}{p^2}; \; y = -2p + \sqrt{p^2 + 9}.$

(f) $4y = 2cx^2 + 3c^2; \; 12y + x^4 = 0.$

(g) $y = cx + (c - r)(c - s); \; 4y + (r + s - x)^2 = 4rs.$

(h) $y = cx + \sqrt{a^2 + c^2}; \; y = |a|\sqrt{1 - x^2}.$

(i) $x^2c^2 - 2cxy + c + y^2 = 0; \; 4xy = 1.$

(j) $(y - cx)(3c - 5) - 15c = 0; \; x = \dfrac{75}{(3p - 5)^2}, y = \dfrac{45p^2}{(3p - 5)^2}.$

(k) $4y^3 + 4cy^{3/2} + c^2 = 9e^{2x}.$

(l) $x = c + p + \dfrac{3p^2}{4}; \; y = \dfrac{p^2 + p^3}{2}.$

(m) $x = \dfrac{c}{a^2 + p^2 + p\sqrt{a^2 + p^2}}; \; y = \dfrac{c}{\sqrt{a^2 + p^2}}.$

(n) $\cos(x + c) = \log y; \; \log^2 y = 1.$

(o) $x = \dfrac{1}{a} \pm \dfrac{\sqrt{1 + p^2}}{ap}; \; y = c \pm \dfrac{1}{a}\log\dfrac{1 + \sqrt{1 + p^2}}{p}.$

(p) $y = cx - c^2$; $4y - x^2 = 0$.

(q) $y = \dfrac{9}{4c} + cx^2$; $y^2 = 9x^2$.

(r) $s = 5p^5 + p^2$; $t = \dfrac{25p^4}{4} + 2p + c$.

(s) $\sin (y - cx) = \pm \dfrac{1}{\sqrt{1 + c^2}}$; $x = \dfrac{1}{1 + p^2}$, $y = \dfrac{p}{1 + p^2}$
$+ \text{arc cot } p$.

(t) $(r - ce^\theta)(r + \cos \theta + c) \left(e^r - c \cot \dfrac{\theta}{2} \right) = 0$.

(u) $\log y = ce^x + c^2$; $4 \log y = -e^{2x}$.

29. Particular.

32. $y^2 + 2cy + c^2 - \dfrac{x^4}{4} = 0$.

33. $y^2 - 2cxy + c^2x^2 + ck = 0$; $xy = \dfrac{k}{4}$.

34. $(x - a)^2 + (y - b)^2 = c^2$.

35. $(y - cx)^2 = \dfrac{c^2k^2}{1 + c^2}$; $x^{2/3} + y^{2/3} = k^{2/3}$.

36. $x = \dfrac{a \cos 7\theta + 7a \cos \theta}{2}$, $y = \dfrac{-a \sin 7\theta + 7a \sin \theta}{2}$.

37. $y = px + \dfrac{4}{27p^2}$.

38. $y = cx - 2c^2$; $8y = x^2$.

39. $y = cx + \dfrac{3c}{c - 1}$; $x = \dfrac{3}{(p - 1)^2}$, $y = \dfrac{3p^2}{(p - 1)^2}$.

Section 28, page 80

2. (a) $y = c_1e^{3x} + c_2e^{-x}$.

(b) $y = c_1 + c_2e^x + c_3e^{-2x/3}$.

(c) $y = c_1 + c_2e^{x/2} + c_3e^{2x}$.

(d) $y = c_1e^{2x} + c_2e^{-4x}$.

(e) $y = c_1e^x + c_2e^{-x} + c_3e^{x\sqrt{3}} + c_4e^{-x\sqrt{3}}$.

(f) $y = c_1e^{ax} + c_2e^{-ax} + c_3e^{bx}$.

(g) $y = c_1 + c_2e^x + c_3e^{2x} + c_4e^{-x}$.

Section 29, page 83

1. (a) $y = c_1x + \dfrac{c_2}{x} + \dfrac{4}{3} x^2$.

(b) $y = x^2 e^x - x e^x \log x - e^x + c_1 x e^x \int \dfrac{dx}{x^2 e^x} + c_2 x e^x.$

(c) $y = c_1 + c_2 \sin x + \sin x \int \operatorname{ctn} x \csc x \log \tan \dfrac{1}{2} x \, dx.$

2. (a) $y = 2 \int \left\{ \int \left[e^x(x+2) \int x^{-1} e^{-x} \, dx \right] dx \right\} dx + c_1 x e^x$
$$+ c_2 x + c_3.$$

(b) $y = \dfrac{c_1 \log x}{x} + \dfrac{c_2}{x} + c_3 + \dfrac{x \log x}{4} - \dfrac{x}{2}.$

(c) $y = c_1 + c_2 x^2 + c_3 x^2 \log x - \dfrac{1}{36x}.$

Section 30, page 88

1. (a) $y = c_1 + c_2 x + c_3 e^{-2x}.$

(b) $y = e^{2x}(c_1 \cos 3x + c_2 \sin 3x).$

(c) $y = e^{-3x}(c_1 \cos x + c_2 \sin x) + c_3.$

(d) $y = c_1 + c_2 x + c_3 e^x + c_4 x e^x.$

(e) $y = c_1 + c_2 x + c_3 x^2 + c_4 e^x + c_5 e^{2x}.$

(f) $y = c_1 e^x + c_2 x e^x + c_3 e^{-2x} + c_4 x e^{-2x}.$

(g) $y = c_1 e^{-x} + c_2 x e^{-x} + c_3 x^2 e^{-x} + c_4 e^{2x}.$

(h) $y = c_1 + c_2 x + e^x(c_3 \cos 2x + c_4 \sin 2x).$

(i) $y = c_1 + c_2 e^x + c_3 x e^x.$

(j) $y = c_1 + c_2 x + (c_3 + c_4 x) \cos 2x + (c_5 + c_6 x) \sin 2x.$

(k) $y = c_1 + c_2 e^x + e^{2x}\left(c_3 \cos \dfrac{x}{2} + c_4 \sin \dfrac{x}{2} \right).$

2. $y = e^x(c_1 + c_2 x) + e^{4x}(c_3 \cos x + c_4 \sin x).$

Section 31, page 91

2. $y = c_1 e^x + c_2 e^{-2x} - x^2 + \dfrac{x}{2} - \dfrac{3}{4}.$

3. $y = c_1 e^x + c_2 e^{2x} + c_3 e^{-2x} + \dfrac{x^4}{4} + x^3 + \dfrac{15x^2}{4} + \dfrac{27x}{4} + \dfrac{67}{8}.$

4. $y = c_1 e^x + c_2 e^{3x} + c_3 e^{-3x} + \dfrac{2x}{9} + \dfrac{5}{9}.$

5. $y = (c_1 + c_2 x)e^x + c_3 e^{-3x} + \dfrac{x^3}{3} + \dfrac{5x^2}{3} + \dfrac{41x}{9} + \dfrac{166}{27}.$

7. $y = c_1 + c_2 e^{2x} + c_3 e^x + \dfrac{x^3}{3} + \dfrac{3x^2}{4} + \dfrac{7x}{4}.$

8. $y = c_1 + c_2 x + c_3 e^x - \dfrac{x^3}{3} - \dfrac{5x^2}{2}$.

9. $y = c_1 + c_2 e^{-x} + c_3 e^{3x} - \dfrac{x^3}{9} + \dfrac{2x^2}{9} + \dfrac{31x}{27}$.

11. $y = c_1 + c_2 e^{3x} + c_3 e^{-x} + \dfrac{3 \sin x}{10} + \dfrac{3 \cos x}{5}$.

12. $y = c_1 e^x + c_2 e^{-x} + c_3 \cos x + c_4 \sin x + \dfrac{\cos 2x - 2 \sin 2x}{15}$.

13. $y = \dfrac{x \sin x}{6} + \dfrac{\sin 3x}{40}$.

15. $y = - \dfrac{x \cos 3x}{9}$.

16. $y = \dfrac{x^2 \sin x}{8}$.

17. $y = \dfrac{x \sin 2x}{16}$.

18. $y = \dfrac{x \sin x}{6} + \dfrac{\sin 3x}{40}$.

20. $y = e^{2x}$.

21. $y = 2e^{-x}$.

22. $y = \dfrac{x^2}{6} + \dfrac{4x}{9} - xe^x$.

24. $y = \dfrac{x^2 e^{3x}}{3}$.

25. (a) $y = - \dfrac{x^2 e^x}{2}$.   (b) $y = - \dfrac{1}{4} e^x + \dfrac{1}{10} xe^{2x} - \dfrac{2}{15} xe^{-3x}$.

26. $y = - \frac{1}{4}e^x + \frac{1}{10}xe^{2x} - \frac{2}{15}xe^{-2x}$.

29. $y = - \dfrac{e^x \sin x}{3}$.

30. $y = - \dfrac{e^{3x}}{27} (3x + 7)$.

32. $y = \dfrac{1}{5} (2e^{3x} - \sin x)$.

33. $y = - \dfrac{x^3}{6} - \dfrac{x^2}{4} + \dfrac{\sin x - 2 \cos x}{5}$.

34. $y = e^x\left(\dfrac{x^3}{6} - \dfrac{3x^2}{4} + \dfrac{7x}{4} + \dfrac{3\sin x + \cos x}{10}\right).$

35. $y = \dfrac{xe^{ax}}{a-b} + \dfrac{2xe^{bx}}{b-a} + \dfrac{(ab-1)\cos x - (a+b)\sin x}{a^2b^2 + a^2 + b^2 + 1}.$

Section 33, page 101

1. (a) $y = c_1 + c_2e^{2x} - \dfrac{2\sin x + \cos x}{5}.$

(b) $y = c_1 + c_2e^x + c_3e^{-3x} - \dfrac{x^2}{6} - \dfrac{8x}{9}.$

(c) $y = c_1e^{ax} + c_2e^{-bx} + \dfrac{2e^{3x}}{(3-a)(3+b)}.$

(d) $y = c_1e^x + c_2e^{-x} + c_3e^{2x} + \dfrac{xe^x}{4}(1+x).$

(e) $y = c_1 + (c_2 + c_3x)e^{2x} + e^x - \dfrac{\sin 2x}{16}.$

5. (a) $y = c_1 + c_2e^{-4x} + c_3e^{2x} - \dfrac{x}{16} - \dfrac{3\sin 2x + \cos 2x}{160}.$

(b) $y = c_1 + c_2x + c_3e^{-3x} + c_4xe^{-3x} + \dfrac{12\cos 2x - 5\sin 2x}{676}$
$$+ \dfrac{5e^x - 2xe^x}{32}.$$

(c) $y = c_1 + c_2e^{-4x} + c_3e^{ax} - \dfrac{x^3}{4a} + \dfrac{(3a-14)x^2}{16a^2}$
$$+ \dfrac{(14a - 3a^2 - 56)x}{32a^3}.$$

(d) $y = c_1 + c_2x + c_3e^{-3x} + \dfrac{x^4}{12} - \dfrac{x^3}{9} - \dfrac{x^2}{18}.$

Section 34, page 105

1. (a) $y = c_1\cos ax + c_2\sin ax + \dfrac{\sin ax}{a^2}\log(\csc ax - \cot ax).$

(b) $y = c_1 + c_2e^{ax} + c_3e^{-ax}$
$$+ e^{2ax}\left[\dfrac{1}{12a^3} + \dfrac{(4 - 11a^2)\sin 2x + 3a(4 - a^2)\cos 2x}{4(a^2+1)(a^2+4)(9a^2+4)}\right].$$

(c) $y = c_1e^{3x} + c_2e^{-4x} - \dfrac{x}{12} + \dfrac{13\sin x}{170} + \dfrac{\cos x}{170} - \dfrac{1}{144}.$

(d) $y = c_1 + c_2\sin x + c_3\cos x + \dfrac{e^x}{2} + x^2 - x.$

2. $y = \dfrac{x^5 \log x}{12} - \dfrac{7x^5}{144}$.

3. $y = \dfrac{\log^3 x}{4x} + \dfrac{3 \log^2 x}{4x} + \dfrac{9 \log x}{8x} + \dfrac{3}{4x}$.

Section 35, page 107

1. (a) $y = c_1 \sin x + c_2 \cos x - \dfrac{\cos^5 x}{3} + \dfrac{5 \cos^3 x}{12} + \dfrac{x \sin x}{4}$.

(b) $y = c_1 + e^x(c_2 \cos x + c_3 \sin x) + \dfrac{x}{4} - \dfrac{\sin 2x}{40} + \dfrac{\cos 2x}{20}$.

(c) $y = (c_1 + c_2 x) \sin 2x + (c_3 + c_4 x) \cos 2x + \dfrac{e^x}{25}$.

Section 37, page 109

1. (a) $y = c_1 x^2 + c_2 x^3$.

(b) $y = c_1 x^2 + c_2 x^4 - \dfrac{x^2 \cosh x}{2} + x^4 \displaystyle\int \dfrac{\sinh x}{2x^2}\, dx$.

(c) $y = c_1 + c_2 x^3 + \dfrac{c_3}{x^2}$.

(d) $y = c_1 + c_2 x^a + \dfrac{c_3}{x^a}$.

(e) $y = c_1 + c_2 x + c_3 x^4 - \dfrac{x^3}{3} + \dfrac{x \log x}{3}$.

3. (a) $y = c_1(2 - x)^5 + c_2(2 - x)^{-3}$.

(b) $y = c_1(1 + 2x)^3 + c_2(1 + 2x)^{-1} - \dfrac{3x}{16} - \dfrac{5}{96}$.

4. $y = c_1 x^5 + \dfrac{c_2}{x}$.

5. (a) $y = \dfrac{c_1}{x} + \dfrac{c_2 \log x}{x}$.

(b) $y = c_1 + c_2 \log x + c_3 (\log x)^2$.

(c) $y = c_1 + c_2 \log x + c_3 x^3$.

6. (a) $y = x(c_1 \cos 3 \log x + c_2 \sin 3 \log x)$.

(b) $y = c_1 \cos 2 \log x + c_2 \sin 2 \log x$.

(c) $y = c_1(1 - 3x) + \dfrac{c_2}{1 - 3x} - \dfrac{\log^2 (1 - 3x)}{9} - \dfrac{2}{9}$.

(d) $y = c_1 + c_2 \sin \log (x + 3) + c_3 \cos \log (x + 3)$.

Section 38, page 112

2. (a) $(x + \sin x)y = c_1 x^2 + c_2 x + c_3 - \cos x.$

(b) $(e^x + 2x)y = \dfrac{1}{24x} + c_1 x^3 + c_2 x^2 + c_3 x + c_4.$

(c) $y \tan \dfrac{x}{2} = \displaystyle\int \tan \dfrac{x}{2} (c_1 x \csc x + c_2 \csc x - \cot x)dx + c_3.$

(d) $y(x^2 + 1)^2 = x^5 \left[\dfrac{\log x}{5} - \dfrac{1}{25} \right] + 2x^3 \left[\dfrac{\log x}{3} - \dfrac{1}{9} \right] + x \log x$
$\qquad - x + c_1(x^4 + 2x^2) + c_2(x^3 + 3x) + c_3.$

(e) $y = c_1 + c_2(x + 2)^{\frac{3+\sqrt{5}}{2}} + c_3(x + 2)^{\frac{3-\sqrt{5}}{2}} + x - \log x.$

4. (f) $x\mu'' + \mu' - x^2\mu = 0.$

Section 39, page 118

1. (a) $\begin{cases} x = e^t + \dfrac{5 \sin t}{17} - \dfrac{3 \cos t}{17} - 3c_1 e^{4t} + c_2, \\[2mm] y = -\dfrac{2}{3} e^t - \dfrac{\sin t}{17} + \dfrac{4 \cos t}{17} + 4c_1 e^{4t}. \end{cases}$

(b) $\begin{cases} x = 2c_1 e^{\frac{(-5+\sqrt{5})t}{2}} + 2c_2 e^{\frac{(-5-\sqrt{5})t}{2}}, \\[2mm] y = (-1 + \sqrt{5})c_1 e^{\frac{(-5+\sqrt{5})t}{2}} - (1 + \sqrt{5})c_2 e^{\frac{(-5-\sqrt{5})t}{2}}. \end{cases}$

(c) $\begin{cases} x = c_1 \cos 2t - c_2 \sin 2t - \dfrac{5}{4}, \\[2mm] y = c_1 \sin 2t + c_2 \cos 2t + \dfrac{3t}{2}. \end{cases}$

(d) $\begin{cases} x = 3c_1 t - c_2 e^{4t} + c_3, \\ y = c_1 + 4c_2 e^{4t}. \end{cases}$

(e) $\begin{cases} x = c_1 + c_2 t - c_3 e^{-2t} + \dfrac{t^3}{6} + \dfrac{t^2}{4} - \dfrac{1}{16} e^{2t} - \dfrac{1}{8} e^{-2t}(1 + 2t), \\[2mm] y = c_4 + 2c_3 e^{-2t} + \dfrac{t}{2} - \dfrac{t^2}{2} + \dfrac{1}{8} e^{2t} + \dfrac{1}{4} e^{-2t} + \dfrac{1}{2} te^{-2t}. \end{cases}$

(f) $\begin{cases} x = 4c_1 e^t + c_2 e^{t/2} + c_3 e^{-t/2} + \frac{4}{15} e^{2t}, \\ y = 3c_1 e^t - t + 1. \end{cases}$

(g) $\begin{cases} x = c_1 e^t + c_2(1 + \sqrt{5})e^{\frac{(1+\sqrt{5})t}{2}} + c_3(1 - \sqrt{5})e^{\frac{(1-\sqrt{5})t}{2}}, \\[2mm] y = c_4 - 2c_2 e^{\frac{(1+\sqrt{5})t}{2}} - 2c_3 e^{\frac{(1-\sqrt{5})t}{2}}. \end{cases}$

(h) $\begin{cases} x = c_1 + c_2 \sin (t \sqrt{2}) + c_3 \cos (t \sqrt{2}) + e^{2t} + \cos t, \\ y = c_4 + c_2 \sqrt{2} \cos (t \sqrt{2}) - c_3 \sqrt{2} \sin (t \sqrt{2}) \\ \qquad\qquad\qquad\qquad\qquad\qquad + 3e^{2t} - \sin t. \end{cases}$

4. (a) $\begin{cases} x = A_1e^{2t} - 2A_2e^{3t}, \\ y = -A_1e^{2t} + A_2e^{3t}. \end{cases}$

(b) $\begin{cases} x = A_1e^{3t} + 3A_2e^{-t}, \\ y = -A_1e^{3t} + A_2e^{-t}. \end{cases}$

6. (a) $\begin{cases} x = A_1e^{3t} + A_2te^{3t}, \\ y = (A_1 - A_2)e^{3t} + A_2te^{3t}. \end{cases}$

(b) $\begin{cases} x = A_1e^{2t} + A_2te^{2t}, \\ y = (A_1 + A_2)e^{2t} + A_2te^{2t}. \end{cases}$

8. (a) $\begin{cases} x = e^{2t}(A_1 \sin t + A_2 \cos t), \\ y = e^{2t}(A_2 \sin t - A_1 \cos t). \end{cases}$

(b) $\begin{cases} x = e^{3t}[5A_1 \sin 2t + 5A_2 \cos 2t], \\ y = e^{3t}[(A_1 + 2A_2) \sin 2t + (A_2 - 2A_1) \cos 2t]. \end{cases}$

10. (a) $\begin{cases} x = 3A_1e^t + 4A_2e^{2t} + 2A_3e^{3t}, \\ y = 2A_1e^t + A_2e^{2t} + 2A_3e^{3t}, \\ z = 3A_1e^t + A_2e^{2t} + 3A_3e^{3t}. \end{cases}$

(b) $\begin{cases} x = 2A_1 + 3A_2e^{2t} + 4A_3e^{-t}, \\ y = 2A_1 + 2A_2e^{2t} + A_3e^{-t}, \\ z = 3A_1 + 3A_2e^{2t} + A_3e^{-t}. \end{cases}$

11. $\begin{cases} 3x = 2e^{2t} + e^{-t}, \\ 3y = 2e^{2t} - 2e^{-t}. \end{cases}$

Section 40, page 122

1. (a) $y = c_1 + c_2e^x + c_3e^{-x}.$

(b) $y = c_1e^x + e^{-\frac{x}{2}}\left(c_2 \cos \dfrac{x\sqrt{15}}{2} + c_3 \sin \dfrac{x\sqrt{15}}{2}\right).$

(c) $y = c_1 + c_2x + (c_3 + c_4x)e^{ax} + \dfrac{x^4}{12a^2} + \dfrac{2x^3}{3a^3} + \dfrac{(6 - a^2)x^2}{2a^4}.$

(d) $y = c_1e^{2x} + c_2e^{-2x} + c_3xe^{-2x} + \dfrac{e^{3x}}{25} - \dfrac{1}{4}.$

(e) $y = c_1 + c_2e^{x/2} + c_3e^x + c_4e^{3x/2} + \dfrac{18}{65} \sin x - \dfrac{14}{65} \cos x.$

(f) $y = c_1e^{-2x} + e^{2x}(c_2 \cos x + c_3 \sin x).$

(g) $y = c_1 + c_2x + e^{4x}(c_3 \cos 2x + c_4 \sin 2x) + \dfrac{x^4}{240} + \dfrac{x^3}{150}$

$\qquad + \dfrac{11x^2}{2000} + \dfrac{1}{45} e^{3x}.$

(h) $y = c_1e^x + c_2xe^x + c_3e^{-2x} + c_4xe^{-2x} + \sin 2x.$

(i) $y = c_1 e^{2x} + c_2 e^{ax} + c_3 e^{-ax} + \dfrac{1}{3(a^2 - 1)} [2 \sinh x + \cosh x]$.

(j) $y = c_1 e^{3x} + c_2 e^{-x/2} + c_3 x e^{-x/2} + e^x$.

(k) $y = e^{ax} \left(c_1 + c_2 x + c_3 x^2 + \dfrac{x^3}{6} \right)$.

(l) $y = (c_1 + c_2 x) \sin ax + (c_3 + c_4 x) \cos ax + \dfrac{1}{4a^4} \cosh ax$.

(m) $y = c_1 x^2 + c_2 x^3 + x^2 \log x + \dfrac{x^4}{2}$.

(n) $y = c_1 x + c_2 x \log x + \dfrac{c_3}{x^2} + \dfrac{x^4 \log x}{9} - \dfrac{x^4}{9} - \dfrac{3x^3 \log x}{10} - \dfrac{x^3}{25}$.

(o) $y = \dfrac{c_1}{2 - x} + c_2 (2 - x)^3$.

(p) $y = c_1 x^2 + c_2 x^2 \log x + 5x$.

(q) $y = c_1 + (3 + 2x)[c_2 \cos \log (3 + 2x) + c_3 \sin \log (3 + 2x)]$.

(r) $y = c_1 + c_2 e^{-x} + e^{2x} \left(c_3 + \dfrac{x^4}{24} - \dfrac{5x^3}{36} + \dfrac{19x^2}{72} - \dfrac{65x}{216} \right)$.

2. (a) $y = 2e^{3x} \sin 2x$.

    (b) $y = e^x - e^{-4x} + 2x$.

    (c) $y = x^3 (2 \cos \log x^2 - \sin \log x^2)$.

3. (a) $(x^2 + 3x)y' + (x - 4)y = 3(x^2 + 3x)^{1\frac{4}{3}} + c_1$,

or

$$y \dfrac{(x^2 + 3x)^{7\!/\!3}}{x^{11\!/\!3}} = \dfrac{9x}{17} (x + 3)^{17\!/\!3} - \dfrac{27}{340} (x + 3)^{20\!/\!3}$$

$$+ c_1 \int \dfrac{(x + 3)^{4\!/\!3} \, dx}{x^{7\!/\!3}} + c_2.$$

    (b) $y' - y \sin x = \dfrac{x^2 \log x}{2} - \dfrac{3x^2}{4} + c_1 x + c_2$,

or

$$e^{\cos x} y = c_3 + \int e^{\cos x} \left[\dfrac{x^2 \log x}{2} - \dfrac{3x^2}{4} + c_1 x + c_2 \right] dx.$$

    (c) $xy' + (\log x - 2)y = \dfrac{x^3}{3} + c_1 x + c_2$,

or

$$y \dfrac{\sqrt{e^{\log^2 x}}}{x^2} = c_3 + \int \sqrt{e^{\log^2 x}} \left(\dfrac{x}{3} + \dfrac{c_1}{x^2} + \dfrac{c_2}{x^3} \right) dx.$$

(d) $y = c_1 x^{-2} + c_2 x^2 + c_3 x + c_4 + \dfrac{4}{5} x^3$.

(e) $y \sin x = \dfrac{\cot x}{4} + \displaystyle\int \log \sin x \, dx + c_1 x^3 + c_2 x^2 + c_3 x + c_4$.

4. (a) $y = \dfrac{e^x}{2} + \dfrac{c_1}{x e^x} + \dfrac{c_2 e^x}{x}$.

(b) $\mu = c_1 x + c_2 x^2$ (c_1, c_2 arbitrary constants).

5. (a) $y = u \cos 2x$, where u is defined by

$$u' = \frac{\sqrt{\sin 2x} \, \log \tan x}{2 \cos^2 2x} + \frac{\sqrt{\sin 2x}}{2 \cos 2x} + \frac{c_1 \sqrt{\sin 2x}}{\cos^2 2x}.$$

(b) $y = ux \sin x$, where

$$u = -\int \cot x \csc x \log \cos x \, dx + c_1 \csc x + c_2.$$

(c) $y = u \log x$, where $u' = \dfrac{1 - \log x}{\log^2 x} \left[c + \displaystyle\int \dfrac{dx}{1 - \log x} \right]$.

(d) $y = \dfrac{3x^3}{4} + c_1 x \log x + c_2 x$.

(e) $y = u e^x$, where

$$u' = \frac{2x - x^2}{e^x} \left[c_1 + c_2 \left(\frac{1}{2 - x} - \frac{1}{x} + \log \frac{x}{2 - x} \right) \right].$$

8. (a) $y = \dfrac{1}{\sqrt{\sin x}} (c_1 e^{2x} + c_2 e^{-2x})$.

(b) $y = \dfrac{1}{\sqrt{x}} \left(c_1 e^x + c_2 e^{-x} + \dfrac{x e^x}{2} \right)$.

(c) $y = e^{-x^2} [c_1 \cos \log x^{\frac{\sqrt{3}}{2}} + c_2 \sin \log x^{\frac{\sqrt{3}}{2}}] \sqrt{x}$.

(d) $y = \sqrt{\dfrac{e^x}{x^x}} \left(c_1 x^2 + \dfrac{c_2}{x} + \dfrac{x^2 \log x}{3} \right)$.

10. (a) $y = e^{e^x}(c_1 + c_2 e^x) + e^x + 2$.

(b) $y = e^{\frac{\cos x}{2}} \left[c_1 \cos \dfrac{\sqrt{3} \cos x}{2} + c_2 \sin \dfrac{\sqrt{3} \cos x}{2} \right]$.

(c) $y = c_1 (\sec x)^{\frac{3 + \sqrt{13}}{2}} + c_2 (\sec x)^{\frac{3 - \sqrt{13}}{2}}$.

11. (a) $y = e^{x^2}(c_1 \cos x + c_2 \sin x + 1)$.

(b) $y = c_1 x^{\frac{-1 + \sqrt{17}}{8}} + c_2 x^{\frac{-1 - \sqrt{17}}{8}} - \log x - 1$.

(c) $y = c_1 \dfrac{x^x}{e^x} + c_2 \dfrac{e^x}{x^x}$.

(d) $y = \sqrt{\cos x}\left(c_1 x^3 + \dfrac{c_2}{x^2} - \dfrac{x^2}{4}\right).$

(e) $y = e^{-\frac{1}{3}x^{3/2}}\left(c_1 e^{3x} + c_2 e^{-3x} - \dfrac{x}{9}\right).$

12. (c) $y = \dfrac{-5x^9 + 4c}{x^{11} + cx^2}.$

(d) $y = -\dfrac{\log x + c \log^3 x + 2c \log x}{1 + c \log^2 x}.$

(e) $y = \dfrac{\csc x(e^{-x} - 4ce^{4x})}{e^{-x} + ce^{4x}}.$

(g) $x(1 - x)(x - \log x)(1 - \log x)y' = x - x^2 - x \log x$
$+ x \log^2 x - y(1 - x^2 - x + x \log^2 x) + y^2(1 - 2x + x \log x)$

13. (a) $x = 3c_1 e^{8t} + c_2 e^{-2t}; \; y = 4c_1 e^{8t} - 2c_2 e^{-2t}.$

(b) $u = e^{-3x}(13c_1 \cos 4x + 13c_2 \sin 4x);$
$v = e^{-3x}[(6c_1 - 4c_2) \cos 4x + (4c_1 + 6c_2) \sin 4x].$

(c) $x = e^{4t}(2c_1 + 2c_2 t); \; y = e^{4t}(2c_1 - c_2 + 2c_2 t).$

(d) $u = 2c_1 e^{4x} + 4c_2 e^{-2x} + c_3 e^x; \; y = 3c_1 e^{4x} + 3c_2 e^{-2x}; \; z = 18c_1 e^{4x}.$

(e) $x = c_1 \cos t + c_2 \sin t + 3t^2 - t - 1;$
$y = c_1 \sin t - c_2 \cos t + t^2 + 2.$

(f) $x = \dfrac{5e^{2t}}{17} + \dfrac{3t}{7} - \dfrac{1}{49} + 2c^{-7t/5};$

$y = -\dfrac{e^{2t}}{17} + \dfrac{t}{7} - \dfrac{26}{49} + 3ce^{-7t/5} + \dfrac{1}{2} e^{-t}.$

(g) $x = 2c_1 + 4c_2 e^{t/2} - t^2 - 4t + \dfrac{\sin 2t + 4 \cos 2t}{34};$

$y = c_1 + c_2 e^{t/2} - \dfrac{t^2}{2} - t + 2 + \dfrac{9 \sin 2t + 2 \cos 2t}{68}.$

(h) $x = c_1 + c_3 e^{t\sqrt{2}} + c_4 e^{-t\sqrt{2}};$
$y = c_2 + c_3(1 - \sqrt{2})e^{t\sqrt{2}} + c_4(1 + \sqrt{2})e^{-t\sqrt{2}}.$

(i) $x = c_1 e^t + c_2 e^{-t} + 7c_3 \cos 3t + 7c_4 \sin 3t + \dfrac{14t}{9};$

$y = -c_1 e^t - c_2 e^{-t} + 3c_3 \cos 3t + 3c_4 \sin 3t - \dfrac{4t}{3}.$

15. $v = -\sqrt{2gR}.$

17. Period $= \dfrac{\pi}{2}$ seconds.

18. (b) Period $= 2\pi \sqrt{\dfrac{l}{g}}.$

19. $x^2 - y^2 = c.$

21. $y = \dfrac{3\omega l^2 x^2 - 2\omega x^4}{48EI}$; maximum $y = \dfrac{5\omega l^4}{384EI}.$

22. (a) $y = \dfrac{\omega}{6EI}(3lx^2 - x^3)$; maximum $y = \dfrac{\omega l^3}{3EI}.$

    (b) $y = \dfrac{1}{24EI}(5400x^2 - 120x^3 + x^4)$; maximum $y = \dfrac{101250}{EI}.$

    (c) $y = \dfrac{1}{48EI}(30720x^2 - 496x^3 + 3x^4)$; maximum $y = \dfrac{1568000}{3EI}.$

24. (a) $L\dfrac{d^2q}{dt^2} + \dfrac{q}{C} = 0.$ (b) $L\dfrac{d^2i}{dt^2} + \dfrac{i}{C} = 0.$

25. (a) $L\dfrac{d^2q}{dt^2} + R\dfrac{dq}{dt} + \dfrac{q}{C} = 0.$ (b) $L\dfrac{d^2i}{dt^2} + R\dfrac{di}{dt} + \dfrac{i}{C} = 0.$

26. (a) $L\dfrac{d^2q}{dt^2} + \dfrac{q}{C} = V.$ (b) $L\dfrac{d^2i}{dt^2} + \dfrac{i}{C} = 0.$

27. (a) $L\dfrac{d^2q}{dt^2} + \dfrac{q}{C} = E\sin\omega t.$ (b) $L\dfrac{d^2i}{dt^2} + \dfrac{i}{C} = E\omega\cos\omega t.$

28. $L\dfrac{d^2i}{dt^2} + R\dfrac{di}{dt} + \dfrac{i}{C} = E\omega\cos\omega t.$

29. $x = \dfrac{3e^t}{4} - \dfrac{3e^{-t}}{4} - \dfrac{\sin t}{2}, \qquad y = \dfrac{3e^t}{8} - \dfrac{3e^{-t}}{8} + \dfrac{\sin t}{4}.$

30. $6s = 1 + \cos(8\sqrt{3}t).$

31. $s = e^{\frac{-16t}{675}}\left[\dfrac{1}{6}\cos\dfrac{8\sqrt{1366871}}{675}t\right.$

$$\left. + \dfrac{1}{3\sqrt{1366871}}\sin\dfrac{8\sqrt{1366871}}{675}t\right] + \dfrac{1}{6}.$$

32. Period $= \dfrac{6\sqrt{\pi}}{5}.$

Section 41, page 136

1. (a) $y = 1.02660.$ (b) $y_2 = 1.02660.$ (c) $y = 1.0266.$

2. $y = 1.005.$

3. $y_4 = 2 - 2x + \dfrac{3x^2}{2} - \dfrac{x^3}{2} + \dfrac{x^4}{8} - \dfrac{x^5}{120};$

$y = 2 - 2x + \dfrac{3x^2}{2} - \dfrac{x^3}{2} + \dfrac{x^4}{8} - \dfrac{x^5}{40} + \cdots .$

6. (a) $y_3 = \dfrac{x^2}{2} + \dfrac{x^5}{20} + \dfrac{x^8}{160} + \dfrac{x^{11}}{4400}.$

(b) $y = \dfrac{x^2}{2} + \dfrac{x^5}{20} + \dfrac{x^8}{160} + \cdots.$

(c) $y_3 = .0049995;\ y = .0049995.$

8. $y_2 = 1 + 2x - \dfrac{x^2}{2} + \dfrac{x^3}{6};\ z_2 = 2 - x - \dfrac{3x^2}{2} - \dfrac{4x^3}{3}.$

9. $y_3 = x + \dfrac{x^2}{2} + \dfrac{x^4}{12} + \dfrac{x^7}{252};\ z_3 = 1 + \dfrac{x^3}{6} - \dfrac{x^4}{12} + \dfrac{x^6}{120}.$

10. $y_3 = 1 + \dfrac{4x^3}{3} + \dfrac{x^4}{2} + \dfrac{x^5}{20};\ z_3 = 2x + \dfrac{x^2}{2} - \dfrac{x^3}{6} + \dfrac{x^4}{3};$

$u_3 = 1 + x - \dfrac{x^2}{2} - \dfrac{x^3}{3}.$

11. (a) $y = 1 + 2x - \dfrac{x^2}{2} - \dfrac{x^3}{2} + \cdots;\ z = 2 - x - \dfrac{3x^2}{2}$
$$- x^3 + \cdots.$$

(b) $y = x + \dfrac{x^2}{2} + \cdots;\ z = 1 + \dfrac{x^3}{6} + \cdots$

(c) $y = 1 + \dfrac{4x^3}{3} + \cdots;\ z = 2x + \dfrac{x^2}{2} - \dfrac{x^3}{6} + \cdots;$

$u = 1 + x - \dfrac{x^2}{2} - \dfrac{x^3}{3} + \cdots$

13. (a) $y = 1 + x - \dfrac{x^2}{2} + \dfrac{5x^3}{6} - \dfrac{5x^4}{12} + \cdots.$

(b) $y_3 = 1 + x - \dfrac{x^2}{2} + \dfrac{5x^3}{6}.$

14. (a) $y = -1 + x - x^2 + \dfrac{2x^3}{3} - \dfrac{x^4}{3} + \cdots.$

(b) $y_3 = -1 + x - x^2 + \dfrac{2x^3}{3} - \dfrac{x^4}{12}.$

Section 42, page 141

1. (a) $y = .473.$ (b) $y = 2.281,\ y = 2.280.$ (c) $y = 2.162,$
$$y = 2.172$$

(d) $y = 2.477.$ (e) $x = 1.1.$ (f) $x = 5.076.$

5. (a) $y = .640,\ z = .223.$ (b) $y = .838,\ z = .371.$
(c) $y = 3.269,\ z = .526.$

6. (a) $y = 1.450.$ (b) $y = -0.247.$

Section 43, page 146

1. (a)

x	0.4	0.5
y	1.5836	1.7974

(b)

x	0.4	0.5
y	1.290	1.339

(c)

x	1.8	2.0	2.2
y	0.7261	0.6065	0.4867

2. (a) 1.175. (b) 0.60.

Section 44, page 149

3. (a) $y = Ax + x^2$.

(b) $y = -\dfrac{1}{2} + \dfrac{1 + 2A}{2}\left(1 + x^2 + \dfrac{x^4}{2} + \dfrac{x^6}{6} + \dfrac{x^8}{24} + \cdots\right)$

$= -\dfrac{1}{2} + ce^{x^2}$.

(c) $y = c + (1 - c)x + cx^2 + \left(\dfrac{1}{2} - c\right)x^3 + \left(c - \dfrac{1}{3}\right)x^4$

$+ \left(\dfrac{3}{8} - c\right)x^5 + \cdots$.

4. (a) $y = A(1 + x) + \dfrac{A - A^2}{2}x^2 + \dfrac{A - 5A^2 + 2A^3}{6}x^3$

$+ \dfrac{A - 17A^2 + 26A^3 - 6A^4}{24}x^4 + \cdots$

(b) $y = A - A^2x + \dfrac{1 + 2A^3}{2}x^2 - \dfrac{A + 3A^4}{3}x^3$

$+ \dfrac{5A^2 + 12A^5}{12}x^4 + \cdots$.

(c) $y = A + \dfrac{A}{1 + A}x + \dfrac{1 + 3A + A^2}{2(1 + A)^3}x^3$

$+ \dfrac{1 + A - 5A^2 - 2A^3}{6(1 + A)^5}x^4 + \cdots$

(d) $y = A - \dfrac{1}{2A}x^2 - \dfrac{1 + 2A}{8A^3}x^4 - \dfrac{8A^2 + 10A + 3}{48A^5}x^6 - \cdots$.

5. $y = A - x - \dfrac{x^2}{2A} - \dfrac{2x^3}{3A^2} - \dfrac{9x^4}{8A^3} - \cdots$

7. (a) $y' = A + x + \dfrac{x^2}{2} - \dfrac{x^3}{3} + \dfrac{x^4}{4} - \dfrac{x^5}{5} + \cdots$

$$= A + 2x - \log(x + 1);$$

$$y = A(x + 1) + x^2 + x - (x + 1)\log(x + 1).$$

(b) $y = x(A - 1) + x^2 - x \log x.$

Section 45, page 157

1. (a) $y = A(1 - x^2) + B\left(x - \dfrac{x^3}{3!} - \dfrac{x^5}{5!} - \dfrac{3x^7}{7!} - \cdots \right.$

$$\left. - \dfrac{3 \cdot 5 \cdot 7 \cdots (2n - 3)}{(2n + 1)!} x^{2n+1} - \cdots \right).$$

(b) $y = A\left(\dfrac{1}{x} + \dfrac{x^2}{3} - \dfrac{x^5}{36} + \dfrac{5x^8}{2268} - \cdots \right)$

$$+ B\left(x - \dfrac{x^4}{15} + \dfrac{x^7}{180} - \dfrac{7x^{10}}{17820} + \cdots \right).$$

(c) $y = A\left(x - \dfrac{x^3}{5} + \dfrac{x^5}{5 \cdot 7} - \cdots \right.$

$$\left. + (-1)^n \dfrac{x^{2n+1}}{5 \cdot 7 \cdot 9 \cdots (2n + 3)} + \cdots \right)$$

$$+ B\left(\dfrac{1}{x^2} - \dfrac{1}{2} + \dfrac{x^2}{2 \cdot 4} - \dfrac{x^4}{2 \cdot 4 \cdot 6} \right.$$

$$\left. + \cdots + (-1)^{n-1} \dfrac{x^{2n}}{2 \cdot 4 \cdot 6 \cdots (2n + 2)} + \cdots \right).$$

(d) $y = A\left(1 + \displaystyle\sum_{n=1} \dfrac{x^{-2n}}{2 \cdot 4 \cdot 6 \cdots (2n)} \right)$

$$+ B\left(\dfrac{1}{x} + \displaystyle\sum_{n=1} \dfrac{x^{-2n-1}}{3 \cdot 5 \cdot 7 \cdots (2n + 1)} \right).$$

(e) $y = A\left(1 - \dfrac{1}{5x^2} \right) + B\left(x^3 + \dfrac{5x}{2} - \dfrac{15}{8x} + \dfrac{5}{48x^3} + \cdots \right).$

(f) $y = Ax + \dfrac{B}{x^3}.$

2. (a) $y = A\left(1 + \displaystyle\sum_{n=1} \dfrac{(-1)^n \cdot x^{3n}}{(3n + 1)!} \right) + B\left(\dfrac{1}{x} + \displaystyle\sum_{n=1} \dfrac{(-1)^n x^{3n-1}}{(3n)!} \right)$

$$+ C\left(\displaystyle\sum_{n=1} \dfrac{(-1)^{n-1} x^{3n-2}}{(3n - 1)!} \right).$$

(b) $y = Cx^2 + A\left(1 - \dfrac{2 \cdot 1}{3 \cdot 4 \cdot 5} \cdot \dfrac{1}{x^3}\right.$

$\left. - \displaystyle\sum_{n=3} \dfrac{2(2 \cdot 5 \cdot 8 \cdots (3n - 4))(2 \cdot 5 \cdot 8 \cdots (3n - 7)))}{(3n - 1)! \cdot x^{3n-3}}\right)$

$+ B\left(x - \dfrac{1 \cdot 2}{4!} \cdot \dfrac{1}{x^2}\right.$

$+ \displaystyle\sum_{n=2} \dfrac{(1 \cdot 4 \cdot 7 \cdots (3n - 2))(-2 \cdot 1 \cdot 4 \cdot 7 \cdots (3n - 5)))}{(3n + 1)! \cdot x^{3n-1}}\Big).$

(c) $y = c_1x^2 + c_2x^{\frac{-7+\sqrt{17}}{2}} + c_3x^{\frac{-7-\sqrt{17}}{2}}.$

3. $y = A + B \tan^{-1} x; \quad y = A + B \tan^{-1} \dfrac{1}{x}.$

4. (a) $y = A\left(1 + \dfrac{1}{3}x^3 + \displaystyle\sum_{n=1} \dfrac{(-1)^n 2 \cdot 5 \cdots (3n - 1)}{3 \cdot 6 \cdots (3n + 3)} x^{3n+3}\right)$

$+ B\left(x^2 + \displaystyle\sum_{n=1} (-1)^n \dfrac{4 \cdot 7 \cdots (3n - 2)}{5 \cdot 8 \cdots (3n + 2)} x^{3n+2}\right);$

also

$y = A\left(x + \dfrac{1}{3x^2} + \displaystyle\sum_{n=1} (-1)^n \dfrac{2 \cdot 5 \cdots (3n - 1)}{3 \cdot 6 \cdots (3n + 3)x^{3n+2}}\right)$

$+ \dfrac{B}{x}\left(1 + \displaystyle\sum_{n=1} (-1)^n \dfrac{1 \cdot 4 \cdots (3n - 2)}{5 \cdot 8 \cdots (3n + 2)x^{3n}}\right).$

4. (b) $y = \dfrac{A + Bx^3}{x^2 + 1}.$

Section 46, page 161

1. (a) $y = (A + B \log x)\left(x^{-2} + \displaystyle\sum_{n=1} \dfrac{2^n x^{3n-2}}{[3 \cdot 6 \cdots (3n)]^2}\right)$

$- \dfrac{2B}{x^2}\left[\displaystyle\sum_{n=1} (2x^3)^n \left(\dfrac{1}{[3 \cdot 6 \cdots (3n)]^2}\right)\left(\dfrac{1}{3} + \dfrac{1}{6} + \cdots + \dfrac{1}{3n}\right)\right].$

(b) $y = (A + B \log x)\left(1 + \displaystyle\sum_{n=1} \dfrac{x^n}{(n!)^2}\right)$

$- 2B \displaystyle\sum_{n=1} \dfrac{x^n}{(n!)^2}\left(1 + \dfrac{1}{2} + \cdots + \dfrac{1}{n}\right).$

(c) $y = (A + B \log x) \left(1 + \displaystyle\sum_{n=1} (-1)^n \cdot \dfrac{1}{[2 \cdot 4 \, \cdots \, (2n)]^2 x^{2n}} \right)$

$- 2B \displaystyle\sum_{n=1} (-1)^{n-1} \cdot \dfrac{1}{x^{2n}} \cdot \dfrac{1}{[2 \cdot 4 \, \cdots \, (2n)]^2} \left(\dfrac{1}{2} + \dfrac{1}{4} + \cdots + \dfrac{1}{2n} \right).$

(d) $y = (A + B \log x)(1 - x) + 4Bx;$

$$\text{also}$$

$$y = (A + B \log x)(x - 1) - 4B.$$

2. (a) $y = (A + B \log x) \displaystyle\sum_{n=0} \dfrac{(n + 1)!}{(n!)^2 x^n}$

$+ B \left[\dfrac{3}{x} + \displaystyle\sum_{n=2} \dfrac{(n + 1)\left(2 + \dfrac{1}{n + 1} - \dfrac{1}{n} - \dfrac{1}{n - 1} - \cdots - \dfrac{1}{2} \right)}{n! x^n} \right].$

(b) $y = (A + B \log x) x \left[1 - \dfrac{1}{4x^2} - \displaystyle\sum_{n=2} \dfrac{1 \cdot 3 \cdot 5 \, \cdots \, (2n - 3)}{(2 \cdot 4 \cdot 6 \, \cdots \, (2n) x^n)^2} \right]$

$+ B \left[- \dfrac{1}{2x} - \right.$

$\left. \displaystyle\sum_{n=2} \dfrac{1 \cdot 3 \cdot 5 \cdots (2n - 3)\left(2 - \dfrac{1}{1} - \dfrac{1}{3} - \cdots - \dfrac{1}{2n - 3} + \dfrac{1}{2} + \dfrac{1}{3} + \cdots + \dfrac{1}{n} \right)}{x^{2n-1}(2 \cdot 4 \cdot 6 \, \cdots \, (2n))^2} \right].$

Section 47, page 165

1. (a) $y = (A + B \log x) \left(- \dfrac{x}{2} + \dfrac{x^3}{2^2 \cdot 4} - \dfrac{x^5}{2^2 \cdot 4^2 \cdot 6} + \cdots \right)$

$+ \dfrac{B}{x} \left[1 + \dfrac{x^2}{4} - \dfrac{x^4}{2^2 \cdot 4} \left(\dfrac{2}{2} + \dfrac{1}{4} \right) + \dfrac{x^6}{2^2 \cdot 4^2 \cdot 6} \left(\dfrac{2}{2} + \dfrac{2}{4} + \dfrac{1}{6} \right) \right.$

$+ \cdots \left. \vphantom{\dfrac{x^2}{4}} \right].$

(b) $y = (A + B \log x) \left(- \dfrac{x^3}{3!(-2)(-1)} + \dfrac{x^4}{4!(-2)(-1)(1)} \right.$

$\left. - \dfrac{x^5}{5!(-2)(-1)(1)(2)} + \cdots \right)$

$+ B \left[1 + \dfrac{x}{2} + \dfrac{x^2}{4} + \dfrac{x^3}{3!(-2)(-1)} \cdot \dfrac{1}{3} \right.$

$- \dfrac{x^4}{4!(-2)(-1)(1)} \left(\dfrac{1}{3} + \dfrac{1}{4} + \dfrac{1}{1} \right)$

$\left. + \dfrac{x^5}{5!(-2)(-1)(1)(2)} \left(\dfrac{1}{3} + \dfrac{1}{4} + \dfrac{1}{5} + \dfrac{1}{1} + \dfrac{1}{2} \right) + \cdots \right].$

(c) $y = (A + B \log x)\left(-\dfrac{x}{2} + \dfrac{x^2}{1^2 \cdot 2 \cdot 3} - \dfrac{x^3}{1^2 \cdot 2^2 \cdot 3 \cdot 4} + \cdots\right)$

$\qquad + \dfrac{B}{x}\left[1 + x + \dfrac{x^2}{4} - \dfrac{x^3}{1^2 \cdot 2 \cdot 3}\left(-1 + \dfrac{2}{1} + \dfrac{1}{2} + \dfrac{1}{3}\right)\right.$

$\qquad + \dfrac{x^4}{1^2 \cdot 2^2 \cdot 3 \cdot 4}\left.\left(-1 + \dfrac{2}{1} + \dfrac{2}{2} + \dfrac{1}{3} + \dfrac{1}{4}\right) - \cdots\right].$

(d) $y = \dfrac{(A + B \log x)}{x^2}\left(-\dfrac{x^3}{6} + \dfrac{x^4}{1^2 \cdot 2 \cdot 3 \cdot 4}\right.$

$\qquad\qquad\qquad\qquad\left. - \dfrac{x^5}{1^2 \cdot 2^2 \cdot 3 \cdot 4 \cdot 5} + \cdots\right)$

$\qquad + \dfrac{B}{x^2}\left[2 + x + \dfrac{x^2}{2} + \dfrac{x^3}{1 \cdot 2 \cdot 3}\left(-\dfrac{1}{2} - \dfrac{1}{1} + \dfrac{1}{1} + \dfrac{1}{2} + \dfrac{1}{3}\right)\right.$

$\qquad - \dfrac{x^4}{1^2 \cdot 2 \cdot 3 \cdot 4}\left.\left(-\dfrac{1}{2} - \dfrac{1}{1} + \dfrac{2}{1} + \dfrac{1}{2} + \dfrac{1}{3} + \dfrac{1}{4}\right) + \cdots\right].$

3. $y = (A + B \log x)x\left(\dfrac{1}{2x^2} + \dfrac{1}{2^2 \cdot 4x^4} + \dfrac{1 \cdot 3}{2^2 \cdot 4^2 \cdot 6x^6}\right.$

$\qquad + \dfrac{1 \cdot 3 \cdot 5}{2^2 \cdot 4^2 \cdot 6^2 \cdot 8x^3} - \cdots\left.\right) + Bx\left(1 + \dfrac{3}{4x^2} + \dfrac{5}{64x^4} + \cdots\right).$

Section 48, page 168

2. (a) $y = \dfrac{x^4}{9}\left[1 - \dfrac{2x^2}{4 \cdot 5} + \dfrac{2 \cdot 3x^4}{(4 \cdot 5)(5 \cdot 7)} - \dfrac{2 \cdot 3 \cdot 4x^6}{(4 \cdot 5 \cdot 6)(5 \cdot 7 \cdot 9)} + \cdots\right].$

(b) $y = \dfrac{1}{2x} + \dfrac{x}{4}\left[1 - \dfrac{2x^3}{4 \cdot 7} + \dfrac{2 \cdot 5x^6}{(4 \cdot 7)(7 \cdot 10)}\right.$

$\qquad\qquad\qquad\qquad\left. - \dfrac{2 \cdot 5 \cdot 8x^9}{(4 \cdot 7 \cdot 10)(7 \cdot 10 \cdot 13)} + \cdots\right].$

(c) $y = \dfrac{2}{x} - \dfrac{1}{9x^3}\left[1 + \dfrac{2}{5^2 \cdot x^2} + \dfrac{2 \cdot 4}{(5 \cdot 7)^2 x^4} + \dfrac{2 \cdot 4 \cdot 6}{(5 \cdot 7 \cdot 9)^2 x^6} + \cdots\right].$

4. (a) $y = \dfrac{1}{5x^3} - \dfrac{2 \log x}{15x} - \dfrac{2}{15} G'(0)$, where

$\qquad G(h) = \dfrac{1}{x} - \dfrac{hx}{(-1 + h)(2 + h)}$

$\qquad\qquad + \dfrac{h(h + 2)x^3}{(-1 + h)(2 + h)(1 + h)(4 + h)} - \cdots.$

(b) $y = \dfrac{1}{3x^2} - \dfrac{\log x}{6x} - \dfrac{G'(0)}{6}$, where

$\qquad G(h) = \dfrac{1}{x} - \dfrac{h}{(-1 + h)(1 + h)} + \dfrac{1}{(-1 + h)(2 + h)} x$

$\qquad\qquad - \dfrac{1}{(-1 + h)(1 + h)(3 + h)} x^2 + \cdots.$

Section 51, page 187

1. (a) $2F\left(-\dfrac{n}{2}, \dfrac{-n+1}{2}, \dfrac{1}{2}, x^2\right).$

   (b) $2nxF\left(\dfrac{-n+1}{2}, \dfrac{-n+2}{2}, \dfrac{3}{2}, x^2\right).$

   (c) $2xF\left(\dfrac{1}{2}, 1, \dfrac{3}{2}, x^2\right).$

   (d) $F(1, 1, 1, -x)$; divergent for $x = \pm 1$.

   (e) $F(1, 1, 1, x)$; divergent for $x = \pm 1$.

   (f) $\underset{\substack{\alpha \to \infty \\ \beta \to \infty}}{\text{Lim}}\ x \cdot F\left(\alpha, \beta, \dfrac{3}{2}, -\dfrac{x^2}{4\alpha\beta}\right).$

   (g) $\underset{\beta \to \infty}{\text{Lim}}\ F\left(1, \beta, 1, \dfrac{x}{\beta}\right).$

2. (a) $y = A \cdot F(1, 2, 3, x) + \dfrac{B}{x^2} \cdot F(-1, 0, -1, x) =$

   $A \cdot F(1, 2, 3, x) + \dfrac{B}{x^2}$; converges for $|x| < 1$ and $x = -1$.

   (b) $y = \dfrac{A}{x^2} \cdot F\left(2, 2, 4, \dfrac{1}{x}\right) + Bx \cdot F\left(-1, -1, -2, \dfrac{1}{x}\right)$

   $= \dfrac{A}{x^2} \cdot F\left(2, 2, 4, \dfrac{1}{x}\right) + B\left(x - \dfrac{1}{2}\right)$; converges for $|x| > 1$

   and $x = -1$.

3. (a) Converges for $8 > x > 2$. (b) Converges for all values of x.

5. $(x^2 + x)y'' + [(\alpha + \beta + 1)x + \gamma]y' + \alpha\beta \cdot y = 0.$

6. $(x^2 + x)y'' + (3x + 2)y' + y = 0.$

7. $\dfrac{\alpha(\alpha + 1) \cdots (\alpha + m - 1) \cdot \beta(\beta + 1) \cdots (\beta + m - 1)}{\gamma(\gamma + 1) \cdots (\gamma + m - 1)} \cdot$
   $F(\alpha + m, \beta + m, \gamma + m, x).$

8. $(z^2 - z)\dfrac{d^2y}{dz^2} + [(\alpha + \beta + 1)z - \gamma]\dfrac{dy}{dz} + \alpha\beta y = 0,$ where

   $\alpha + \beta + 1 = \dfrac{D}{A}, \ \alpha\beta = \dfrac{F}{A}, \ \gamma = \dfrac{Dm + E}{2Am + B}.$

Section 52, page 188

1. (a) $y = \dfrac{A}{x}\left(1 - \dfrac{x}{2}\right) + Bx^2\left(\dfrac{1}{6} - \dfrac{2x}{4!} + \dfrac{3x^2}{5!} - \dfrac{4x^3}{6!} + \cdots\right).$

(b) $y = A\left(1 - \dfrac{x^2}{2} + \dfrac{x^4}{8} + \dfrac{x^6}{80} + \cdots\right)$

$$+ Bx\left(1 - \dfrac{x^2}{2} + \dfrac{x^4}{40} + \dfrac{3x^6}{560} + \cdots\right).$$

(c) $y = (A + B\log x)\left(x + \displaystyle\sum_{n=1} \dfrac{(-1)^n x^{2n+1}}{4\cdot 16\,\cdots\,(2n)^2}\right)$

$$+ 2Bx\sum_{n=1} \dfrac{(-1)^{n-1}x^{2n}}{4\cdot 16\,\cdots\,(2n)^2}\left(\dfrac{1}{2} + \dfrac{1}{4} + \cdots + \dfrac{1}{2n}\right).$$

(d) $y = A\left(x^3 + \dfrac{3x}{4}\right) + B\left(1 + \dfrac{9x^2}{2} + \dfrac{15x^4}{8} - \dfrac{7x^6}{16} + \cdots\right);$

also

$$y = A\left(x^3 + \dfrac{3x}{4}\right) + B\left(\dfrac{1}{x^3} - \dfrac{3}{4x^5} + \dfrac{9}{16x^7} - \dfrac{7}{16x^9} + \cdots\right).$$

(e) $y = A\left(1 + \dfrac{x^3}{3}\displaystyle\sum_{n=2} \dfrac{(-1)^{n-1}\,x^{3n}}{(3\cdot 6\,\cdots\,3n)(2\cdot 5\,\cdots\,(3n-4))}\right)$

$$+ Bx^4\left(1 + \sum_{n=1} (-1)^n\cdot\dfrac{x^{3n}}{(3\cdot 6\,\cdots\,3n)(7\cdot 10\,\cdots\,(3n+4))}\right).$$

(f) $y = Ax^3\left(1 + \dfrac{2}{x^2} - \dfrac{1}{x^4}\right) + B\left[1 - \dfrac{1}{2\cdot 5}\cdot\dfrac{1}{x^2} -\right.$

$$\left.\dfrac{1\cdot 1}{(2\cdot 4)(5\cdot 7)}\cdot\dfrac{1}{x^4} - \dfrac{1\cdot 3}{(2\cdot 4\cdot 6)(5\cdot 7\cdot 9)}\cdot\dfrac{1}{x^6} - \cdots\right] + \dfrac{1}{x} +$$

$$\dfrac{1}{2x^2}\left[1 + \sum_{n=1} \dfrac{1\cdot 3\,\cdots\,(2n-1)}{(4\cdot 6\,\cdots\,(2n+2))(7\cdot 9\,\cdots\,(2n+5))}\cdot\dfrac{1}{x^{2n}}\right].$$

(g) Particular integral is

$$y = -\dfrac{1}{8x} + \dfrac{x}{64} - \dfrac{y_1\log x}{384} - \dfrac{G'(0)}{384}, \text{ where}$$

$$y_1 = x^3 - \dfrac{3x^5}{8\cdot 2} + \dfrac{3\cdot 5x^7}{(8\cdot 2)(10\cdot 4)} - \dfrac{3\cdot 5\cdot 7x^9}{(8\cdot 2)(10\cdot 4)(12\cdot 6)} + \cdots$$

and $\quad G(h) = x^3 - \dfrac{3+h}{(8+h)(2+h)}\,x^5$

$$+ \dfrac{(3+h)(5+h)}{(8+h)(2+h)(10+h)(4+h)}\,x^7 - \cdots.$$

8. (a) $xF\left(\dfrac{1}{2}, \dfrac{1}{2}, \dfrac{3}{2}, x^2\right)$.

   (b) $xF\left(\dfrac{1}{2}, 1, \dfrac{3}{2}, -x^2\right)$.

   (c) $\displaystyle\operatorname*{Lim}_{\substack{\alpha\to\infty \\ \beta\to\infty}} F\left(\alpha, \beta, \dfrac{1}{2}, \dfrac{x^2}{4\alpha\beta}\right)$.

10. $(x^2 + x)y'' + [(\beta - n + 1)x + \beta]y' - n\beta y = 0$ (β arbitrary).

Section 56, page 195

1. (a) $x^2 y - x + y \cos z - z^2 = c$.

   (b) $x^2 + y^2 - 2 \tan^{-1}\dfrac{x}{y} + 2z = c$.

   (c) $x^2 + y^2 + \log z + \dfrac{x}{z} = c$.

   (d) $x - \dfrac{z}{y + a} = c$.

   (e) $y + \sqrt{4 - z^2 - (x - 1)^2} = c$.

   (f) $e^{xy} + e^{yz} + e^{zx} = c$.

   (g) $x \sinh y + y \sinh z + z \sinh x = c$.

2. (a) $\log x - \dfrac{z}{x} + zy = c$.

   (b) $e^x(x + y + z) = c$.

   (d) $y(z - \sin^{-1} x) - z\sqrt{1 - x^2} = c$.

   (f) $x \sec y + z \tan y - \sec y = c$.

4. (a) $x^2(yz + xy + x^2) = c$.

   (b) $xy^2(xz + y^2) = c$.

   (c) $y^2\left(\dfrac{y}{z} - \log\dfrac{x}{z}\right) = c$.

   (d) $x + z = cy$.

6. (a) $x + z = cy^2$.

   (b) $z^5 - x^4 y = cx^4 z^5$.

   (c) $4x^4 + 4xy^2z + z^4 = c$.

9. (a) $xy + yz + zt + tx = c$.

   (c) $x^3 y^2 + 2yz + tz = c$.

10. (a) $(y + xz - t)e^{x^2} = c$.

   (b) $\log x + y^2 + z - \dfrac{1}{t} + u + v^2 = c$.

12. $x^4 + x^3 y + x^2 yz + xyzt = c$.

Section 59, page 202

1. (a) $\begin{cases} xy + y^2z = c_1, \\ x^3y = c_2z. \end{cases}$

(b) $\begin{cases} x^6 - y^3 = c_1, \\ x^4 - z^2 = c_2. \end{cases}$

(c) $\begin{cases} (xz - y^2)e^y = c_1, \\ yze^y = c_2. \end{cases}$

(d) $\begin{cases} \dfrac{1}{x^2} - y^4 = c_1, \\ y^4 - z^2 = c_2. \end{cases}$

(e) $\begin{cases} x + y + z = c_1, \\ x^2 + y^2 + z^2 = c_2. \end{cases}$

(f) $\begin{cases} x^3 - y^3 = c_1, \\ y^3 + 3e^{-z} = c_2. \end{cases}$

2. (a) $\begin{cases} x^2 - y^2 = c_1, \\ x + y = c_2z. \end{cases}$

(b) $\begin{cases} x^2y + y^2z = c_1, \\ xz^2 = c_2. \end{cases}$

(c) $\begin{cases} y^2z = c_1, \\ x^2z^2 - 4y^2z^2 \log z + 1 = c_2z. \end{cases}$

(d) $\begin{cases} x^2 + y^2 = c_1, \\ yz + x\sqrt{1 - z^2} = c_2. \end{cases}$

(e) $\begin{cases} uv = c_1, \\ 4u - z^2 = c_2. \end{cases}$

(f) $\begin{cases} (z - x)^2(z - 4x) = c_1, \\ (x + y)e^{x-z} = c_2. \end{cases}$

(g) $\begin{cases} z = c_1, \\ \log(x^2 + y^2 - 10x - 10y + 50) - \\ \qquad\qquad 2\tan^{-1}\left(\dfrac{x + y - 10}{x - y}\right) = c_2. \end{cases}$

(h) $\begin{cases} x^2y^2 = c_1(x + y)^3, \\ xyz^9 = c_2. \end{cases}$

3. (a) $\begin{cases} x + 4y + 9z = c_1, \\ x^2 + 4y^2 + 9z^2 = c_2. \end{cases}$

(b) $\begin{cases} 2x - 3y + z = c_1, \\ z + 2x = (3y - z)[c_2 + \log(3y - z)]. \end{cases}$

(c) $\begin{cases} 2x + 3y + 4z = c_1, \\ xyz = c_2. \end{cases}$

(d) $\begin{cases} x^2 + y^2 = c_1, \\ x^2 - 3z^2 = c_2. \end{cases}$

(e) $\begin{cases} 9x^2 + 4y^2 + z^2 = c_1, \\ x = c_2yz. \end{cases}$

(f) $\begin{cases} xyz = c_1, \\ x^3 + y^3 + z^3 = c_2. \end{cases}$

5. (b) $\begin{cases} y = c_1e^{4x} + 2c_2xe^{4x}, \\ z = c_1e^{4x} - c_2e^{4x} + 2c_2xe^{4x}. \end{cases}$

(c) $\begin{cases} y = 2c_1e^{-x} + c_2e^{-7x}, \\ z = -3c_1e^{-x} + 3c_2e^{-7x}. \end{cases}$

(d) $\begin{cases} y = c_1e^{-4x} + c_2e^{-7x} + \dfrac{7}{40}e^x + \dfrac{1}{27}e^{2x}, \\[2mm] z = c_1e^{-4x} - 2c_2e^{-7x} + \dfrac{1}{20}e^x + \dfrac{7}{27}e^{2x}. \end{cases}$

(e) $\begin{cases} y = 4c_1 + c_2e^{5x} - \dfrac{(25\cos x + 21\sin x)}{26}, \\[2mm] z = -c_1 + c_2e^{5x} + \dfrac{\cos x + 5\sin x}{26}. \end{cases}$

(f) $\begin{cases} y = e^{2x}(c_1 + c_2x + 6x^2 + x^3), \\ z = e^{2x}(c_2 - c_1 - 12 - c_2x + 12x - 3x^2 - x^3). \end{cases}$

(g) $\begin{cases} y = \dfrac{e^{\alpha x}}{\beta}\Big\{ c_1\cosh\beta x + c_2\sinh\beta x + \sinh\beta x \cdot \\ \quad \displaystyle\int e^{-\alpha x}h(x)\cosh\beta x\,dx - \cosh\beta x\int e^{-\alpha x}h(x)\sinh\beta x\,dx\Big\}, \\[2mm] z = \dfrac{y' - ay - f(x)}{b},\ \text{where} \\[2mm] \alpha = \dfrac{a+g}{2},\ \beta = \dfrac{1}{2}\sqrt{(a-g)^2 + 4bc},\ h(x) \equiv f'(x) \\ \qquad\qquad\qquad\qquad\qquad\qquad + b\varphi(x) - gf(x). \end{cases}$

7. (a) $\begin{cases} e^{x^3}(y - z) = -\dfrac{1}{2}e^{2x^3} + \displaystyle\int e^{2x^3}\,dx + c_1, \\[2mm] e^{2x^3}(y + 2z) = \dfrac{2}{3}e^{3x^3} + \displaystyle\int e^{3x^3}\,dx + c_2. \end{cases}$

(b) $\begin{cases} 5x^5(y - z) + 2x^5 = c_1, \\ 3x^3(y - 3z) + x^6 = c_2. \end{cases}$

(c) $\begin{cases} e^{\frac{(-1+\sqrt{33})x}{2}}\left(y + \dfrac{3 + \sqrt{33}}{2}z\right) = \\[2mm] \quad \displaystyle\int e^{\frac{(-1+\sqrt{33})x}{2}}\left[\sinh x + \dfrac{3 + \sqrt{33}}{2}\cosh x\right]dx + c_1, \\[2mm] e^{\frac{(-1-\sqrt{33})x}{2}}\left(y + \dfrac{3 - \sqrt{33}}{2}z\right) = \\[2mm] \quad \displaystyle\int e^{\frac{(-1-\sqrt{33})x}{2}}\left[\sinh x + \dfrac{3 - \sqrt{33}}{2}\cosh x\right]dx + c_2. \end{cases}$

$$(d) \begin{cases} (\cos x)^{\frac{-1-\sqrt{33}}{2}} \left(y + \dfrac{1+\sqrt{33}}{2} z \right) = \\[4pt] \displaystyle\iint \left\{ (\cos x)^{\frac{-3-\sqrt{33}}{2}} + \dfrac{1+\sqrt{33}}{2} (\cos x)^{\frac{-5-\sqrt{33}}{2}} \right\} dx + c_1, \\[10pt] (\cos x)^{\frac{-1+\sqrt{33}}{2}} \left(y + \dfrac{1-\sqrt{33}}{2} z \right) = \\[4pt] \displaystyle\iint \left\{ (\cos x)^{\frac{-3+\sqrt{33}}{2}} + \dfrac{1-\sqrt{33}}{2} (\cos x)^{\frac{-5+\sqrt{33}}{2}} \right\} dx + c_2. \end{cases}$$

Section 60, page 207

1. $\begin{cases} x^2 + y^2 + z^2 = c, \\ \log (x^2 + xy + y^2) + \dfrac{10}{\sqrt{3}} \tan^{-1} \left(\dfrac{2y + x}{x \sqrt{3}} \right) = c_1. \end{cases}$

2. $\begin{cases} ax + by + cz = d, \\ a^2x^2 + b^2y^2 + 3abxy + acxz + bcyz = c_1. \end{cases}$

3. $\begin{cases} x^2 + z^2 = 1, \\ x^2(a \cos^2 y + b \sin^2 y - 1)^{a+b} = c_1. \end{cases}$

4. $\begin{cases} x = c, \\ xy + \dfrac{z^2}{2} = c_1. \end{cases}$

5. $\begin{cases} 2z^2 = x^2y^2, \\ 2x + y = cxy. \end{cases}$

6. $\begin{cases} z = f(y), \\ x - z - \displaystyle\int f(y) \, dy = c. \end{cases}$

Section 65, page 218

2. (a) $\dfrac{dz}{0} = \dfrac{dx_1}{x_2 - x_3} = \dfrac{dx_2}{x_3 - x_1} = \dfrac{dx_3}{x_1 - x_2}.$

(b) $\dfrac{dz}{0} = \dfrac{dx_1}{0} = \dfrac{dx_2}{0} = \dfrac{dx_3}{x_3} = \dfrac{dx_4}{-x_4}.$

(c) $dz = dx_1 = dx_2 = 0.$

3. $u' \equiv -\sqrt[4]{\dfrac{2}{3}} z^{3/2}, \; u'' \equiv -\sqrt[4]{\dfrac{2}{3}} z^{1/2}(x_1 + x_2),$

$$u''' \equiv -\sqrt[4]{\dfrac{2}{3}} z^{1/2}(x_1 + x_3), \; u^{iv} \equiv -\sqrt[4]{\dfrac{2}{3}} z^{1/2}(x_1 - x_4).$$

4. $x_1 x_2^2 = c_1,\ z = c_2 x_2,\ x_3 = c_3.$

5. $\begin{cases} x_1^2 = c_1(x_2 + x_3 + x_4), \\ x_1 x_2 - x_1 x_4 = c_2, \\ x_1 x_2 - x_1 x_3 = c_3. \end{cases}$

6. $\begin{cases} u^{1\!/\!4}(5x_1 - u) = c_1, \\ u^{1\!/\!4}(5x_2 - u) = c_2, \\ u^{1\!/\!4}(5x_3 - u) = c_3, \\ u^{1\!/\!4}(5x_4 - u) = c_4, \text{ where } u \equiv x_1 + x_2 + x_3 + x_4 + x_5. \end{cases}$

7. $z = c_1 x_1^a = c_2 x_2^a = c_3 x_3^a.$

8. $x_1 = c_1 x_2 = c_2 x_3,\ (a - 1)x_3 x_4 + x_1 x_2 = c_3 x_3^{a+1}.$

9. $1.$

10. $(x + y).$

13. $xyzw = c_1,\ x^2 y + y^2 z + z^2 w + w^2 x = c_2,\ w^2 x + yz = c_3.$

14. $x + \log (wy + wz) = c_1,\ x + yz + wz = c_2,\ x^2 yz = c_3.$

Section 67, page 225

1. (a) $\phi(mx - ly,\ nx - lz) = 0.$

(b) $\phi\left(y^2 - z^2,\ \dfrac{x}{y + z}\right) = 0.$

(c) $\phi\left(y,\ \dfrac{z}{y} - \log x\right) = 0.$

(d) $\phi\left(x^2 - y^2,\ \dfrac{z}{5} - \log (x + y)\right) = 0.$

(e) $\phi\left(x - y - z,\ \{a^2 c x^2 + a(b - a)(by + cz)x - a(by + cz)^2\}. \right.$

$\left. \left\{\dfrac{2acx + (b - a - \sqrt{a^2 - 2ab + b^2 + 4ac})(by + cz)}{2acx + (b - a + \sqrt{a^2 - 2ab + b^2 + 4ac})(by + cz)}\right\}^{\frac{a+b}{\sqrt{a^2 - 2ab + b^2 + 4ac}}} \right) = 0.$

(f) $\phi(x + 2y + 3z,\ 13x^2 + 10y^2 + 5z^2 - 4xy - 12yz - 6zx)$
$$= 0.$$

(g) $\phi(x + y + z,\ x^2 + y^2 + z^2) = 0.$

(h) $\phi(x^2 - y^2,\ y^2 + 2z^2) = 0.$

(i) $\phi\left(\dfrac{\cos z}{\cos y},\ \dfrac{\cos z}{\cos x}\right) = 0.$

(j) $\phi(x^2 + z^2,\ y^3 + z^3) = 0.$

(k) $\phi(y^2 + z^2,\ xz^3) = 0.$

(l) $\phi(x^4 + y^4 + z^4, xyz^2) = 0.$

(m) $\phi\left(\dfrac{x}{y}, xz\right) = 0.$

(n) $\phi(xy, x \sin z) = 0.$

2. $\phi(x^2 - z^2, x + y + z) - \phi(-8, 6) = 0.$

3. $\phi\left(x + 2\log y, \dfrac{y}{z}\right) - \phi(0, 1) = 0.$

4. $x + 2\log y - \dfrac{3y}{z} = 0.$

5. $x^3 + y^2 - z = 8.$

6. $y^2 - z^2 - z - x - 4 = 0.$

7. $z = 0.$

8. $(xz^2 - xy^2)z_x + (x^2y - z^2y)z_y = y^2z - x^2z.$

9. $xz_x + 2yz_y + 2 = 0.$

10. $z = a(x + y) + b.$

11. $z = a\left(\dfrac{1}{xz} + \dfrac{\log y}{e^z}\right) + b.$

12. $z_x + az_y = b; \; \phi(ax - y, bx - z) = 0.$

13. $xz_x + yz_y = z; \; \phi\left(\dfrac{z}{x}, \dfrac{z}{y}\right) = 0.$

14. $(x - a)z_x + (y - b)z_y = (z - c); \; \phi\left(\dfrac{z - c}{x - a}, \dfrac{z - c}{y - b}\right) = 0.$

15. $(\gamma y - \beta z)z_x + (\alpha z - \gamma x)z_y = \beta x - \alpha y.$

16. $(\gamma y - \beta z - \gamma b + \beta c)z_x + (\alpha z - \gamma x - \alpha c + \gamma a)z_y =$
$$\beta x - \alpha y - \beta a + \alpha b.$$

17. $xz_x + yz_y = 0; \; \phi\left(z, \dfrac{x}{y}\right) = 0.$

19. $\phi(\mu x^2, \mu y^2) = 0.$

Section 69, page 230

1. $\phi[x - y + z, (y - z)e^{-t}, (yt - zt - x - t - z - 1)e^{-t}] = 0.$

2. $\phi(z, l^2x_1^2 + m^2x_2^2 + n^2x_3^2, l^2x_1 + m^2x_2 + n^2x_3) = 0.$

3. $\phi\left(\dfrac{4x_2 - x_1 - x_3 - x_4 - z}{4x_1 - x_2 - x_3 - x_4 - z}, \dfrac{4x_3 - x_1 - x_2 - x_4 - z}{4x_1 - x_2 - x_3 - x_4 - z},\right.$
$$\left.\dfrac{4x_4 - x_1 - x_2 - x_3 - z}{4x_1 - x_2 - x_3 - x_4 - z}, \dfrac{4z - x_1 - x_2 - x_3 - x_4}{4x_1 - x_2 - x_3 - x_4 - z}\right) = 0.$$

4. $\phi(z^2 - x_1^2,\ z^2 - x_2^2,\ z^2 - x_3^2) = 0.$

5. $\phi\left(z,\ x_1^2 - x_3^2,\ \dfrac{x_1 + x_3}{x_2}\right) = 0.$

Section 71, page 239

1. $z = 2a^2x + 2ay + b.$

2. $2z = 2ax + (a^2 + 1)y + b.$

3. $z = ax + (1 - a^{2/3})^{3/2}y + b.$

4. $z = 2x \cos a + 2y \sin a + b.$

5. $z = ax + \dfrac{2ay}{a + 1} + b.$

6. $z = a_1 + a_2x_1 + a_3x_2 - (a_2 + a_3)x_3.$

7. $z = ax_1 + bx_2 + \sqrt{1 - a^2 - b^2}\,x_3 + c.$

8. $z = ax_1 + bx_2 + \dfrac{ab}{a - b}x_3 + c.$

9. $4(z + a^2)^3 - 4b(z + a^2)^{3/2} + b^2 - 90x^2 - 180axy - 90a^2y^2 = 0.$

10. $2(x + ay) = \log\left(\dfrac{-1 \pm \sqrt{1 + 4az^2}}{2a}\right) + \dfrac{4az^2}{-1 \pm \sqrt{1 + 4az^2}} + b.$

11. Each of the following is a solution:

    i. $a\sqrt{a^2 - 4 + 4z} + a^2 \log(-a + \sqrt{a^2 - 4 + 4z}) - x$
$$- ay - b = 0;$$

    ii. $a\sqrt{a^2 - 4 + 4z} + a^2 \log(-a + \sqrt{a^2 - 4 + 4z}) - x$
$$+ ay - b = 0;$$

    iii. $z = b.$

12. $5x^2 + 10axy + 5a^2y^2 + 10bx + 10aby + 5b^2 - 4(1 + a^2)z = 0,$
$z = 0.$

13. $2\sqrt{1 - z} + \log\left(\dfrac{\sqrt{1 - z} - 1}{\sqrt{1 - z} + 1}\right) \pm \dfrac{x + ay}{\sqrt{a}} = b.$

14. $(z - b)(z - ax - a^2y - b)(z^2 - 6x - 6ay - b) = 0.$

15. $z = b(xy^a)^{\frac{-1 \pm \sqrt{1 + 4a^2}}{2a^2}}$

16. $(z - b)(\log z - x - ay - b)(a^2 \log z + x + ay + b) = 0.$

17. $ab^4z^2 - 2a^3b^2z + (a^5 - ab^2)\log(b^2z^2 + a^2z + 1)$
$$+ \dfrac{3a^3b^2 - a^7}{\sqrt{a^4 - 4b^2}}\log\dfrac{2b^2z + a^2 - \sqrt{a^4 - 4b^2}}{2b^2z + a^2 + \sqrt{a^4 - 4b^2}}$$
$$- bx_1 - abx_2 - b^2x_3 = c.$

18. $\pm\sqrt{1 + 4az} + \log(-1 \pm \sqrt{1 + 4az}) - x - ay - b = 0$,
$z = 0$.

19. $z = be^{\pm a(x+ay)}$.

20. $z = be^{\pm 2a(x+a^2y)}$.

21. $ax + y + b = \int \dfrac{(1 - a^2)dz}{z \pm \sqrt{a^2z^2 + 1 - a^2}}$,
$z = 1$.

22. $3z = x^3 + y^3 + ax + ay + b$.

23. $4z = 3(a + x)^{4/3} + 4ay + b$.

24. $z = \pm\dfrac{2\sqrt{a}}{3}x^{3/2} + \dfrac{y^2}{2} + ay + b$,
$z = 0$.

25. $z = \dfrac{ax^2}{2} + \dfrac{y^2}{2a^2} + b$.

26. $z = -a\cos x - \cos y + \dfrac{y}{a} + b$.

28. $z = ax + by + 2a + 3b^2$,
$z = -\dfrac{y^2}{12}$.

29. $z = ax + by + a^2 + b^2 + 1$,
$z = -\dfrac{x^2}{4} - \dfrac{y^2}{4} + 1$.

30. $z = ax + by + 5a^3 - 2a - b$.

31. $(z - ax - by)^2 = ab$.

32. $z = ax_1 + bx_2 + cx_3 + abc$.

33. $z = a_1x_1 + a_2x_2 + a_3x_3 + a_4x_4 + a_1a_2 + a_3a_4$.
$z = -x_1x_2 - x_3x_4$.

34. $(x - a)^2 + (y - b)^2 - z^2 = 1$.

35. $\dfrac{x^2}{a^2} + \dfrac{y^2}{b^2} + \dfrac{z^2}{a^2b^2} = 1$.

36. $\dfrac{x}{a} + \dfrac{y}{b} + \dfrac{z}{1 - a - b} = 1$.

37. $(x - a)^2 - (y - b)^2 - z^2 = 1$.

38. $(x - a)^2 + \dfrac{(y - b)^2}{5} - z^2 = 0$; $z = 0$.

39. $z = ax + by + \log ab$, $z = -2 - \log xy$.

40. $x^2(y - a)^2 + \dfrac{3}{4} x^4 + xz = b.$

41. $z = ax + b + a^2y - b^2x.$

42. $z^2 = x^2 + ax + \dfrac{2}{3} (y + a)^{3/2} + b.$

43. $z^2 = a_1x_1 + a_2x_2 + (1 - a_1^2 - a_2^3)x_3 + a_3.$

44. $(1 - a_1a_2) \log z = (a_1 + a_2)(x_1 + a_1x_2 + a_2x_3 + a_3); z = 0.$

45. $z^2 = a_1e^{x_1} + a_2e^{x_2} + (a_1 + a_2)^2e^{x_3} + a_3.$

46. $e^z = a_1x_1^3 + a_2x_2^2 + a_3x_3.$

47. $z = \dfrac{\dfrac{3}{4} (x_1 + c_1x_2 + c_2x_3 + c_3x_4)^{4/3}}{(c_1c_2c_3)^{1/3}} + c_4; z = c.$

48. $z = \dfrac{7c_1^2c_2^2c_3^2}{8} \left(\dfrac{x_1 + c_1x_2 + c_2x_3 + c_3x_4}{c_1^2c_2^2c_3^2}\right)^{8/7} + c_4.$

Section 74, page 247

1. $z = F_1(y + 2x) + F_2(y + 5x).$

2. $z = F_1(y - x) + F_2(y + 3x).$

3. $z = F_1(y + x) + F_2(y + 2x) + F_3(y + 3x).$

4. $z = F_1(y - x) + F_2(y + x) + F_3(y - 2x).$

5. $z = F_1(y + x) + F_2(y - x) + F_3(y + 2x) + F_4(y - 2x).$

6. $z = F_1(y) + F_2(y - x) + F_3(y - 3x) + F_4(y + 2x).$

7. $z = F_1(y + x + x \sqrt{3}) + F_2(y + x - x \sqrt{3}).$

8. $z = F_1(y - 2x + x \sqrt{10}) + F_2(y - 2x - x \sqrt{10}).$

9. $z = F_1(y + 3x) + F_2(y - 2x + x \sqrt{2}) + F_3(y - 2x - x \sqrt{2}).$

10. $z = F_1(y - 2x) + F_2(y + 3x + x \sqrt{2}) + F_3(y + 3x - x \sqrt{2}).$

11. $z = F_1(y + x + x \sqrt{5}) + F_2(y + x - x \sqrt{5})$
$\qquad + F_3(y - 2x + x \sqrt{2}) + F_4(y - 2x - x \sqrt{2}).$

12. $z = F_1(y - 3x + 2x \sqrt{2}) + F_2(y - 3x - 2x \sqrt{2})$
$\qquad + F_3(y + 3x + x \sqrt{14}) + F_4(y + 3x - x \sqrt{14}).$

13. $z = F_1(y - 2x) + xF_2(y - 2x).$

14. $z = F_1(2y + 3x) + xF_2(2y + 3x).$

15. $z = F_1(y - x) + xF_2(y - x) + x^2F_3(y - x).$

16. $z = F_1(2y + x) + xF_2(2y + x) + x^2F_3(2y + x)$.

17. $z = F_1(y + 3x) + F_2(2y - x) + F_3(y + 2x) + xF_4(y + 2x)$.

18. $z = F_1(2y + x) + xF_2(2y + x) + F_3(2y + 3x) + xF_4(2y + 3x)$.

19. $z = \sum_i \{c_i e^{(y+x)g_i} \cos(g_i x) + d_i e^{(y+x)h_i} \sin(h_i x)\}$.

20. $z = \sum_i \{c_i e^{(3y+x)g_i} \cos(2g_i x) + d_i e^{(3y+x)h_i} \sin(2h_i x)\}$.

21. $z = F_1(3y + x) + \sum_i \{c_i e^{(y-2x)g_i} \cos(2g_i x) +$
$$d_i e^{(y-2x)h_i} \sin(2h_i x)\}.$$

22. $z = F_1(2y + x) + \sum_i \{c_i e^{(y-x)g_i} \cos(3g_i x) +$
$$d_i e^{(y-x)h_i} \sin(3h_i x)\}.$$

23. $z = \sum_i \{(a_i + b_i x)e^{(y-x)g_i} \cos(g_i x) +$
$$(c_i + d_i x)e^{(y-x)h_i} \sin(h_i x)\}.$$

24. $z = \sum_i \{(a_i + b_i x)e^{(2y+3x)g_i} \cos(g_i x) +$
$$(c_i + d_i x)e^{(2y+3x)h_i} \sin(h_i x)\}.$$

Section 76, page 249

1. $z = F_1(y + 2x) + F_2(y + 5x) + \dfrac{231}{20} x^5 + \dfrac{43}{4} x^4 y + \dfrac{7}{2} x^3 y^2$
$$+ \dfrac{1}{2} x^2 y^3.$$

2. $z = F_1(y + x + x\sqrt{3}) + F_2(y + x - x\sqrt{3})$
$$+ \dfrac{11x^9}{630} + \dfrac{2x^8 y}{35} + \dfrac{3x^7 y^2}{35} + \dfrac{x^6 y^3}{15} + \dfrac{x^5 y^4}{20}.$$

3. $z = F_1(y + 3x) + F_2(y - 2x + x\sqrt{2}) + F_3(y - 2x - x\sqrt{2})$
$$+ \dfrac{x^4}{24} - \dfrac{y^5}{360}.$$

4. $z = F_1(y - 2x + x\sqrt{2}) + F_2(y - 2x - x\sqrt{2})$
$$+ F_3(y + x + x\sqrt{5}) + F_4(y + x - x\sqrt{5}) + \dfrac{x^8}{720}$$
$$- \dfrac{x^7 y}{630} + \dfrac{x^6 y^2}{360} + \dfrac{x^6}{360}.$$

5. $z = F_1(y + 3x) + F_2(y - x) + \dfrac{20}{3} \cos (y + 2x)$.

6. $z = F_1(y) + F_2(y - x) + F_3(y - 3x) + F_4(y + 2x)$
$$- \frac{1}{27} \cos (2y + 3x) + \frac{1}{135} \sin (2y + 3x).$$

7. $z = F_1(2y + 3x) + xF_2(2y + 3x) - \cos (x + y) -$
$$\frac{1}{49} \cos (2x - y).$$

8. $z = F_1(y + 2x) + F_2(y + 3x) - x \sin (y + 2x)$.

9. $z = F_1(y + 2x) + xF_2(y + 2x) + \dfrac{x^2}{2} \cos (y + 2x)$.

10. $z = F_1(y + 3x) + F_2(y + 2x) + x \cos (y + 2x)$.

11. $z = F_1(y + 2x) + F_2(y + 3x) + 3x \cos (y + 2x)$
$$+ x \sin (y + 3x).$$

12. $z = F_1(y - 2x) + xF_2(y - 2x) + x^2 F_3(y - 2x) - \sin x$
$$+ \frac{x^3}{6} \sin (y - 2x).$$

13. $z = F_1(y - 2x) + xF_2(y - 2x) + \dfrac{5}{64} e^{2x+3y}$.

14. $z = F_1(2y + x + x \sqrt{33}) + F_2(2y + x - x \sqrt{33})$
$$+ F_3(y + 3x) + \frac{1}{24} e^{3x-y}.$$

15. $z = F_1(y + 2x) + F_2(y + 5x) - \dfrac{1}{3} xe^{y+2x}$.

16. $z = F_1(y - 2x) + xF_2(y - 2x) + x^2 F_3(y - 2x) + \dfrac{1}{6} x^3 e^{y-2x}$.

17. $z = F_1(y + 2x) + F_2(y + x) + xF_3(y + x) - \dfrac{1}{2} x^2 e^{y+x}$
$$+ xe^{y+2x} + \frac{1}{4} e^{y+3x}.$$

Section 79, page 255

1. (a) $z = F_1(y + 2x) + F_2(y + 5x) + \dfrac{1}{2x}$.

(b) $z = F_1(y + x) + xF_2(y + x) + \dfrac{1}{4} (1 + x)e^{3x+5y}$.

(c) $z = F_1(y + x) + F_2(y - x) + F_3(y - 2x) -$
$$\frac{8}{525}(3x - 2y)^{7/2}.$$

(d) $z = F_1(y - x) + xF_2(y - x) + x^2F_3(y - x) + \frac{y^3}{6}\phi(y - x).$

(e) $z = F_1(2y + x) + xF_2(2y + x) + x^2F_3(2y + x)$
$$+ \frac{x^3}{48}f(2y + x) + \frac{3x^7}{13440} + \frac{x^6y}{960}.$$

(f) $z = F_1(y - 3x + 2x\sqrt{2}) + F_2(y - 3x - 2x\sqrt{2})$
$+ F_3(y + 3x + x\sqrt{14}) + F_4(y + 3x - x\sqrt{14})$
$$- \frac{1}{176}x\cos(y - 3x) - \frac{3}{968}\sin(y - 3x).$$

(g) $z = F_1(y + 3x) + F_2(y - 2x) + \frac{2x^4}{3} + \frac{x^3y}{3} + \frac{x^2y^2}{2}.$

(h) $z = F_1(y + x) + F_2(y + 2x) + F_3(y + 3x)$
$$- \frac{x\sin(y + x)}{2} + x\cos(y + 2x) + \frac{xe^{y+3x}}{2}.$$

(i) $z = F_1(y + x) + F_2(y - x) + F_3(y - 2x) +$
$\frac{x^2}{20}\cos(2x - 3y) + \frac{21x}{200}\sin(2x - 3y) - \frac{441}{4000}\cos(2x - 3y)$
$$+ \frac{3x}{80}(x + y)^{5/3}.$$

(j) $z = F_1(y - 2x + x\sqrt{10}) + F_2(y - 2x - x\sqrt{10})$
$$- (x - 5y + 46)e^{x+y}.$$

(k) $z = F_1(y + x) + F_2(y - x) + F_3(y + 2x) + F_4(y - 2x)$
$$- \frac{x^7}{360} + \frac{x^5y^2}{120} - (x^2 - y^2 - 8x + 10)e^x$$

(l) $z = \sum_i \{c_i e^{(3y+x)g_i}\cos(2g_ix) + d_i e^{(3y+x)h_i}\sin(2h_ix)\}$
$$+ e^x\cos y.$$

3. (a) $z = -\frac{16}{17955}(2x + y)^{9/2}.$

(b) $z = \frac{1}{6283}\cdot\frac{3!}{9!}(4x + 3y)^9 + \frac{1}{4}e^{x-y}.$

(c) $z = -\frac{1}{8}\sin 2x + \frac{1}{7}\cos(x - y).$

5. (a) $z = \frac{x^4}{4!}(3x + y)e^{3x+y}$

(b) $z = \dfrac{x^3}{3!} \cosh(y - x)$.

(c) $z = \dfrac{x^2}{2!} \sqrt{y - 2x}$.

7. $z = \Phi_1(x_3 - b_1 x_1,\, x_2 - a_1 x_1) + \Phi_2(x_3 - b_2 x_1,\, x_2 - a_2 x_1)$.

8. $z = \Phi_1(x_3 - 3x_1,\, x_2 + 2x_1) + \Phi_2(x_3 + 2x_1,\, x_2 - x_1)$
$$- \frac{1}{12} e^{3x_1 + x_2 - x_3}$$

9. $z = \Phi_1(x_3 - x_1,\, x_2 + x_1) + \Phi_2(x_3 - 2x_1,\, x_2 - 2x_1)$
$$- \sin x_1 - \frac{x_1}{2} \sin(x_2 - x_3).$$

Section 82, page 259

1. $z = f_1(x) + e^{3x} f_2(y - 2x) + e^x f_3(y - x)$.

2. $z = f_1(x) + e^{3x} f_2(y - 2x) + e^x f_3(y - x)$
$$+ \frac{x^2 y}{3} - \frac{xy^2}{3} - \frac{4y^2}{9} - \frac{2xy}{9} - \frac{4y}{3}.$$

3. $z = f_1(y) + xf_2(y) + e^{-5x} f_3(y + 4x)$.

4. $z = f_1(y) + xf_2(y) + e^{-5x} f_3(y + 4x) + e^{2x+y} \left(\dfrac{x}{12} - \dfrac{y}{12} - \dfrac{2}{9} \right)$.

5. $z = e^x f_1(y - 2x) + f_2(x) + f_3(y) + xf_4(y)$.

6. $z = e^x f_1(y - 2x) + f_2(x) + f_3(y) + xf_4(y)$
$$+ \frac{13 \sin(x - 7y) + \cos(x - 7y)}{1190}.$$

7. $z = e^{-x} f_1(y - x) + e^{-2x} f_2(y - x) + f_3(y - x)$.

8. $z = e^{-x} f_1(y - x) + e^{-2x} f_2(y - x) + f_3(y - x) + \dfrac{e^{5x-y} \sinh(x - y)}{120}$.

9. $z = f_1(y - 2x) + e^{-x} f_2(y + 2x)$.

10. $z = f_1(y - 2x) + e^{-x} f_2(y + 2x) + \dfrac{y^4}{8} - x^2 + 6y^2 + 25y$
$$+ y^3 + \frac{x^3}{3} - \frac{1}{70} e^{x - 4y}.$$

11. $z = e^x f_1(y - 2x) + e^{3x} f_2(y + x) + e^{5x} f_3(y - x)$.

12. $z = e^x f_1(y - 2x) + e^{3x} f_2(y + x) + e^{5x} f_3(y - x)$
$$- \frac{1}{9240} [31 \cosh(x + 5y + 6) + 101 \sinh(x + 5y + 6)].$$

13. $z = e^{-x}f_1(y) + e^x f_2(y - x).$

14. $z = e^{-x}f_1(y) + e^x f_2(y - x) + \dfrac{1}{4} e^{3x-y+1}.$

Section 84, page 261

1. (a) $z = \dfrac{1}{19} e^{2x-y} + \displaystyle\sum_i c_i e^{a_i x + b_i y}$ where $a_i^3 - 2a_i b_i$

$$+ b_i^2 - a_i + 8 = 0.$$

(b) $z = \dfrac{1}{5} \sin(x - y) - \dfrac{2}{5} \cos(x - y) + \dfrac{3}{34} \sin(x - 2y) +$

$\dfrac{5}{34} \cos(x - 2y) + \displaystyle\sum_i c_i e^{a_i x + b_i y}$ where $a_i^2 + a_i b_i - b_i^2 + a_i - b_i = 0.$

(c) $z = \dfrac{1}{4155} e^{4x-5y+6}\{37 \cos(x + 2y) - 4 \sin(x + 2y)\}$

$$+ \displaystyle\sum_i c_i e^{a_i x + b_i y} \text{ where } a_i^3 + 3b_i^2 + a_i - 8 = 0.$$

(d) $z = \dfrac{1}{625} (125y^3 + 125x^2 + 225y^2 + 270y + 112)$

$$+ \displaystyle\sum_i c_i e^{a_i x + b_i y} \text{ where } a_i^2 + 2a_i b_i^2 - 3b_i + 5 = 0.$$

(e) $z = \dfrac{1}{32} \{\sinh(3x - y) + \cosh(3x - y)\}$

$$+ \displaystyle\sum_i c_i e^{a_i x + b_i y} \text{ where } a_i^3 + 3b_i^3 + a_i - 5b_i = 0.$$

(f) $z = \dfrac{e^{2x}}{2401} \{343x^2 - 1029xy^2 + 294xy + 735y^2 - 532x - 126y$

$+ 258\} + \displaystyle\sum_i c_i e^{a_i x + b_i y}$ where $a_i^2 + a_i b_i + a_i - b_i + 1 = 0.$

(g) $z = \dfrac{1}{6} e^{3x-2y} + \displaystyle\sum_i c_i e^{a_i x + b_i y}$ where $a_i^3 + 3b_i^3 + 3 = 0.$

(h) $z = -\dfrac{1}{10} \sin(3x + 2y) + \displaystyle\sum_i c_i e^{a_i x + b_i y}$ where $a_i^2 + a_i b_i + b_i^2$

$$+ 2a_i - 3b_i + 9 = 0.$$

(i) $z = -\dfrac{7x}{6} + \dfrac{5y}{4} + \displaystyle\sum_i c_i x^{a_i} y^{b_i}$ where $a_i^2 - 2a_i b_i - b_i^2 - 2a_i$

$$+ 2b_i - 5 = 0$$

Section 85, page 265

3. (a) 0.449, (b) 0.123.

4. (a) $\rho^2 v_{\rho\rho} + v_{\varphi\varphi} + \csc^2 \varphi\, v_{\theta\theta} + 2\rho v_\rho + \cot \varphi\, v_\varphi = 0.$

Section 90, page 283

1. $z = f_1(y + ax) + f_2(y - ax).$

2. $y = f_1(z) + f_2(x).$

3. $z = x f_1(y - x) + f_2(y - x).$

4. $z = (x + y) \log y + f_1(x) + f_2(x + y).$

5. $z = f(x + \cos y) + g(x - \cos y).$

6. $p \operatorname{sech} x + q \operatorname{sech} y = f_1 (\sinh x + \sinh y)$

$$\text{or}$$

$p \operatorname{sech} x - q \operatorname{sech} y = f_2(\sinh x - \sinh y),$
$\therefore z = F_1(\sinh x + \sinh y) + F_2(\sinh x - \sinh y).$

7. $z = x f_1 \left(\dfrac{y}{x} \right) + f_2 \left(\dfrac{y}{x} \right).$

8. $z = e^{\frac{2y}{x+y}} \left[f_1(x + y) + \dfrac{1}{x + y} \int e^{\frac{-2y}{a}} f_2(2y - a)\, dy \right]$
with a replaced by $x + y$ after the integration.

9. $y + x f_1(x + 2y + 3z) + f_2(x + 2y + 3z) = 0.$

10. $\dfrac{2p - q}{x - 2y} = f(xy)$ or $\dfrac{px - qy}{x - 2y} = f(x + 2y),$
$\therefore z = f_1(x + 2y) + f_2(xy).$

11. $p - 4x - 3y = f(q - 3x - 3y)$ whence
$$z = 2x^2 + 3xy - ax - by + \frac{3}{2} y^2 + c$$

$$\text{or}$$

$$z = 2x^2 + 3xy + nx + \frac{3}{2} y^2 + \phi(y + mx).$$

12. $4p + y - 5x = f(4q + x - 5y)$ whence
$$8z = 5x^2 - 2xy + 5y^2 + 2ax + 2by + c$$

$$\text{or}$$

$$8z = 5x^2 - 2xy + 5y^2 + 2nx + \phi(y + mx).$$

13. $2p - 3x + 4y = f(2q - x + 4y)$ whence
$$4z = 3x^2 - 8xy - 4y^2 + ax + by + c$$

or

$$4z = 3x^2 - 8xy - 4y^2 + nx - 5mx^2 + \phi(y + mx);$$
$2p - 3x - y = f(q + 2x + 2y)$ whence
$$4z = 3x^2 + 2xy - 4y^2 + ax + by + c$$

or

$$4z = 3x^2 + 2xy - 4y^2 + nx + 5mx^2 + \phi(y + mx).$$

14. $2p + x - y = f(3q - x + y)$ whence
$$12z = -3x^2 + 6xy - 2y^2 + ax + by + c$$

or

$$12z = -3x^2 + 6xy - 2y^2 + ax + mx^2 + \phi(y + mx);$$
$6p + 3x - 2y = f(6q - 3x + 2y)$ whence
$$12z = -3x^2 + 4xy - 2y^2 + ax + by + c$$

or

$$12z = -3x^2 + 4xy - 2y^2 + ax - mx^2 + \phi(y + mx).$$

15. $px + y = f(qy + x)$ whence
$$z = n \log x + mx + \frac{y}{m} + \phi(x^m y).$$

16. $px^2 + q = f(qy^2 + p)$ whence
$$z = \frac{n}{2m} \log \frac{x - m}{x + m} + \phi\left(\frac{(x - m)(1 - my)}{(x + m)(1 + my)}\right).$$

17. $px^2 + qy = f(qy^2 + px)$ whence
$$z = n \log \frac{my}{my - 1} + \phi\left(\frac{(x - m)(my - 1)^m}{xy^m}\right).$$

Section 91, page 288

1. $z = \dfrac{x}{3} + \dfrac{y}{3} - \dfrac{1}{6} + e^{-3(x+2y)}f_1(x + y) + e^{-2(x+y)}f_2(x + 2y).$

2. $15(2y - x)^2(2x - 3y) z =$
$$5(2y - x)^3(2x - 3y)^4 + 3(2y - x)^5(2x - 3y)^2$$
$$+ f_1(2y - x) + f_2(2x - 3y).$$

3. $z = -\dfrac{1}{4}\left(x - \dfrac{1}{y}\right) - \dfrac{1}{8} + e^{2\left(x - \frac{1}{y}\right)} f_1(y) + e^{-\frac{2}{y}} f_2\left(x - \dfrac{1}{y}\right).$

4. $z = f_1(y - \sinh x) + f_2(y + \sinh x)$.

5. $z = f_1(x - y) + f_2(xy)$.

6. $z = xy + f_1(x^2 + y^2) + f_2\left(\dfrac{y}{x}\right)$.

7. $z = e^{2(x-2y)}f_1(x - y) + e^{3(x-2y)}f_2(x - y) + 1$.

8. $z = 2(x + y)^2 + e^{-10xy-5y^2}f(x + y) + e^{-2xy-y^2}g(x + y)$.

9. $z = 2x - 10y - y^{-5}f_1(x - 5y) + y^{-1}f_2(x - 5y)$.

10. $z = \dfrac{y^3}{6} + \dfrac{y^2\phi(x + y)}{2} + yf_1(x + y) + f_2(x + y)$.

11. $z = y^3f_1\left(\dfrac{x}{y}\right) + y^{-3}f_2\left(\dfrac{x}{y}\right) - \dfrac{1}{9}\log\dfrac{x}{y}$.

12. $z = (4 + y)f_1\left(\dfrac{x + y}{x}\right) + (4 + y)^2f_2\left(\dfrac{x + y}{x}\right)$

$$+ (4 + y)^3\left(\dfrac{x + y}{x}\right).$$

Index

A

Adjoint equation, 113
Approximation, numerical, 134ff.
Arbitrary constants, 5, 8
  number of, 11, 117
Arbitrary functions, 222

B

Bernoulli, 37
Bernoulli's equation, 37
Bessel, 177
Bessel's equation, 177
Bessel's function, 178, 180, 181

C

Catenary, 47
Cauchy, 108
Cauchy's linear equation, 108
C-discriminant, 63
Characteristic equation, 84
Characteristics, 210, 233
Charpit's method, 230
Clairaut, 59
Clairaut's equation, 59
Complementary function, **70, 78,** 248
Complete solution, 8, 223
Complex roots, 85, 244
Conditions:
  for exactness, 19, 111, 192
  for functional dependence, 53, 208
  for integrability, 194, 198
  for linear dependence, 72, 73
  for solubility, 8, 16
Constants, arbitrary, 5, 8
Cross ratio, 40
Curvature, radius of, 13
Curve, integral, 8

D

Degree, 1
Dependence:
  functional, 53, 208

Dependence (*cont.*):
  linear, 72, 73
Determinants:
  functional, 53, 208
  Wronskian, 73, 103
Determinate system, 209
Discriminant:
  c-discriminant, 63
  p-discriminant, 64

E

Elementary functions, 38
Envelope, 61, 233
Euler, 30
Euler equation, 108
Euler's theorem on homogeneous
  functions, 30
Exact equations, 19, 111, 192
Exactness, conditions for, 19, 111, 192
Exactness, generalized, 213
Existence theorems, 8, 16

F

Factor, integrating, 24, 113, 193
Factorization of operators, 78, 250
Fractions, partial, method by, 98, 252
Functional dependence, 53, 208
Functional determinant, 53, 208
Functions:
  arbitrary, 222
  Bessel's, 178, 180, 181
  complementary, 70, 78, 248
  elementary, 38
  homogeneous, 28, 196
  orthogonal, 173

G

Gauss, 184
Gauss equation, 184
General solution, 7, 8, 69, 191, 223,
  233, 244
Generalized exactness, 213

H

Homogeneous equation, 28, 196
Homogeneous function, 28, 196
  Euler's theorem on, 30
Homogeneous linear equation, 70, 75, 242
Hypergeometric series, 185, 186

I

Independence, linear, 72
Indeterminate system, 217
Indicial equation, 152
Infinite series, solution by, 14, 134, 147
Infinite solution, 66
Inspection, integrating factor by, 24
Integrability, conditions for, 194, 198
Integral:
  curve, 8
  intermediate, 268, 269
  particular, 70, 165, 257
Integrating factor, 24, 113, 193
Inverse operators, 94, 106, 250

J

Jacobi, 208
Jacobian, 53, 208
Jacobi's method, 236
Jacobi's multipliers, 212, 217

K

Kutta, 143

L

Lagrange, 102, 211
Lagrange's system, 224, 229
Lagrange's method, variation of parameters, 35, 102
Laplace, 262
Laplace's equation, 262
Laplace's transformation, 284
Legendre, 66, 170
Legendre's equation, 170
Legendre polynomial, 171
Legendre's transformation, 66
Leibnitz's rule, 21
Linear dependence, 72, 73
Linear differential equation, 33, 69, 151, 223
Linear independence, 72

M

Matrix, rank of, 209
Method:
  by partial fractions, 98, 252
  Charpit's, 230
  Jacobi's, 236
  Lagrange's, variation of parameters, 35, 102
  Milne's, 144
  Monge's, 270, 275
  Picard's, 135
  Runge's, 139, 142
Milne, 144
Monge, 270
Monge's method, 270, 275
Multiple roots, 84, 245
Multipliers, Jacobi's, 212, 217

N

Non-integrable equations, 206
Number:
  of arbitrary constants, 11, 117
  of linearly independent solutions, 73

O

Operators, 76, 242
  factorization of, 78, 250
  inverse, 94, 106, 250
Order:
  of differential equation, 1
  reduction of, 80
Ordinary differential equation, 2
Orthogonal functions, 173
Orthogonal trajectories, 42

P

Parameters, variation of, 35, 102
Partial differential equation, 2
Partial fractions, method by, 98, 252
Particular integral, 70, 165, 257
Particular solution, 8, 223, 229
P-discriminant, 64
Picard, 135
Picard's method, 135
Points, singular, 10
Polynomial, of Legendre, 171
Primitive, of a differential equation, 4

Q

Quotient:
  of two integrating factors, 53
  of two Jacobi multipliers, 219

R

Radius of curvature, 13
Rank of matrix, 209
Ratio, cross, 40
Reduced equation, 70, 248
Reduction of order, 80
Relation:
 c-discriminant, 63
 p-discriminant, 64
Roots:
 case of complex, 85, 244
 case of multiple, 84, 245
Runge, 139
Runge's method, 139, 142
 as modified by Kutta, 143

S

Separation of variables, 18
Series:
 hypergeometric, 185, 186
 infinite, solution by, 14, 134, 147
 Taylor's, 14, 135
Simultaneous equations, system of,
 16, 114, 198
Singular points, 10
Singular solution, 9, 61, 232
Solubility, conditions for, 8, 16
Solutions:
 complete, 8, 223

Solutions (cont.):
 definition of, 3, 268
 general, 7, 8, 69, 191, 223, 233, 244
 infinite, 66
 in series, 14, 134, 147
 particular, 8, 223, 229
 singular, 9, 61, 232
Systems:
 determinate, 209
 indeterminate, 217
 of simultaneous equations, 16, 114,
 198

T

Taylor's series, 14, 135
Taylor's theorem, 14, 135
Total differential equation, 191
Trajectory, orthogonal, 42
Transformation:
 of Laplace, 284
 of Legendre, 66

V

Variables separable, 18
Variation of parameters, 35, 102

W

Wronskian, 73, 103